HOLT
SCIENCE &
TECHNOLOGY

Inside the Restless Earth

HOLT, RINEHART AND WINSTON

A Harcourt Education Company

Orlando • **Austin** • New York • San Diego • Toronto • London

Acknowledgments

Contributing Authors

Kathleen Meehan Berry
Science Chairman
Canon-McMillan School District
Canonsburg, Pennsylvania

Robert H. Fronk, Ph.D.
Chair of Science and Mathematics Education
Florida Institute of Technology
West Melbourne, Florida

Peter E. Malin, Ph.D.
Professor of Geology
Division of Earth and Ocean Sciences
Duke University
Durham, North Carolina

Inclusion and Special Needs Consultant

Karen Clay
Inclusion Consultant
Boston, Massachusetts

Safety Reviewer

Jack Gerlovich, Ph.D.
Associate Professor
School of Education
Drake University
Des Moines, Iowa

Academic Reviewers

Roger J. Cuffey, Ph.D.
Professor of Paleontology
Department of Geosciences
Pennsylvania State University
University Park, Pennsylvania

Turgay Ertekin, Ph.D.
Professor and Chairman of Petroleum and Natural Gas Engineering
Energy and Geo-Environmental Engineering
Pennsylvania State University
University Park, Pennsylvania

Richard N. Hey, Ph.D.
Professor of Geophysics
Department of Geophysics & Planetology
University of Hawaii at Manoa
Honolulu, Hawaii

Ken Hon, Ph.D.
Associate Professor of Volcanology
Geology Department
University of Hawaii at Hilo
Hilo, Hawaii

Susan Hough, Ph.D.
United States Geological Survey (USGS)
Pasadena, California

Joel S. Leventhal, Ph.D.
Emeritus Scientist, Geochemistry
U.S. Geological Survey
Lakewood, Colorado

Kenneth K. Peace
Manager of Transportation
WestArch Coal, Inc.
St. Louis, Missouri

Kenneth H. Rubin, Ph.D.
Associate Professor
Department of Geology & Geophysics
University of Hawaii at Manoa
Honolulu, Hawaii

Colin D. Sumrall, Ph.D.
Lecturer of Paleontology
Earth and Planetary Sciences
The University of Tennessee
Knoxville, Tennessee

Peter W. Weigand, Ph.D.
Professor Emeritus
Department of Geological Sciences
California State University
Northridge, California

Teacher Reviewers

Diedre S. Adams
Physical Science Instructor
West Vigo Middle School
West Terre Haute, Indiana

Laura Buchanan
Science Teacher and Department Chair
Corkran Middle School
Glen Burnie, Maryland

Robin K. Clanton
Science Department Head
Berrien Middle School
Nashville, Georgia

Meredith Hanson
Science Teacher
Westside Middle School
Rocky Face, Georgia

James Kerr
Oklahoma Teacher of the Year 2002–2003
Union Public Schools
Tulsa, Oklahoma

Laura Kitselman
Science Teacher and Coordinator
Loudoun Country Day School
Leesburg, Virginia

Printed in the United States of America

ISBN 0-03-050052-4

3 4 5 6 7 048 09 08 07

F | Inside the Restless Earth

Labs and Activities

Go to go.hrw.com and type in the red keyword.

PRE-READING ACTIVITY

FOLDNOTES

Graphic Organizer

START-UP ACTIVITY

Quick Lab

Labs

INTERNET ACTIVITY

SCHOOL to HOME

READING STRATEGY

Brainstorming

Discussion

Paired Summarizing

Reading Organizer—Concept Map

Reading Organizer—Flowchart

Reading Organizer—Outline

How to Use Your Textbook

Your Roadmap for Success with Holt Science and Technology

What You Will Learn

At the beginning of every section you will find the section's objectives and vocabulary terms. The objectives tell you what you'll need to know after you finish reading the section.

Vocabulary terms are listed for each section. Learn the definitions of these terms because you will most likely be tested on them. Each term is highlighted in the text and is defined at point of use and in the margin. You can also use the glossary to locate definitions quickly.

STUDY TIP Reread the objectives and the definitions to the terms when studying for a test to be sure you know the material.

Get Organized

A Reading Strategy at the beginning of every section provides tips to help you organize and remember the information covered in the section. Keep a science notebook so that you are ready to take notes when your teacher reviews the material in class. Keep your assignments in this notebook so that you can review them when studying for the chapter test.

SECTION 5

Time Marches On

How old is the Earth? Well, if the Earth celebrated its birthday every million years, there would be 4,600 candles on its birthday cake! Humans have been around only long enough to light the last candle on the cake.

Try to think of the Earth's history in "fast-forward." If you could watch the Earth change from this perspective, you would see mountains rise up like wrinkles in fabric and quickly wear away. You would see life-forms appear and then go extinct. In this section, you will learn that geologists must "fast-forward" the Earth's history when they write or talk about it. You will also learn about some incredible events in the history of life on Earth.

Geologic Time

Shown in **Figure 1** is the rock wall at the Dinosaur Quarry Visitor Center in Dinosaur National Monument, Utah. Contained within this wall are approximately 1,500 fossil bones that have been excavated by paleontologists. These are the remains of dinosaurs that inhabited the area about 150 million years ago. Granted, 150 million years seems to be an incredibly long period of time. However, in terms of the Earth's history, 150 million years is little more than 3% of the time our planet has existed. It is a little less than 4% of the time represented by the Earth's oldest known rocks.

What You Will Learn
- Explain how geologic time is recorded in rock layers.
- Identify important dates on the geologic time scale.
- Explain how environmental changes resulted in the extinction of some species.

Vocabulary
geologic time scale   period
eon   epoch
era   extinction

READING STRATEGY

Brainstorming The key idea of this section is the geologic time scale. Brainstorm words and phrases related to the geologic time scale.

Figure 1 *Bones of dinosaurs that lived about 150 million years ago are exposed in the quarry wall at Dinosaur National Monument in Utah.*

172

↗ Be Resourceful—Use the Web

SciLinks boxes in your textbook take you to resources that you can use for science projects, reports, and research papers. Go to **scilinks.org** and type in the **SciLinks code** to find information on a topic.

Visit go.hrw.com
Check out the **Current Science**® magazine articles and other materials that go with your textbook at **go.hrw.com**. Click on the textbook icon and the table of contents to see all of the resources for each chapter.

Figure 2 *Well-preserved plant and animal fossils are common in the Green River formation. Clockwise from the upper right are a fossil leaf, a dragonfly, a fish, and a turtle.*

The Rock Record and Geologic Time

One of the best places in North America to see the Earth's history recorded in rock layers is in Grand Canyon National Park. The Colorado River has cut the canyon nearly 2 km deep in some places. Over the course of 6 million years, the river has eroded countless layers of rock. These layers represent almost half, or nearly 2 billion years, of Earth's history.

Reading Check How much geologic time is represented by the rock layers in *Reading Checks*

The Fossil

Figure 2 show formation. T Utah, and C were once p period of m common in the fine-grai delicate stru

The Cenozoic Era—The Age of Mammals

The Cenozoic era, as shown in **Figure 7**, began about 65.5 million years ago and continues to the present. This era is known as the *Age of Mammals*. During the Mesozoic era, mammals had to compete with dinosaurs and other animals for food and habitat. After the mass extinction at the end of the Mesozoic era, mammals flourished. Unique traits, such as regulating body temperature internally and bearing young that develop inside the mother, may have helped mammals survive the environmental changes that probably caused the extinction of the dinosaurs.

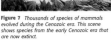

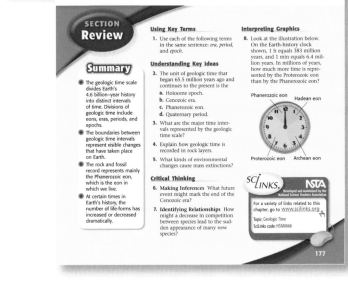

Figure 7 *Thousands of species of mammals evolved during the Cenozoic era. This scene shows species from the early Cenozoic era that are now extinct.*

SECTION Review

Summary

● The geologic time scale divides Earth's 4.6 billion–year history into distinct intervals of time. Divisions of geologic time include eons, eras, periods, and epochs.

● The boundaries between geologic time intervals represent visible changes that have taken place on Earth.

● The rock and fossil record represents mainly the Phanerozoic eon, which is the eon in which we live.

● At certain times in Earth's history, the number of life-forms has increased or decreased dramatically.

Using Key Terms

1. Use each of the following terms in the same sentence: *era, period,* and *epoch.*

Understanding Key Ideas

2. The unit of geologic time that began 65.5 million years ago and continues to the present is the
   a. Holocene epoch.
   b. Cenozoic era.
   c. Phanerozoic eon.
   d. Quaternary period.

3. What are the major time intervals represented by the geologic time scale?

4. Explain how geologic time is recorded in rock layers.

5. What kinds of environmental changes cause mass extinctions?

Critical Thinking

6. **Making Inferences** What future event might mark the end of the Cenozoic era?

7. **Identifying Relationships** How might a decrease in competition between species lead to the sudden appearance of many new species?

Interpreting Graphics

8. Look at the illustration below. On the Earth-history clock shown, 1 h equals 383 million years, and 1 min equals 6.4 million years. In millions of years, how much more time is represented by the Proterozoic eon than by the Phanerozoic eon?

Phanerozoic eon   Hadean eon

Proterozoic eon   Archean eon

SciLINKS.
NSTA
Developed and maintained by the National Science Teachers Association

For a variety of links related to this chapter, go to www.scilinks.org

Topic: Geologic Time
SciLinks code: HSM0668

177

Use the Illustrations and Photos

Art shows complex ideas and processes. Learn to analyze the art so that you better understand the material you read in the text.

Tables and graphs display important information in an organized way to help you see relationships.

A picture is worth a thousand words. Look at the photographs to see relevant examples of science concepts that you are reading about.

Answer the Section Reviews

Section Reviews test your knowledge of the main points of the section. Critical Thinking items challenge you to think about the material in greater depth and to find connections that you infer from the text.

STUDY TIP When you can't answer a question, reread the section. The answer is usually there.

Do Your Homework

Your teacher may assign worksheets to help you understand and remember the material in the chapter.

STUDY TIP Don't try to answer the questions without reading the text and reviewing your class notes. A little preparation up front will make your homework assignments a lot easier. Answering the items in the Chapter Review will help prepare you for the chapter test.

Visit Holt Online Learning

If your teacher gives you a special password to log onto the **Holt Online Learning** site, you'll find your complete textbook on the Web. In addition, you'll find some great learning tools and practice quizzes. You'll be able to see how well you know the material from your textbook.

SAFETY FIRST!

Exploring, inventing, and investigating are essential to the study of science. However, these activities can also be dangerous. To make sure that your experiments and explorations are safe, you must be aware of a variety of safety guidelines. You have probably heard of the saying, "It is better to be safe than sorry." This is particularly true in a science classroom where experiments and explorations are being performed. Being uninformed and careless can result in serious injuries. Don't take chances with your own safety or with anyone else's.

The following pages describe important guidelines for staying safe in the science classroom. Your teacher may also have safety guidelines and tips that are specific to your classroom and laboratory. Take the time to be safe.

Safety Rules!

Start Out Right

Always get your teacher's permission before attempting any laboratory exploration. Read the procedures carefully, and pay particular attention to safety information and caution statements. If you are unsure about what a safety symbol means, look it up or ask your teacher. You cannot be too careful when it comes to safety. If an accident does occur, inform your teacher immediately regardless of how minor you think the accident is.

If you are instructed to note the odor of a substance, wave the fumes toward your nose with your hand. Never put your nose close to the source.

Safety Symbols

All of the experiments and investigations in this book and their related worksheets include important safety symbols to alert you to particular safety concerns. Become familiar with these symbols so that when you see them, you will know what they mean and what to do. It is important that you read this entire safety section to learn about specific dangers in the laboratory.

Eye protection

Clothing protection

Hand safety

Heating safety

Electric safety

Chemical safety

Animal safety

Sharp object

Plant safety

Eye Safety

Wear safety goggles when working around chemicals, acids, bases, or any type of flame or heating device. Wear safety goggles any time there is even the slightest chance that harm could come to your eyes. If any substance gets into your eyes, notify your teacher immediately and flush your eyes with running water for at least 15 minutes. Treat any unknown chemical as if it were a dangerous chemical. Never look directly into the sun. Doing so could cause permanent blindness.

Avoid wearing contact lenses in a laboratory situation. Even if you are wearing safety goggles, chemicals can get between the contact lenses and your eyes. If your doctor requires that you wear contact lenses instead of glasses, wear eye-cup safety goggles in the lab.

Safety Equipment

Know the locations of the nearest fire alarms and any other safety equipment, such as fire blankets and eyewash fountains, as identified by your teacher, and know the procedures for using the equipment.

Neatness

Keep your work area free of all unnecessary books and papers. Tie back long hair, and secure loose sleeves or other loose articles of clothing, such as ties and bows. Remove dangling jewelry. Don't wear open-toed shoes or sandals in the laboratory. Never eat, drink, or apply cosmetics in a laboratory setting. Food, drink, and cosmetics can easily become contaminated with dangerous materials.

Certain hair products (such as aerosol hair spray) are flammable and should not be worn while working near an open flame. Avoid wearing hair spray or hair gel on lab days.

Sharp/Pointed Objects

Use knives and other sharp instruments with extreme care. Never cut objects while holding them in your hands. Place objects on a suitable work surface for cutting.

Be extra careful when using any glassware. When adding a heavy object to a graduated cylinder, tilt the cylinder so that the object slides slowly to the bottom.

Heat

Wear safety goggles when using a heating device or a flame. Whenever possible, use an electric hot plate as a heat source instead of using an open flame. When heating materials in a test tube, always angle the test tube away from yourself and others. To avoid burns, wear heat-resistant gloves whenever instructed to do so.

Electricity

Be careful with electrical cords. When using a microscope with a lamp, do not place the cord where it could trip someone. Do not let cords hang over a table edge in a way that could cause equipment to fall if the cord is accidentally pulled. Do not use equipment with damaged cords. Be sure that your hands are dry and that the electrical equipment is in the "off" position before plugging it in. Turn off and unplug electrical equipment when you are finished.

Chemicals

Wear safety goggles when handling any potentially dangerous chemicals, acids, or bases. If a chemical is unknown, handle it as you would a dangerous chemical. Wear an apron and protective gloves when you work with acids or bases or whenever you are told to do so. If a spill gets on your skin or clothing, rinse it off immediately with water for at least 5 minutes while calling to your teacher.

Never mix chemicals unless your teacher tells you to do so. Never taste, touch, or smell chemicals unless you are specifically directed to do so. Before working with a flammable liquid or gas, check for the presence of any source of flame, spark, or heat.

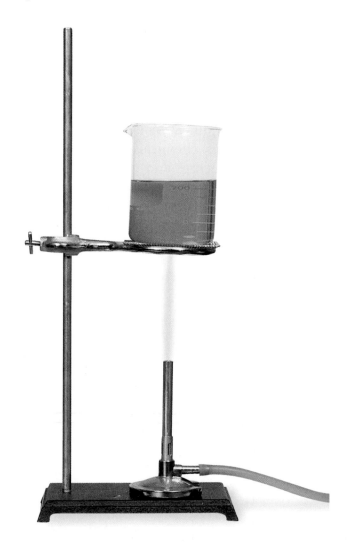

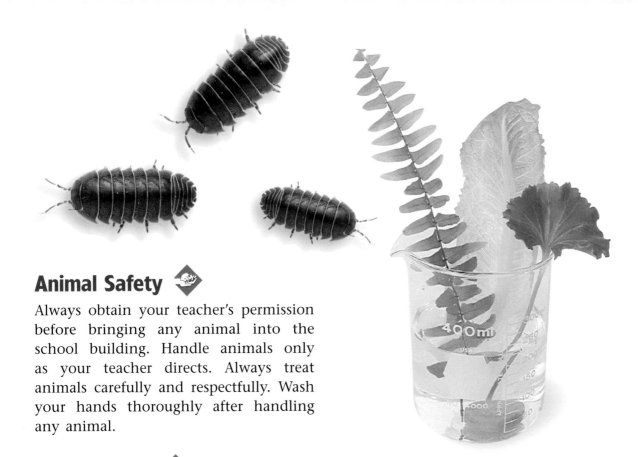

Animal Safety

Always obtain your teacher's permission before bringing any animal into the school building. Handle animals only as your teacher directs. Always treat animals carefully and respectfully. Wash your hands thoroughly after handling any animal.

Plant Safety

Do not eat any part of a plant or plant seed used in the laboratory. Wash your hands thoroughly after handling any part of a plant. When in nature, do not pick any wild plants unless your teacher instructs you to do so.

Glassware

Examine all glassware before use. Be sure that glassware is clean and free of chips and cracks. Report damaged glassware to your teacher. Glass containers used for heating should be made of heat-resistant glass.

Minerals of the Earth's Crust

The Big Idea

Minerals have characteristic physical and chemical properties that determine how each mineral is used by humans.

About the PHOTO

Fluorescence is the ability that some minerals have to glow under ultraviolet light. The beauty of mineral fluorescence is well represented at the Sterling Hill Mine in Franklin, New Jersey. In this picture taken at the mine, minerals in the rock glow as brightly as if they had been freshly painted by an artist.

PRE-READING ACTIVITY

Graphic Organizer

Concept Map Before you read the chapter, create the graphic organizer entitled "Concept Map" described in the **Study Skills** section of the Appendix. As you read the chapter, fill in the concept map with details about minerals.

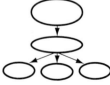

START-UP ACTIVITY

What Is Your Classroom Made Of?

One of the properties of minerals is that minerals are made from nonliving material. Complete the following activity to see if you can determine whether items in your classroom are made from living or nonliving materials.

Procedure

1. On a **sheet of paper,** make two columns. Label one column "Materials made from living things." Label the second column "Materials made from nonliving things."

2. Look around your classroom. Choose a variety of items to put on your list. Some items that you might select are your clothing, your desk, books, notebook paper, pencils, the classroom windows, doors, walls, the ceiling, and the floor.

3. With a partner, discuss each item that you have chosen. Decide into which column each item should be placed. Write down the reason for your decision.

Analysis

1. Are most of the items that you chose made of living or nonliving materials?

What Is a Mineral?

You may think that all minerals look like gems. But, in fact, most minerals look more like rocks. Does this mean that minerals are the same as rocks? Well, not really. So, what's the difference?

For one thing, rocks are made of minerals, but minerals are not made of rocks. A **mineral** is a naturally formed, inorganic solid that has a definite crystalline structure.

Mineral Structure

By answering the four questions in **Figure 1,** you can tell whether an object is a mineral. If you cannot answer "yes" to all four questions, you don't have a mineral. Three of the four questions may be easy to answer. The question about crystalline structure may be more difficult. To understand what crystalline structure is, you need to know a little about the elements that make up a mineral. **Elements** are pure substances that cannot be broken down into simpler substances by ordinary chemical means. All minerals contain one or more of the 92 naturally occurring elements.

What You Will Learn

● Describe the structure of minerals.
● Describe the two major groups of minerals.

Vocabulary

mineral
element
compound
crystal
silicate mineral
nonsilicate mineral

READING STRATEGY

Paired Summarizing Read this section silently. In pairs, take turns summarizing the material. Stop to discuss ideas that seem confusing.

Does it have a crystalline structure? Minerals are crystals, which have a repeating inner structure that is often reflected in the shape of the crystal. Minerals generally have the same chemical composition throughout.

Is it nonliving material? A mineral is inorganic, meaning it isn't made of living things.

Is it a solid? Minerals can't be gases or liquids.

Is it formed in nature? Crystalline materials made by people aren't classified as minerals.

Figure 1 *The answers to these four questions will determine whether an object is a mineral.*

Atoms and Compounds

Each element is made of only one kind of atom. An *atom* is the smallest part of an element that has all the properties of that element. Like other substances, minerals are made up of atoms of one or more elements.

Most minerals are made of compounds of several different elements. A **compound** is a substance made of two or more elements that have been chemically joined, or bonded. Halite, NaCl, for example, is a compound of sodium, Na, and chlorine, Cl, as shown in **Figure 2.** A few minerals, such as gold and silver, are composed of only one element. A mineral that is composed of only one element is called a *native element.*

✓ Reading Check How does a compound differ from an element? (*See the Appendix for answers to Reading Checks.*)

Crystals

Solid, geometric forms of minerals produced by a repeating pattern of atoms or molecules that is present throughout the mineral are called **crystals.** A crystal's shape is determined by the arrangement of the atoms or molecules within the crystal. The arrangement of atoms or molecules in turn is determined by the kinds of atoms or molecules that make up the mineral. Each mineral has a definite crystalline structure. All minerals can be grouped into crystal classes according to the kinds of crystals they form. **Figure 3** shows how the arrangement of atoms in gold may form cubic crystals.

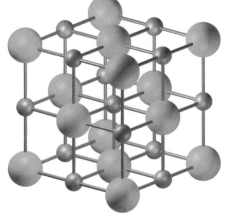

Figure 2 *When atoms of sodium (purple) and chlorine (green) join, they form a compound commonly known as rock salt, or the mineral halite.*

mineral a naturally formed, inorganic solid that has a definite crystalline structure

element a substance that cannot be separated or broken down into simpler substances by chemical means

compound a substance made up of atoms of two or more different elements joined by chemical bonds

crystal a solid whose atoms, ions, or molecules are arranged in a definite pattern

---

Figure 3 **Composition of the Mineral Gold**

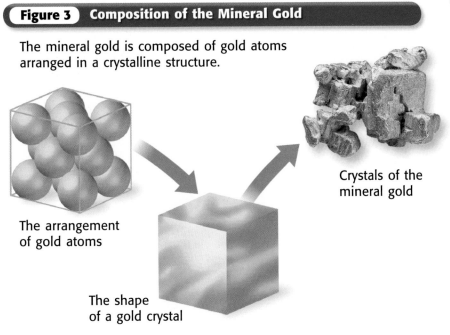

The mineral gold is composed of gold atoms arranged in a crystalline structure.

The arrangement of gold atoms

The shape of a gold crystal

Crystals of the mineral gold

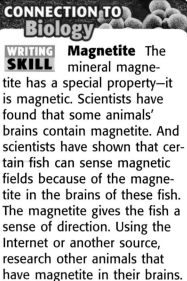
Two Groups of Minerals

The most common classification of minerals is based on chemical composition. Minerals are divided into two groups based on their chemical composition. These groups are the silicate minerals and the nonsilicate minerals.

Silicate Minerals

Silicon and oxygen are the two most common elements in the Earth's crust. Minerals that contain a combination of these two elements are called **silicate minerals.** Silicate minerals make up more than 90% of the Earth's crust. The rest of the Earth's crust is made up of nonsilicate minerals. Silicon and oxygen usually combine with other elements, such as aluminum, iron, magnesium, and potassium, to make up silicate minerals. Some of the more common silicate minerals are shown in **Figure 4.**

Nonsilicate Minerals

Minerals that do not contain a combination of the elements silicon and oxygen form a group called the **nonsilicate minerals.** Some of these minerals are made up of elements such as carbon, oxygen, fluorine, and sulfur. **Figure 5** on the following page shows the most important classes of nonsilicate minerals.

Reading Check How do silicate minerals differ from nonsilicate minerals?

silicate mineral a mineral that contains a combination of silicon, oxygen, and one or more metals

nonsilicate mineral a mineral that does not contain compounds of silicon and oxygen

Figure 4 Common Silicate Minerals

Quartz is the basic building block of many rocks.

Feldspar minerals are the main component of most rocks on the Earth's surface.

Mica minerals separate easily into sheets when they break. Biotite is one of several kinds of mica.

Figure 5 Classes of Nonsilicate Minerals

Native elements are minerals that are composed of only one element. Some examples are copper, Cu, gold, Au, and silver, Ag. Native elements are used in communications and electronics equipment.

Copper

Oxides are compounds that form when an element, such as aluminum or iron, combines chemically with oxygen. Oxide minerals are used to make abrasives, aircraft parts, and paint.

Corundum

Carbonates are minerals that contain combinations of carbon and oxygen in their chemical structure. We use carbonate minerals in cement, building stones, and fireworks.

Calcite

Sulfates are minerals that contain sulfur and oxygen, SO_4. Sulfates are used in cosmetics, toothpaste, cement, and paint.

Gypsum

Halides are compounds that form when fluorine, chlorine, iodine, or bromine combine with sodium, potassium, or calcium. Halide minerals are used in the chemical industry and in detergents.

Fluorite

Sulfides are minerals that contain one or more elements, such as lead, iron, or nickel, combined with sulfur. Sulfide minerals are used to make batteries, medicines, and electronic parts.

Galena

SECTION Review

Summary

- A mineral is a naturally formed, inorganic solid that has a definite crystalline structure.
- Minerals may be either elements or compounds.
- Mineral crystals are solid, geometric forms that are produced by a repeating pattern of atoms.
- Minerals are classified as either silicate minerals or nonsilicate minerals based on the elements of which they are composed.

Using Key Terms

1. In your own words, write a definition for each of the following terms: *element*, *compound*, and *mineral*.

Understanding Key Ideas

2. Which of the following minerals is a nonsilicate mineral?
   a. mica
   b. quartz
   c. gypsum
   d. feldspar

3. What is a crystal, and what determines a crystal's shape?

4. Describe the two major groups of minerals.

Math Skills

5. If there are approximately 3,600 known minerals and about 20 of the minerals are native elements, what percentage of all minerals are native elements?

Critical Thinking

6. **Applying Concepts** Explain why each of the following is not considered a mineral: water, oxygen, honey, and teeth.

7. **Applying Concepts** Explain why scientists consider ice to be a mineral.

8. **Making Comparisons** In what ways are sulfate and sulfide minerals the same. In what ways are they different?

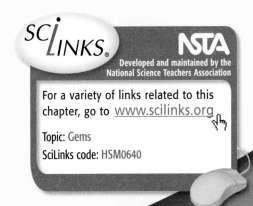

SCiLINKS

NSTA
Developed and maintained by the
National Science Teachers Association

For a variety of links related to this chapter, go to www.scilinks.org

Topic: Gems
SciLinks code: HSM0640

Identifying Minerals

If you closed your eyes and tasted different foods, you could probably determine what the foods are by noting properties such as saltiness or sweetness. You can also determine the identity of a mineral by noting different properties.

In this section, you will learn about the properties that will help you identify minerals.

What You Will Learn

● Identify seven ways to determine the identity of minerals.
● Explain special properties of minerals.

Vocabulary

luster	fracture
streak	hardness
cleavage	density

READING STRATEGY

Reading Organizer As you read this section, create an outline of the section. Use the headings from the section in your outline.

luster the way in which a mineral reflects light

Color

The same mineral can come in a variety of colors. For example, in its purest state quartz is clear. Samples of quartz that contain various types of and various amounts of impurities, however, can be a variety of colors.

Besides impurities, other factors can change the appearance of minerals. The mineral pyrite, often called fool's gold, normally has a golden color. But if pyrite is exposed to air and water for a long period, it can turn brown or black. Because of factors such as impurities, color usually is not the best way to identify a mineral.

Luster

The way a surface reflects light is called **luster.** When you say an object is shiny or dull, you are describing its luster. Minerals have metallic, submetallic, or nonmetallic luster. If a mineral is shiny, it has a metallic luster. If the mineral is dull, its luster is either submetallic or nonmetallic. The different types of lusters are shown in **Figure 1.**

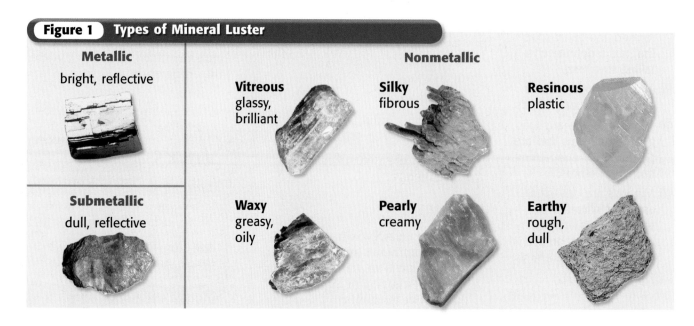

Figure 1 Types of Mineral Luster

Metallic
bright, reflective

Submetallic
dull, reflective

Nonmetallic

Vitreous
glassy,
brilliant

Waxy
greasy,
oily

Silky
fibrous

Pearly
creamy

Resinous
plastic

Earthy
rough,
dull

Streak

The color of a mineral in powdered form is called the mineral's **streak.** A mineral's streak can be found by rubbing the mineral against a piece of unglazed porcelain called a *streak plate.* The mark left on the streak plate is the streak. The streak is a thin layer of powdered mineral. The color of a mineral's streak is not always the same as the color of the mineral sample. The difference between color and streak is shown in **Figure 2.** Unlike the surface of a mineral sample, the streak is not affected by air or water. For this reason, using streak is more reliable than using color in identifying a mineral.

Reading Check Why is using streak more reliable in identifying a mineral than using color is? (*See the Appendix for answers to Reading Checks.*)

Figure 2 *The color of the mineral hematite may vary, but hematite's streak is always red-brown.*

Cleavage and Fracture

Different types of minerals break in different ways. The way a mineral breaks is determined by the arrangement of its atoms. **Cleavage** is the tendency of some minerals to break along smooth, flat surfaces. **Figure 3** shows the cleavage patterns of the minerals mica and halite.

Fracture is the tendency of some minerals to break unevenly along curved or irregular surfaces. One type of fracture is shown in **Figure 4.**

streak the color of the powder of a mineral

cleavage the splitting of a mineral along smooth, flat surfaces

fracture the manner in which a mineral breaks along either curved or irregular surfaces

Figure 3 *Cleavage varies with mineral type.*

Mica breaks easily ▶
into distinct sheets.

Halite breaks at 90°
angles in three directions.
▼

Figure 4 *This sample of quartz shows a curved fracture pattern called* conchoidal fracture *(kahn KOYD uhl FRAK chuhr).*

Figure 5 Mohs Hardness Scale

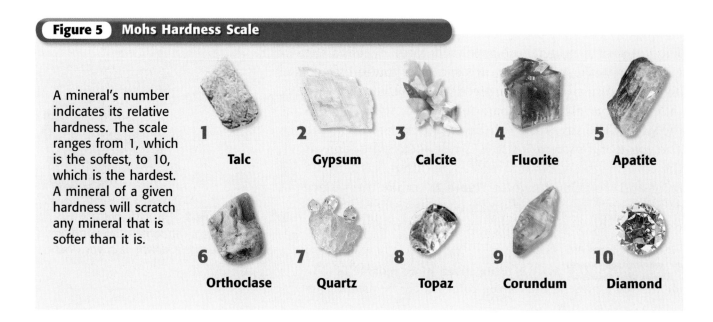

A mineral's number indicates its relative hardness. The scale ranges from 1, which is the softest, to 10, which is the hardest. A mineral of a given hardness will scratch any mineral that is softer than it is.

1 Talc
2 Gypsum
3 Calcite
4 Fluorite
5 Apatite
6 Orthoclase
7 Quartz
8 Topaz
9 Corundum
10 Diamond

hardness a measure of the ability of a mineral to resist scratching

density the ratio of the mass of a substance to the volume of the substance

Scratch Test

1. You will need a **penny,** a **pencil,** and your **finger-nail.** Which one of these three materials is the hardest?

2. Use your fingernail to try to scratch the graphite at the tip of a pencil.

3. Now try to scratch the penny with your fingernail.

4. Rank the three materials in order from softest to hardest.

Hardness

A mineral's resistance to being scratched is called **hardness.** To determine the hardness of minerals, scientists use *Mohs hardness scale,* shown in **Figure 5.** Notice that talc has a rating of 1 and diamond has a rating of 10. The greater a mineral's resistance to being scratched is, the higher the mineral's rating is. To identify a mineral by using Mohs scale, try to scratch the surface of a mineral with the edge of one of the 10 reference minerals. If the reference mineral scratches your mineral, the reference mineral is harder than your mineral.

✓ *Reading Check* How would you determine the hardness of an unidentified mineral sample?

Density

If you pick up a golf ball and a table-tennis ball, which will feel heavier? Although the balls are of similar size, the golf ball will feel heavier because it is denser. **Density** is the measure of how much matter is in a given amount of space. In other words, density is a ratio of an object's mass to its volume. Density is usually measured in grams per cubic centimeter. Because water has a density of 1 g/cm^3, it is used as a reference point for other substances. The ratio of an object's density to the density of water is called the object's *specific gravity.* The specific gravity of gold, for example, is 19. So, gold has a density of 19 g/cm^3. In other words, 1 cm^3 of gold contains 19 times as much matter than 1 cm^3 of water contains.

Special Properties

Some properties are particular to only a few types of minerals. The properties shown in **Figure 6** can help you quickly identify the minerals shown. To identify some properties, however, you will need specialized equipment.

Figure 6 Special Properties of Some Minerals

Fluorescence
Calcite and fluorite glow under ultraviolet light. The same fluorite sample is shown in ultraviolet light (top) and in white light (bottom).

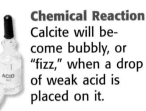
Chemical Reaction
Calcite will become bubbly, or "fizz," when a drop of weak acid is placed on it.

Optical Properties
A thin, clear piece of calcite placed over an image will cause a double image.

Magnetism
Both magnetite and pyrrhotite are natural magnets that attract iron.

Taste
Halite has a salty taste.

Radioactivity
Minerals that contain radium or uranium can be detected by a Geiger counter.

SECTION Review

Summary

- Properties that can be used to identify minerals are color, luster, streak, cleavage, fracture, hardness, and density.

- Some minerals can be identified by special properties they have, such as taste, magnetism, fluorescence, radioactivity, chemical reaction, and optical properties.

Using Key Terms

1. Use each of the following terms in a separate sentence: *luster, streak,* and *cleavage.*

Understanding Key Ideas

2. Which of the following properties of minerals is expressed in numbers?
   a. fracture
   b. cleavage
   c. hardness
   d. streak

3. How do you determine a mineral's streak?

4. Briefly describe the special properties of minerals.

Math Skills

5. If a mineral has a specific gravity of 5.5, how much more matter is there in 1 cm^3 of this mineral than in 1 cm^3 of water?

Critical Thinking

6. **Applying Concepts** What properties would you use to determine whether two mineral samples are different minerals?

7. **Applying Concepts** If a mineral scratches calcite but is scratched by apatite, what is the mineral's hardness?

8. **Analyzing Methods** What would be the easiest way to identify calcite?

SCiLINKS®

Developed and maintained by the National Science Teachers Association

For a variety of links related to this chapter, go to www.scilinks.org

Topic: Identifying Minerals
SciLinks code: HSM0782

The Formation, Mining, and Use of Minerals

If you wanted to find a mineral, where do you think you would look?

Minerals form in a variety of environments in the Earth's crust. Each of these environments has a different set of physical and chemical conditions. Therefore, the environment in which a mineral forms determines the mineral's properties. Environments in which minerals form may be on or near the Earth's surface or deep beneath the Earth's surface.

What You Will Learn

- Describe the environments in which minerals form.
- Compare the two types of mining.
- Describe two ways to reduce the effects of mining.
- Describe different uses for metallic and nonmetallic minerals.

Vocabulary

ore
reclamation

READING STRATEGY

Discussion Read this section silently. Write down questions that you have about this section. Discuss your questions in a small group.

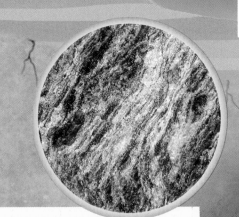

Limestones Surface water and ground-water carry dissolved materials into lakes and seas, where they crystallize on the bottom. Minerals that form in this environment include calcite and dolomite.

Evaporating Salt Water When a body of salt water dries up, minerals such as gypsum and halite are left behind. As the salt water evaporates, these minerals crystallize.

Metamorphic Rocks When changes in pressure, temperature, or chemical makeup alter a rock, *metamorphism* takes place. Minerals that form in metamorphic rock include calcite, garnet, graphite, hematite, magnetite, mica, and talc.

INTERNET ACTIVITY

For another activity related to this chapter, go to go.hrw.com and type in the keyword **HZ5MINW**.

Hot-Water Solutions
Groundwater works its way downward and is heated by magma. It then reacts with minerals to form a hot liquid solution. Dissolved metals and other elements crystallize out of the hot fluid to form new minerals. Gold, copper, sulfur, pyrite, and galena form in such hot-water environments.

Pegmatites As magma moves upward, it can form teardrop-shaped bodies called *pegmatites.* The mineral crystals in pegmatites become extremely large, sometimes growing to several meters across! Many gemstones, such as topaz and tourmaline, form in pegmatites.

Plutons As magma rises upward through the crust, it sometimes stops moving before it reaches the surface and cools slowly, forming millions of mineral crystals. Eventually, the entire magma body solidifies to form a *pluton.* Mica, feldspar, magnetite, and quartz are some of the minerals that form from magma.

Surface Coal Mining
Producing 1 metric ton of coal requires that up to 30 metric tons of earth be removed first. Some surface coal mines produce up to 50,000 metric tons of coal per day. How many metric tons of earth might have to be removed in order to mine 50,000 metric tons of coal?

ore a natural material whose concentration of economically valuable minerals is high enough for the material to be mined profitably

Mining

Many kinds of rocks and minerals must be mined to extract the valuable elements they contain. Geologists use the term **ore** to describe a mineral deposit large enough and pure enough to be mined for profit. Rocks and minerals are removed from the ground by one of two methods—surface mining or sub-surface mining. The method miners choose depends on how close to the surface or how far down in the Earth the mineral is located.

Surface Mining

When mineral deposits are located at or near the surface of the Earth, surface-mining methods are used to remove the minerals. Types of surface mines include open pits, surface coal mines, and quarries.

Open-pit mining is used to remove large, near-surface deposits of economically important minerals such as gold and copper. As shown in **Figure 1,** ore is mined downward, layer by layer, in an open-pit mine. Explosives are often used to break up the ore. The ore is then loaded into haul trucks and transported from the mine for processing. Quarries are open pits that are used to mine building stone, crushed rock, sand, and gravel. Coal that is near the surface is removed by surface coal mining. Surface coal mining is sometimes known as strip mining because the coal is removed in strips that may be as wide as 50 m and as long as 1 km.

Figure 1 *In open-pit mines, the ore is mined downward in layers. The stair-step excavation of the walls keeps the sides of the mine from collapsing. Giant haul trucks (inset) are used to transport ore from the mine.*

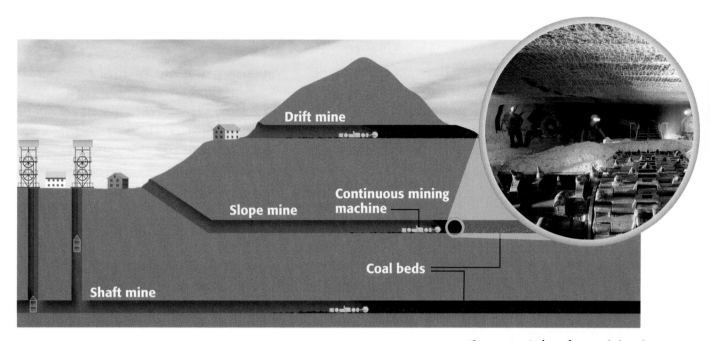

Drift mine

Continuous mining machine

Slope mine

Coal beds

Shaft mine

Subsurface Mining

Subsurface mining methods are used when mineral deposits are located too deep within the Earth to be surface mined. Subsurface mining often requires that passageways be dug into the Earth to reach the ore. As shown in **Figure 2,** these passageways may be dug horizontally or at an angle. If a mineral deposit extends deep within the Earth, however, a vertical shaft is sunk. This shaft may connect a number of passageways that intersect the ore at different levels.

✔️ **Reading Check** Compare surface and subsurface mining.
(*See the Appendix for answers to Reading Checks.*)

Responsible Mining

Mining gives us the minerals we need, but it may also create problems. Mining can destroy or disturb the habitats of plants and animals. Also, the waste products from a mine may get into water sources, which pollutes surface water and groundwater.

Mine Reclamation

One way to reduce the potential harmful effects of mining is to return the land to its original state after the mining is completed. The process by which land used for mining is returned to its original state or better is called **reclamation.** Reclamation of mined public and private land has been required by law since the mid-1970s. Another way to reduce the effects of mining is to reduce our need for minerals. We reduce our need for minerals by recycling many of the mineral products that we currently use, such as aluminum.

Figure 2 *Subsurface mining is the removal of minerals or other materials from deep within the Earth. Passageways must be dug underground to reach the ore. Machines such as continuous mining machines (inset) are used to mine ore in subsurface mines.*

reclamation the process of returning land to its original condition after mining is completed

Recycling Minerals at Home

With a parent or guardian, locate products in your home that are made of minerals. Decide which of these products could be recycled. In your **science journal,** make a list of the products that could be recycled to save minerals.

ACTiViTY

Table 1	Common Uses of Minerals
Mineral	**Uses**
Copper	electrical wire, plumbing, coins
Diamond	jewelry, cutting tools, drill bits
Galena	batteries, ammunition
Gibbsite	cans, foil, appliances, utensils
Gold	jewelry, computers, spacecraft, dentistry
Gypsum	wallboards, plaster, cement
Halite	nutrition, highway de-icer, water softener
Quartz	glass, computer chips
Silver	photography, electronics products, jewelry
Sphalerite	jet aircraft, spacecraft, paints

The Use of Minerals

As shown in **Table 1,** some minerals are of major economic and industrial importance. Some minerals can be used just as they are. Other minerals must be processed to get the element or elements that the minerals contain. **Figure 3** shows some processed minerals used to make the parts of a bicycle.

Metallic Minerals

Some minerals are metallic. Metallic minerals have shiny surfaces, do not let light pass through them, and are good conductors of heat and electricity. Metallic minerals can be processed into metals that are strong and do not rust. Other metals can be pounded or pressed into various shapes or stretched thinly without breaking. These properties make metals desirable for use in aircraft, automobiles, computers, communications and electronic equipment, and spacecraft. Examples of metallic minerals that have many industrial uses are gold, silver, and copper.

Nonmetallic Minerals

Other minerals are nonmetals. Nonmetallic minerals have shiny or dull surfaces, may let light pass through them, and are good insulators of electricity. Nonmetallic minerals are some of the most widely used minerals in industry. For example, calcite is a major component of concrete, which is used in building roads, buildings, bridges, and other structures. Industrial sand and gravel, or silica, have uses that range from glassmaking to producing computer chips.

Figure 3 Some Materials Used in the Parts of a Bicycle

Handlebars titanium from ilmenite

Frame aluminum from bauxite

Spokes iron from magnetite

Pedals beryllium from beryl

Gemstones

Some nonmetallic minerals, called *gemstones*, are highly valued for their beauty and rarity rather than for their usefulness. Important gemstones include diamond, ruby, sapphire, emerald, aquamarine, topaz, and tourmaline. An example of a diamond is shown in **Figure 4**. Color is the most important characteristic of a gemstone. The more attractive the color is, the more valuable the gem is. Gemstones must also be durable. That is, they must be hard enough to be cut and polished. The mass of a gemstone is expressed in a unit known as a *carat*. One carat is equal to 200 mg.

✓ **Reading Check** In your own words, define the term *gemstone*.

Figure 4 *The Cullinan diamond, at the center of this scepter, is part of the largest diamond ever found.*

SECTION Review

Summary

- Environments in which minerals form may be located at or near the Earth's surface or deep below the surface.

- The two types of mining are surface mining and subsurface mining.

- Two ways to reduce the effects of mining are the reclamation of mined land and the recycling of mineral products.

- Some metallic and nonmetallic minerals have many important economic and industrial uses.

Using Key Terms

Complete each of the following sentences by choosing the correct term from the word bank.

    ore   reclamation

1. _____ is the process of returning land to its original condition after mining is completed.

2. _____ is the term used to describe a mineral deposit that is large enough and pure enough to be mined for profit.

Understanding Key Ideas

3. Which of the following conditions is NOT important in the formation of minerals?
    a. presence of groundwater
    b. evaporation
    c. volcanic activity
    d. wind

4. What are the two main types of mining, and how do they differ?

5. List some uses of metallic minerals.

6. List some uses of nonmetallic minerals.

Math Skills

7. A diamond cutter has a raw diamond that weighs 19.5 carats and from which two 5-carat diamonds will be cut. How much did the raw diamond weigh in milligrams? How much will each of the two cut diamonds weigh in milligrams?

Critical Thinking

8. **Analyzing Ideas** How does reclamation protect the environment around a mine?

9. **Applying Concepts** Suppose you find a mineral crystal that is as tall as you are. What kinds of environmental factors would cause such a crystal to form?

SCILINKS®

NSTA
Developed and maintained by the National Science Teachers Association

For a variety of links related to this chapter, go to www.scilinks.org

Topic: Mining Minerals
SciLinks code: HSM0968

Skills Practice Lab

Is It Fool's Gold?
A Dense Situation

Have you heard of fool's gold? Maybe you've seen a piece of it. This mineral is actually pyrite, and it was often passed off as real gold. However, there are simple tests that you can do to keep from being tricked. Minerals can be identified by their properties. Some properties, such as color, vary from sample to sample. Other properties, such as density and specific gravity, remain consistent across samples. In this activity, you will try to verify the identity of some mineral samples.

Ask a Question

1. How can I determine if an unknown mineral is not gold or silver?

Form a Hypothesis

2. Write a hypothesis that is a possible answer to the question above. Explain your reasoning.

Test the Hypothesis

3. Copy the data table. Use it to record your observations.

Observation Chart		
Measurement	**Galena**	**Pyrite**
Mass in air (g)		
Weight in air (N)		
Volume of mineral (mL)	DO NOT WRITE IN BOOK	
Weight in water (N)		

4. Find the mass of each sample by laying the mineral on the balance. Record the mass of each sample in your data table.

5. Attach the spring scale to the ring stand.

6. Tie a string around the sample of galena, and leave a loop at the loose end. Suspend the galena from the spring scale, and find its mass and weight in air. Do not remove the sample from the spring scale yet. Enter these data in your data table.

Galena

Pyrite

7. Fill a beaker halfway with water. Record the beginning volume of water in your data table.

8. Carefully lift the beaker around the galena until the mineral is completely submerged. Be careful not to splash any water out of the beaker! Do not allow the mineral to touch the beaker.

9. Record the new volume and weight in your data table.

10. Subtract the original volume of water from the new volume to find the amount of water displaced by the mineral. This is the volume of the mineral sample itself. Record this value in your data table.

11. Repeat steps 6–10 for the sample of pyrite.

Analyze the Results

1. **Constructing Tables** Copy the data table below. (Note: 1 mL = 1 cm³)

Density Data Table		
Mineral	**Density (g/cm³)**	**Specific gravity**
Silver	10.5	10.5
Galena	DO NOT WRITE IN BOOK	
Pyrite		
Gold	19.0	19.0

2. **Organizing Data** Use the following equations to calculate the density and specific gravity of each mineral, and record your answers in your data table.

$$density = \frac{mass\ in\ air}{volume}$$

$$specific\ gravity = \frac{weight\ in\ air}{weight\ in\ air\ -\ weight\ in\ water}$$

Draw Conclusions

3. **Drawing Conclusions** The density of pure gold is 19 g/cm³. How can you use this information to prove that your sample of pyrite is not gold?

4. **Drawing Conclusions** The density of pure silver is 10.5 g/cm³. How can you use this information to prove that your sample of galena is not silver?

5. **Applying Conclusions** If you found a gold-colored nugget, how could you find out if the nugget was real gold or fool's gold?

Chapter Review

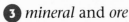
1 Use each of the following terms in a separate sentence: *element, compound,* and *mineral*.

For each pair of terms, explain how the meanings of the terms differ.

2 *color* and *streak*

3 *mineral* and *ore*

4 *silicate mineral* and *nonsilicate mineral*

UNDERSTANDING KEY IDEAS

Multiple Choice

5 Which of the following properties of minerals does Mohs scale measure?

a. luster

b. hardness

c. density

d. streak

6 Pure substances that cannot be broken down into simpler substances by ordinary chemical means are called

a. molecules.

b. elements.

c. compounds.

d. crystals.

7 Which of the following properties is considered a special property that applies to only a few minerals?

a. luster

b. hardness

c. taste

d. density

8 Silicate minerals contain a combination of the elements

a. sulfur and oxygen.

b. carbon and oxygen.

c. iron and oxygen.

d. silicon and oxygen.

9 The process by which land used for mining is returned to its original state is called

a. recycling.

b. regeneration.

c. reclamation.

d. renovation.

10 Which of the following minerals is an example of a gemstone?

a. mica

b. diamond

c. gypsum

d. copper

Short Answer

11 Compare surface and subsurface mining.

12 Explain the four characteristics of a mineral.

13 Describe two environments in which minerals form.

14 List two uses for metallic minerals and two uses for nonmetallic minerals.

15 Describe two ways to reduce the effects of mining.

16 Describe three special properties of minerals.

CRITICAL THINKING

17 **Concept Mapping** Use the following terms to create a concept map: *minerals, calcite, silicate minerals, gypsum, carbonates, nonsilicate minerals, quartz,* and *sulfates.*

18 **Making Inferences** Imagine that you are trying to determine the identity of a mineral. You decide to do a streak test. You rub the mineral across the streak plate, but the mineral does not leave a streak. Has your test failed? Explain your answer.

19 **Applying Concepts** Why would cleavage be important to gem cutters, who cut and shape gemstones?

20 **Applying Concepts** Imagine that you work at a jeweler's shop and someone brings in some gold nuggets for sale. You are not sure if the nuggets are real gold. Which identification tests would help you decide whether the nuggets are gold?

21 **Identifying Relationships** Suppose you are in a desert. You are walking across the floor of a dry lake, and you see crusts of cubic halite crystals. How do you suppose the halite crystals formed? Explain your answer.

INTERPRETING GRAPHICS

The table below shows the temperatures at which various minerals melt. Use the table below to answer the questions that follow.

Melting Points of Various Minerals	
Mineral	**Melting Point (°C)**
Mercury	−39
Sulfur	+113
Halite	801
Silver	961
Gold	1,062
Copper	1,083
Pyrite	1,171
Fluorite	1,360
Quartz	1,710
Zircon	2,500

22 According to the table, what is the approximate difference in temperature between the melting points of the mineral that has the lowest melting point and the mineral that has the highest melting point?

23 Which of the minerals listed in the table do you think is a liquid at room temperature?

24 Pyrite is often called *fool's gold.* Using the information in the table, how could you determine if a mineral sample is pyrite or gold?

25 Convert the melting points of the minerals shown in the table from degrees Celsius to degrees Fahrenheit. Use the formula $°F = (9/5 \times °C) + 32$.

Standardized Test Preparation

Read each of the passages below. Then, answer the questions that follow each passage.

Passage 1 In North America, copper was mined at least 6,700 years ago by the ancestors of the Native Americans who live on Michigan's upper peninsula. Much of this mining took place on Isle Royale, an island in Lake Superior. These <u>ancient</u> people removed copper from the rock by using stone hammers and wedges. The rock was sometimes heated first to make breaking it up easier. Copper that was mined was used to make jewelry, tools, weapons, fish hooks, and other objects. These objects were often marked with designs. The Lake Superior copper was traded over long distances along ancient trade routes. Copper objects have been found in Ohio, Florida, the Southwest, and the Northwest.

1. In the passage, what does *ancient* mean?
   - **A** young
   - **B** future
   - **C** modern
   - **D** early

2. According to the passage, what did the ancient copper miners do?
   - **F** They mined copper in Ohio, Florida, the Southwest, and the Northwest.
   - **G** They mined copper by cooling the rock in which the copper was found.
   - **H** They mined copper by using stone tools.
   - **I** They mined copper for their use only.

3. Which of the following statements is a fact according to the passage?
   - **A** Copper could be shaped into different objects.
   - **B** Copper was unknown outside of Michigan's upper peninsula.
   - **C** Copper could be mined easily from the rock in which it was found.
   - **D** Copper could not be marked with designs.

Passage 2 Most mineral names end in *-ite*. The <u>practice</u> of so naming minerals dates back to the ancient Romans and Greeks, who added *-ites* and *-itis* to common words to indicate a color, a use, or the chemistry of a mineral. More recently, mineral names have been used to honor people, such as scientists, mineral collectors, and even rulers of countries. Other minerals have been named after the place where they were discovered. These place names include mines, quarries, hills, mountains, towns, regions, and even countries. Finally, some minerals have been named after gods in Greek, Roman, and Scandinavian mythology.

1. In the passage, what does *practice* mean?
   - **A** skill
   - **B** custom
   - **C** profession
   - **D** use

2. According to the passage, the ancient Greeks and Romans did not name minerals after what?
   - **F** colors
   - **G** chemical properties
   - **H** people
   - **I** uses

3. Which of the following statements is a fact according to the passage?
   - **A** Minerals are sometimes named for the country in which they are discovered.
   - **B** Minerals are never named after their collectors.
   - **C** All mineral names end in *-ite*.
   - **D** All of the known minerals were named by the Greeks and Romans.

A sample of feldspar was analyzed to find out what it was made of. The graph below shows the results of the analysis. Use the graph below to answer the questions that follow.

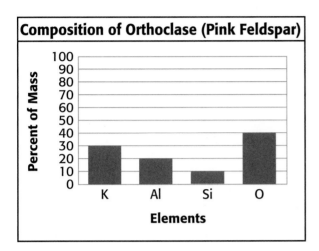

Composition of Orthoclase (Pink Feldspar)

1. The sample consists of four elements: potassium, K, aluminum, Al, silicon, Si, and oxygen, O. Which element makes up the largest percentage of your sample?

   A potassium
   B aluminum
   C silicon
   D oxygen

2. Silicate minerals, such as feldspar, contain a combination of silicon and oxygen. What percentage of your sample is composed of silicon and oxygen combined?

   F 30%
   G 40%
   H 50%
   I 70%

3. If your sample has a mass of 10 g, how many grams of oxygen does it contain?

   A 1 g
   B 2 g
   C 4 g
   D 8 g

4. Your sample of orthoclase has a hardness of 6. Which of the following minerals will scratch your sample?

   F gypsum
   G corundum
   H calcite
   I apatite

Read each question below, and choose the best answer.

1. Gold classified as 24-karat is 100% gold. Gold classified as 18-karat is 18 parts gold and 6 parts another, similar metal. The gold is therefore 18/24, or 3/4, pure. What is the percentage of pure gold in 18-karat gold?

   A 10%
   B 25%
   C 50%
   D 75%

2. Gold's specific gravity is 19. Pyrite's specific gravity is 5. What is the difference in the specific gravities of gold and pyrite?

   F 8 g/cm^3
   G 10 g/cm^3
   H 12 g/cm^3
   I 14 g/cm^3

3. In a quartz crystal, there is one silicon atom for every two oxygen atoms. So, the ratio of silicon atoms to oxygen atoms is 1:2. If there were 8 million oxygen atoms in a sample of quartz, how many silicon atoms would there be in the sample?

   A 2 million
   B 4 million
   C 8 million
   D 16 million

Science in Action

Science Fiction

"The Metal Man" by Jack Williamson

In a dark, dusty corner of Tyburn College Museum stands a life-sized statue of a man. Except for its strange greenish color, the statue looks quite ordinary. But if you look closely, you will see the perfect detail of the hair and skin. On the statue's chest, you will also see a strange mark—a dark crimson shape with six sides. No one knows how the statue ended up in the dark corner. But most people in Tyburn believe that the metal man is, or once was, Professor Thomas Kelvin of Tyburn College's geology department. Read for yourself the strange story of Professor Kelvin and the Metal Man, which is in the *Holt Anthology of Science Fiction*.

Language Arts ACTIVITY

WRITING SKILL Read "The Metal Man" by Jack Williamson. Write a short essay explaining how the ideas in the story are related to what you are learning.

Weird Science

Wieliczka Salt Mine

Imagine an underground city that is made entirely of salt. Within the city are churches, chapels, rooms of many kinds, and salt lakes. Sculptures of biblical scenes, saints, and famous historical figures carved from salt are found throughout the city. Even chandeliers of salt hang from the ceilings. Such a city is located 16 km southeast of Krakow, Poland, inside the Wieliczka (VEE uh LEETS kuh) Salt Mine. As the mine grew over the past 700 years, it turned into an elaborate underground city. Miners constructed chapels to patron saints so they could pray for a safe day in the mine. Miners also developed superstitions about the mine. So, images that were meant to bring good luck were carved in salt. In 1978, the mine was added to UNESCO's list of endangered world heritage sites. Many of the sculptures in the mine have begun to dissolve because of the humidity in the air. Efforts to save the treasures in the mine from further damage were begun in 1996.

Social Studies ACTIVITY

WRITING SKILL Research some aspect of the role of salt in human history. For example, subjects might include the Saharan and Tibetan salt trade or the use of salt as a form of money in ancient Poland. Report your findings in a one-page essay.

Jamie Hill

The Emerald Man Jamie Hill was raised in the Brushy Mountains of North Carolina. While growing up, Hill gained firsthand knowledge of the fabulous green crystals that could be found in the mountains. These green crystals were emeralds. Emerald is the green variety of the silicate mineral beryl and is a valuable gemstone. Emerald crystals form in pockets, or openings, in rock known as *pegmatite*.

Since 1985, Hill has been searching for pockets containing emeralds in rock near the small town of Hiddenite, North Carolina. He has been amazingly successful. Hill has discovered some spectacular emerald crystals. The largest of these crystals weighs 858 carats and is on display at the North Carolina Museum of Natural Science. Estimates of the total value of the emeralds that Hill has discovered so far are well in the millions of dollars. Hill's discoveries have made him a celebrity, and he has appeared both on national TV and in magazines.

Math ACTIVITY

An emerald discovered by Jamie Hill in 1999 was cut into a 7.85-carat stone that sold for $64,000 per carat. What was the total value of the cut stone?

To learn more about these Science in Action topics, visit go.hrw.com and type in the keyword HZ5MINF.

Current Science

Check out Current Science® articles related to this chapter by visiting go.hrw.com. Just type in the keyword HZ5CS03.

2

Rocks: Mineral Mixtures

The Big Idea

Rock changes through the rock cycle and is classified by how it formed, by its composition, and by its texture.

About the

Irish legend claims that the mythical hero Finn MacCool built the Giant's Causeway, shown here. But this rock formation is the result of the cooling of huge amounts of molten rock. As the molten rock cooled, it formed tall pillars separated by cracks called *columnar joints*.

PRE-READING ACTIVITY

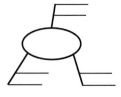

Graphic Organizer **Spider Map** Before you read the chapter, create the graphic organizer entitled "Spider Map" described in the **Study Skills** section of the Appendix. Label the circle "Rock." Create a leg for each of the sections in this chapter. As you read the chapter, fill in the map with details about the material presented in each section of the chapter.

START-UP ACTIVITY

Classifying Objects

Scientists use the physical and chemical properties of rocks to classify rocks. Classifying objects such as rocks requires looking at many properties. Do this exercise for some classification practice.

Procedure

1. Your teacher will give you a **bag** containing **several objects.** Examine the objects, and note features such as size, color, shape, texture, smell, and any unique properties.

2. Develop three different ways to sort these objects.

3. Create a chart that organizes objects by properties.

Analysis

1. What properties did you use to sort the items?

2. Were there any objects that could fit into more than one group? How did you solve this problem?

3. Which properties might you use to classify rocks? Explain your answer.

The Rock Cycle

You know that paper, plastic, and aluminum can be recycled. But did you know that the Earth also recycles? And one of the things that Earth recycles is rock.

Scientists define **rock** as a naturally occurring solid mixture of one or more minerals and organic matter. It may be hard to believe, but rocks are always changing. The continual process by which new rock forms from old rock material is called the **rock cycle.**

What You Will Learn

- Describe two ways rocks have been used by humans.
- Describe four processes that shape Earth's features.
- Describe how each type of rock changes into another type as it moves through the rock cycle.
- List two characteristics of rock that are used to help classify it.

Vocabulary

rock cycle   deposition
rock   composition
erosion   texture

READING STRATEGY

Reading Organizer As you read this section, make a flowchart of the steps of the rock cycle.

The Value of Rock

Rock has been an important natural resource as long as humans have existed. Early humans used rocks as hammers to make other tools. They discovered that they could make arrowheads, spear points, knives, and scrapers by carefully shaping rocks such as chert and obsidian.

Rock has also been used for centuries to make buildings, monuments, and roads. **Figure 1** shows how rock has been used as a construction material by both ancient and modern civilizations. Buildings have been made out of granite, limestone, marble, sandstone, slate, and other rocks. Modern buildings also contain concrete and plaster, in which rock is an important ingredient.

✓ **Reading Check** Name some types of rock that have been used to construct buildings. (*See the Appendix for answers to Reading Checks.*)

Figure 1 *The ancient Egyptians used a sedimentary rock called* limestone *to construct the pyramids at Giza (left). Granite, an igneous rock, was used to construct the Texas state capitol building in Austin (right).*

Processes That Shape the Earth

Certain geological processes make and destroy rock. These processes shape the features of our planet. These processes also influence the type of rock that is found in a certain area of Earth's surface.

Weathering, Erosion, and Deposition

The process in which water, wind, ice, and heat break down rock is called *weathering*. Weathering is important because it breaks down rock into fragments. These rock and mineral fragments are the sediment of which much sedimentary rock is made.

The process by which sediment is removed from its source is called **erosion.** Water, wind, ice, and gravity can erode and move sediments and cause them to collect. **Figure 2** shows an example of the way land looks after weathering and erosion.

The process in which sediment moved by erosion is dropped and comes to rest is called **deposition.** Sediment is deposited in bodies of water and other low-lying areas. In those places, sediment may be pressed and cemented together by minerals dissolved in water to form sedimentary rock.

Heat and Pressure

Sedimentary rock made of sediment can also form when buried sediment is squeezed by the weight of overlying layers of sediment. If the temperature and pressure are high enough at the bottom of the sediment, the rock can change into metamorphic rock. In some cases, the rock gets hot enough to melt. This melting creates the magma that eventually cools to form igneous rock.

How the Cycle Continues

Buried rock is exposed at the Earth's surface by a combination of uplift and erosion. *Uplift* is movement within the Earth that causes rocks inside the Earth to be moved to the Earth's surface. When uplifted rock reaches the Earth's surface, weathering, erosion, and deposition begin.

rock a naturally occurring solid mixture of one or more minerals or organic matter

rock cycle the series of processes in which a rock forms, changes from one type to another, is destroyed, and forms again by geological processes

erosion the process by which wind, water, ice, or gravity transports soil and sediment from one location to another

deposition the process in which material is laid down

Figure 2 *Bryce Canyon, in Utah, is an excellent example of how the processes of weathering and erosion shape the face of our planet.*

Illustrating the Rock Cycle

You have learned about various geological processes, such as weathering, erosion, heat, and pressure, that create and destroy rock. The diagram on these two pages illustrates one way that sand grains can change as different geological processes act on them. In the following steps, you will see how these processes change the original sand grains into sedimentary rock, metamorphic rock, and igneous rock.

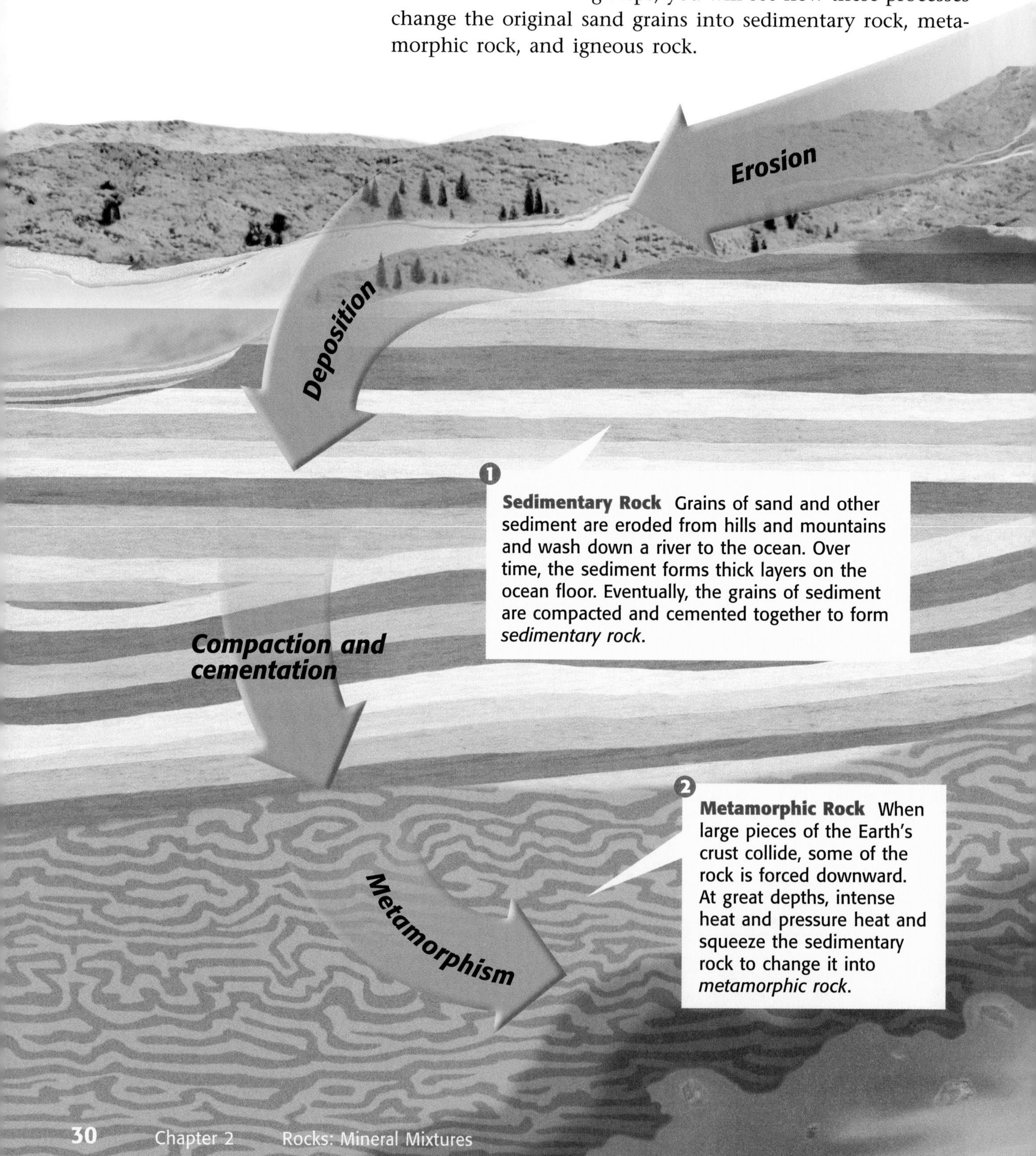

Erosion

Deposition

1

Sedimentary Rock Grains of sand and other sediment are eroded from hills and mountains and wash down a river to the ocean. Over time, the sediment forms thick layers on the ocean floor. Eventually, the grains of sediment are compacted and cemented together to form *sedimentary rock*.

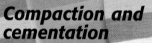

Compaction and cementation

Metamorphism

2

Metamorphic Rock When large pieces of the Earth's crust collide, some of the rock is forced downward. At great depths, intense heat and pressure heat and squeeze the sedimentary rock to change it into *metamorphic rock*.

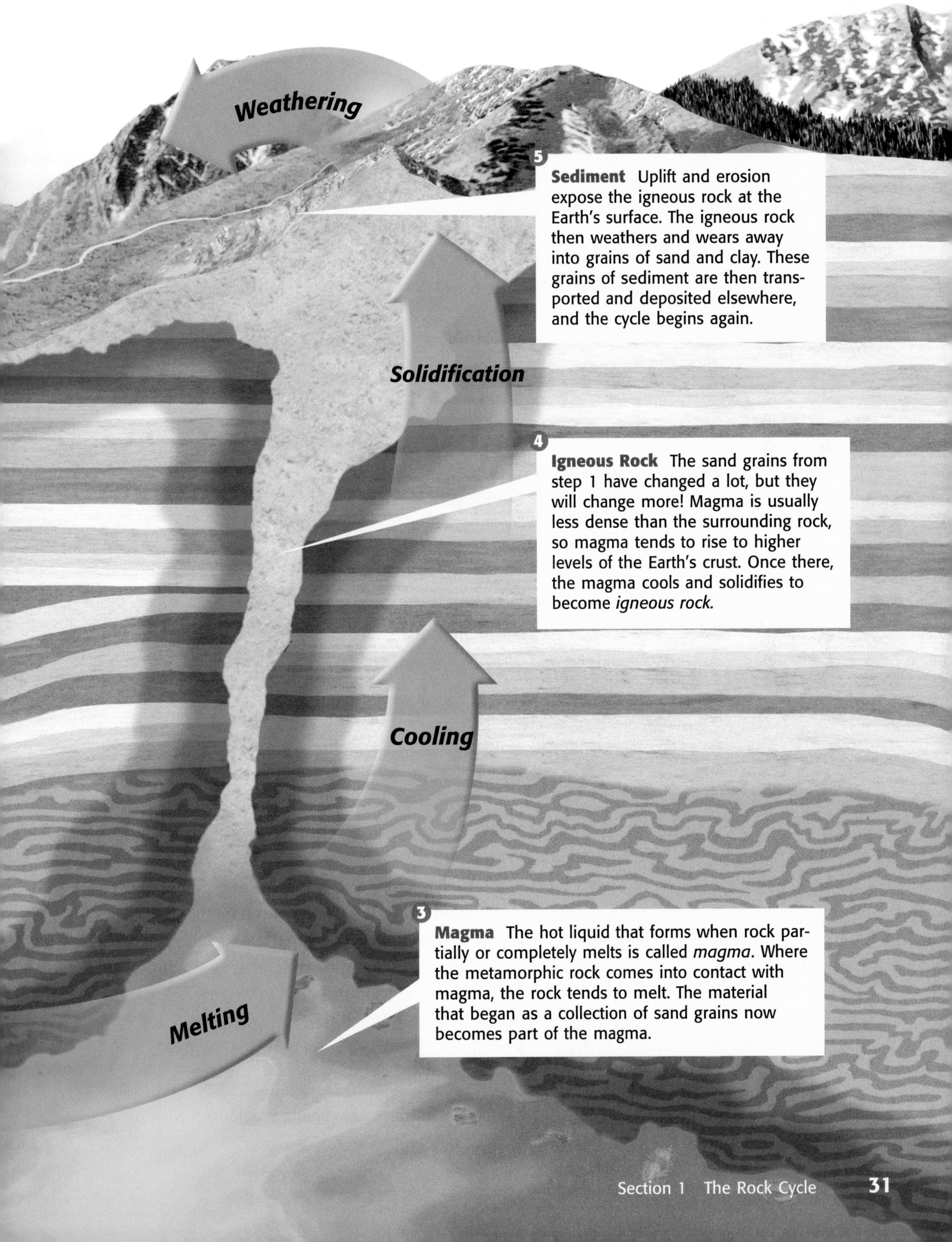

Weathering

Sediment Uplift and erosion expose the igneous rock at the Earth's surface. The igneous rock then weathers and wears away into grains of sand and clay. These grains of sediment are then transported and deposited elsewhere, and the cycle begins again.

Solidification

Igneous Rock The sand grains from step 1 have changed a lot, but they will change more! Magma is usually less dense than the surrounding rock, so magma tends to rise to higher levels of the Earth's crust. Once there, the magma cools and solidifies to become *igneous rock.*

Cooling

Magma The hot liquid that forms when rock partially or completely melts is called *magma.* Where the metamorphic rock comes into contact with magma, the rock tends to melt. The material that began as a collection of sand grains now becomes part of the magma.

Melting

Figure 3 The Rock Cycle

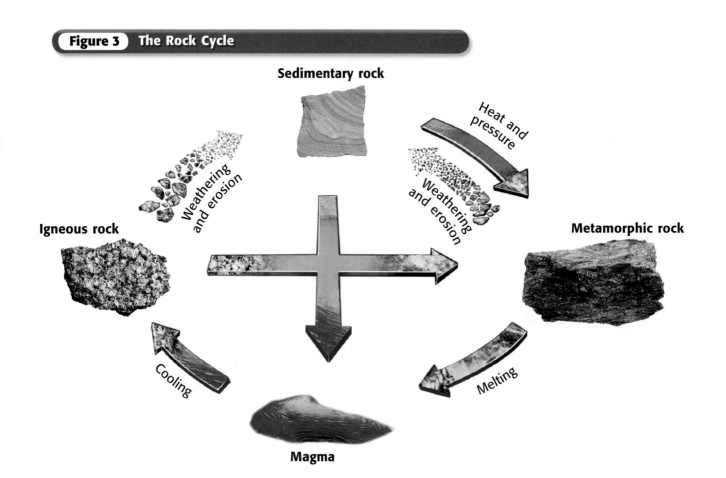

Sedimentary rock

Heat and pressure

Weathering and erosion

Weathering and erosion

Igneous rock

Metamorphic rock

Cooling

Melting

Magma

Round and Round It Goes

You have seen how different geological processes can change rock. Each rock type can change into one of the three types of rock. For example, igneous rock can change into sedimentary rock, metamorphic rock, or even back into igneous rock. This cycle, in which rock is changed by geological processes into different types of rock, is known as the rock cycle.

Rocks may follow various pathways in the rock cycle. As one rock type is changed to another type, several variables, including time, heat, pressure, weathering, and erosion may alter a rock's identity. The location of a rock determines which natural forces will have the biggest impact on the process of change. For example, rock at the Earth's surface is primarily affected by forces of weathering and erosion, whereas deep inside the Earth, rocks change because of extreme heat and pressure. **Figure 3** shows the different ways rock may change when it goes through the rock cycle and the different forces that affect rock during the cycle.

✓ *Reading Check* What processes change rock deep within the Earth?

Rock Classification

You have already learned that scientists divide all rock into three main classes based on how the rock formed: igneous, sedimentary, and metamorphic. But did you know that each class of rock can be divided further? These divisions are also based on differences in the way rocks form. For example, all igneous rock forms when magma cools and solidifies. But some igneous rocks form when magma cools *on* the Earth's surface, and others form when magma cools *beneath* the surface. Therefore, igneous rock can be divided again based on how and where it forms. Sedimentary and metamorphic rocks are also divided into groups. How do scientists know how to classify rocks? They study rocks in detail using two important criteria—composition and texture.

Composition

The minerals a rock contains determine the **composition** of that rock, as shown in **Figure 4.** For example, a rock made of mostly the mineral quartz will have a composition very similar to that of quartz. But a rock made of 50% quartz and 50% feldspar will have a very different composition than quartz does.

✓ **Reading Check** What determines a rock's composition?

What's in It?

Assume that a granite sample you are studying is made of 30% quartz and 55% feldspar by volume. The rest is made of biotite mica. What percentage of the sample is biotite mica?

composition the chemical makeup of a rock; describes either the minerals or other materials in the rock

---

Figure 4 **Two Examples of Rock Composition**

The composition of a rock depends on the minerals the rock contains.

Limestone

95% Calcite   5% Aragonite

Granite

10% Biotite mica

35% Quartz   55% Feldspar

Figure 5   Three Examples of Sedimentary Rock Texture

Fine-grained

Siltstone

Medium-grained

Sandstone

Coarse-grained

Conglomerate

Texture

texture the quality of a rock that is based on the sizes, shapes, and positions of the rock's grains

The size, shape, and positions of the grains that make up a rock determine a rock's **texture.** Sedimentary rock can have a fine-grained, medium-grained, or coarse-grained texture, depending on the size of the grains that make up the rock. Three samples of textures are shown in **Figure 5.** The texture of igneous rock can be fine-grained or coarse-grained, depending on how much time magma has to cool. Based on the degree of temperature and pressure a rock is exposed to, metamorphic rock can also have a fine-grained or coarse-grained texture.

The texture of a rock can provide clues as to how and where the rock formed. Look at the rocks shown in **Figure 6.** The rocks look different because they formed in very different ways. The texture of a rock can reveal the process that formed it.

✓ *Reading Check* Give three examples of sedimentary rock textures.

Figure 6   **Texture and Rock Formation**

Basalt, a fine-grained igneous rock, forms when lava that erupts onto Earth's surface cools rapidly.

Sandstone, a medium-grained sedimentary rock, forms when sand grains deposited in dunes, on beaches, or on the ocean floor are buried and cemented.

Summary

- Rock has been an important natural resource for as long as humans have existed. Early humans used rock to make tools. Ancient and modern civilizations have used rock as a construction material.

- Weathering, erosion, deposition, and uplift are all processes that shape the surface features of the Earth.

- The rock cycle is the continual process by which new rock forms from old rock material.

- The sequence of events in the rock cycle depends on processes, such as weathering, erosion, deposition, pressure, and heat, that change the rock material.

- Composition and texture are two characteristics that scientists use to classify rocks.

- The composition of a rock is determined by the minerals that make up the rock.

- The texture of a rock is determined by the size, shape, and positions of the grains that make up the rock.

Using Key Terms

Complete each of the following sentences by choosing the correct term from the word bank.

rock	composition
rock cycle	texture

1. The minerals that a rock is made of determine the ___ of that rock.

2. ___ is a naturally occurring, solid mixture of crystals of one or more minerals.

Understanding Key Ideas

3. Sediments are transported or moved from their original source by a process called
   a. deposition.
   b. erosion.
   c. uplift.
   d. weathering.

4. Describe two ways that rocks have been used by humans.

5. Name four processes that change rock inside the Earth.

6. Describe four processes that shape Earth's surface.

7. Give an example of how texture can provide clues as to how and where a rock formed.

Critical Thinking

8. **Making Comparisons** Explain the difference between texture and composition.

9. **Analyzing Processes** Explain how rock is continually recycled in the rock cycle.

Interpreting Graphics

10. Look at the table below. Sandstone is a type of sedimentary rock. If you had a sample of sandstone that had an average particle size of 2 mm, what texture would your sandstone have?

Classification of Clastic Sedimentary Rocks	
Texture	**Particle size**
coarse grained	> 2 mm
medium grained	0.06 to 2 mm
fine grained	< 0.06 mm

Igneous Rock

Where do igneous rocks come from? Here's a hint: The word **igneous** comes from a Latin word that means "fire."

Igneous rock forms when hot, liquid rock, or *magma*, cools and solidifies. The type of igneous rock that forms depends on the composition of the magma and the amount of time it takes the magma to cool.

Origins of Igneous Rock

Igneous rock begins as magma. As shown in **Figure 1,** there are three ways magma can form: when rock is heated, when pressure is released, or when rock changes composition.

When magma cools enough, it solidifies to form igneous rock. Magma solidifies in much the same way that water freezes. But there are also differences between the way magma freezes and the way water freezes. One main difference is that water freezes at 0°C. Magma freezes between 700°C and 1,250°C. Also, liquid magma is a complex mixture containing many melted minerals. Because these minerals have different melting points, some minerals in the magma will freeze or become solid before other minerals do.

What You Will Learn

- Describe three ways that igneous rock forms.
- Explain how the cooling rate of magma affects the texture of igneous rock.
- Distinguish between igneous rock that cools within Earth's crust and igneous rock that cools at Earth's surface.

Vocabulary

intrusive igneous rock
extrusive igneous rock

READING STRATEGY

Reading Organizer As you read this section, make a table comparing intrusive rock and extrusive rock.

Figure 1 **The Formation of Magma**

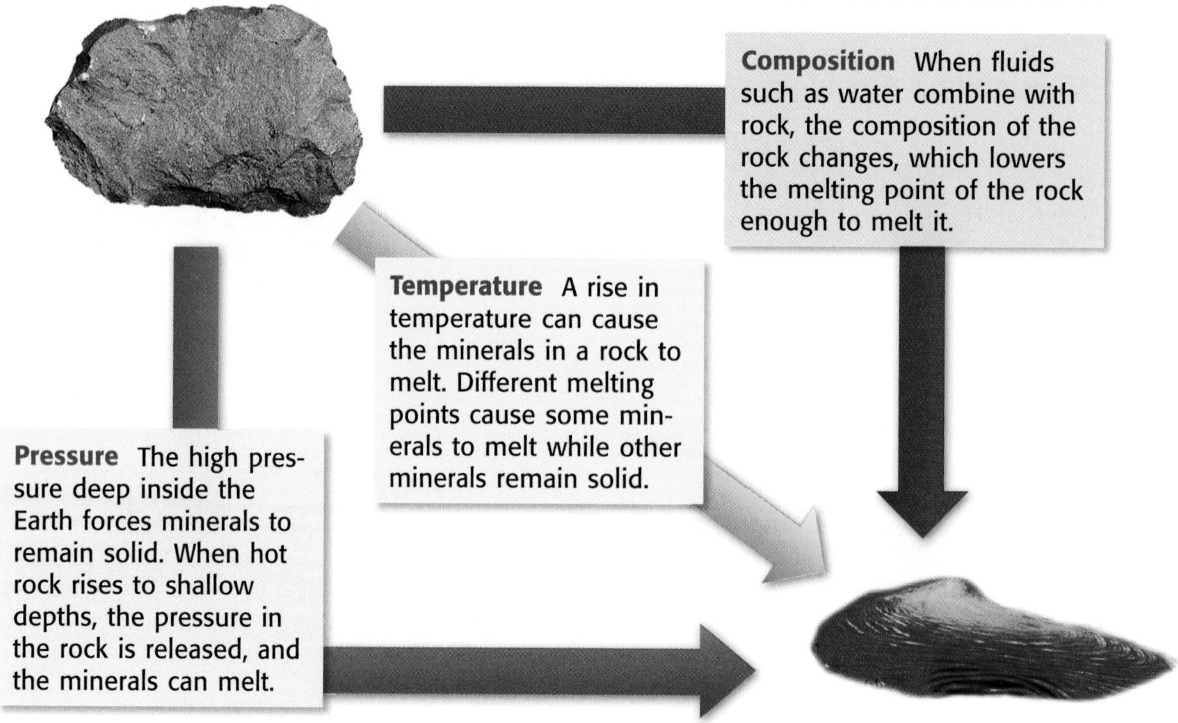

Composition When fluids such as water combine with rock, the composition of the rock changes, which lowers the melting point of the rock enough to melt it.

Temperature A rise in temperature can cause the minerals in a rock to melt. Different melting points cause some minerals to melt while other minerals remain solid.

Pressure The high pressure deep inside the Earth forces minerals to remain solid. When hot rock rises to shallow depths, the pressure in the rock is released, and the minerals can melt.

Figure 2 Igneous Rock Texture

	Coarse-grained	Fine-grained
Felsic	Granite	Rhyolite
Mafic	Gabbro	Basalt

Composition and Texture of Igneous Rock

Look at the rocks in **Figure 2.** All of the rocks are igneous rocks even though they look different from one another. These rocks differ from one another in what they are made of and how fast they cooled.

The light-colored rocks are less dense than the dark-colored rocks are. The light-colored rocks are rich in elements such as aluminum, potassium, silicon, and sodium. These rocks are called *felsic rocks*. The dark-colored rocks, called *mafic rocks*, are rich in calcium, iron, and magnesium, and poor in silicon.

Figure 3 shows what happens to magma when it cools at different rates. The longer it takes for the magma or lava to cool, the more time mineral crystals have to grow. The more time the crystals have to grow, the larger the crystals are and the coarser the texture of the resulting igneous rock is.

In contrast, the less time magma takes to cool, the less time crystals have to grow. Therefore, the rock that is formed will be fine grained. Fine-grained igneous rock contains very small crystals, or if the cooling is very rapid, it contains no crystals.

✓ Reading Check Explain the difference between felsic rock and mafic rock. (*See the Appendix for answers to Reading Checks.*)

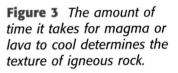

Figure 3 *The amount of time it takes for magma or lava to cool determines the texture of igneous rock.*

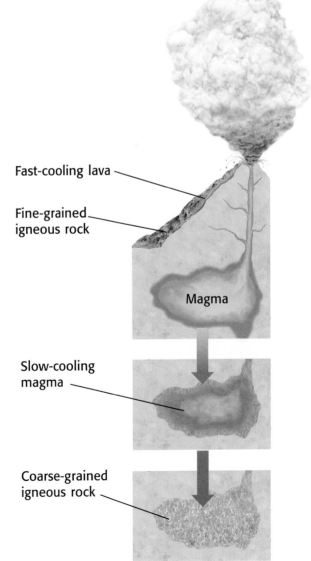

Fast-cooling lava

Fine-grained igneous rock

Magma

Slow-cooling magma

Coarse-grained igneous rock

For another activity related to this chapter, go to **go.hrw.com** and type in the keyword **HZ5RCKW.**

Igneous Rock Formations

Igneous rock formations are located above and below the surface of the Earth. You may be familiar with igneous rock formations that were caused by lava cooling on the Earth's surface, such as volcanoes. But not all magma reaches the surface. Some magma cools and solidifies deep within the Earth's crust.

Intrusive Igneous Rock

intrusive igneous rock rock formed from the cooling and solidification of magma beneath the Earth's surface

When magma *intrudes,* or pushes, into surrounding rock below the Earth's surface and cools, the rock that forms is called **intrusive igneous rock.** Intrusive igneous rock usually has a coarse-grained texture because it is well insulated by surrounding rock and cools very slowly. The minerals that form are large, visible crystals.

Masses of intrusive igneous rock are named for their size and shape. Common intrusive shapes are shown in **Figure 4.** *Plutons* are large, irregular-shaped intrusive bodies. The largest of all igneous intrusions are *batholiths. Stocks* are intrusive bodies that are exposed over smaller areas than batholiths. Sheetlike intrusions that cut across previous rock units are called *dikes,* whereas *sills* are sheetlike intrusions that are oriented parallel to previous rock units.

Figure 4 *Igneous intrusive bodies have different shapes and sizes.*

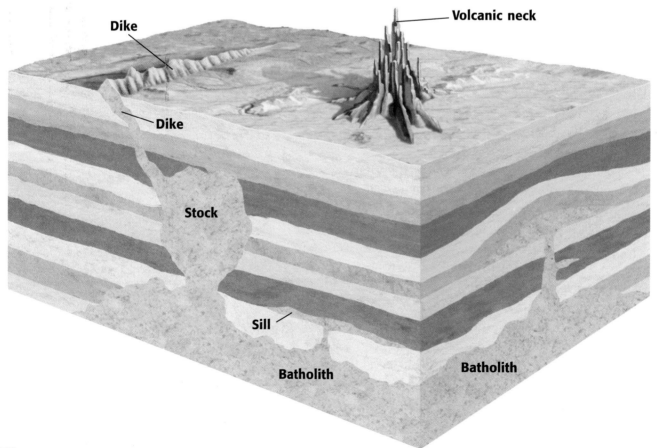

Extrusive Igneous Rock

Igneous rock that forms from magma that erupts, or extrudes, onto the Earth's surface is called **extrusive igneous rock.** Extrusive rock is common around volcanoes. It cools quickly on the surface and contains very small crystals or no crystals.

When lava erupts from a volcano, a *lava flow* forms. **Figure 5** shows an active lava flow. Lava does not always flow from volcanoes. Sometimes lava erupts and flows from long cracks in the Earth's crust called *fissures.* Lava flows from fissures on the ocean floor at places where tension is causing the ocean floor to be pulled apart. This lava cools to form new ocean floor. When a large amount of lava flows out of fissures onto land, the lava can cover a large area and form a plain called a *lava plateau.* Pre-existing landforms are often buried by these lava flows.

Reading Check How does new ocean floor form?

Figure 5 *An active lava flow is shown in this photo. When exposed to Earth's surface conditions, lava quickly cools and solidifies to form a fine-grained igneous rock.*

extrusive igneous rock rock that forms as a result of volcanic activity at or near the Earth's surface

---

SECTION Review

Summary

- Igneous rock forms when magma cools and hardens.
- The texture of igneous rock is determined by the rate at which the rock cools.
- Igneous rock that solidifies at Earth's surface is extrusive. Igneous rock that solidifies within Earth's surface is intrusive.
- Shapes of common igneous intrusive bodies include batholiths, stocks, sills, and dikes.

Using Key Terms

1. In your own words, write a definition for each of the following terms: *intrusive igneous rock* and *extrusive igneous rock.*

Understanding Key Ideas

2. ___ is an example of a coarse-grained, felsic, igneous rock.
   a. Basalt
   b. Gabbro
   c. Granite
   d. Rhyolite

3. Explain three ways in which magma can form.

4. What determines the texture of igneous rocks?

Math Skills

5. The summit of a granite batholith has an elevation of 1,825 ft. What is the height of the batholith in meters?

Critical Thinking

6. **Making Comparisons** Dikes and sills are both types of igneous intrusive bodies. What is the difference between a dike and a sill?

7. **Predicting Consequences** An igneous rock forms from slow-cooling magma deep beneath the surface of the Earth. What type of texture is this rock most likely to have? Explain.

SCILINKS.

NSTA
Developed and maintained by the
National Science Teachers Association

For a variety of links related to this chapter, go to www.scilinks.org

Topic: Igneous Rock
SciLinks code: HSM0783

Sedimentary Rock

Have you ever tried to build a sand castle at the beach? Did you ever wonder where the sand came from?

Sand is a product of weathering, which breaks rock into pieces. Over time, sand grains may be compacted, or compressed, and then cemented together to form a rock called *sandstone*. Sandstone is just one of many types of sedimentary rock.

What You Will Learn

● Describe the origin of sedimentary rock.
● Describe the three main categories of sedimentary rock.
● Describe three types of sedimentary structures.

Vocabulary

strata
stratification

READING STRATEGY

Reading Organizer As you read this section, create an outline of this section. Use the headings from the section in your outline.

Origins of Sedimentary Rock

Wind, water, ice, sunlight, and gravity all cause rock to physically weather into fragments. Through the process of erosion, these rock and mineral fragments, called *sediment*, are moved from one place to another. Eventually, the sediment is deposited in layers. As new layers of sediment are deposited, they cover older layers. Older layers become compacted. Dissolved minerals, such as calcite and quartz, separate from water that passes through the sediment to form a natural cement that binds the rock and mineral fragments together into sedimentary rock.

Sedimentary rock forms at or near the Earth's surface. It forms without the heat and pressure that are involved in the formation of igneous and metamorphic rocks.

The most noticeable feature of sedimentary rock is its layers, or **strata.** A single, horizontal layer of rock is sometimes visible for many miles. Road cuts are good places to observe strata. **Figure 1** shows the spectacular views that sedimentary rock formations carved by erosion can provide.

Figure 1 *The red sandstone "monuments" for which Monument Valley in Arizona has been named are the products of millions of years of erosion.*

Figure 2 Classification of Clastic Sedimentary Rock

Conglomerate   Sandstone   Siltstone   Shale

Coarse grained ←————————————————————→ Fine grained

Composition of Sedimentary Rock

Sedimentary rock is classified by the way it forms. *Clastic sedimentary rock* forms when rock or mineral fragments, called *clasts,* are cemented together. *Chemical sedimentary rock* forms when minerals crystallize out of a solution, such as sea water, to become rock. *Organic sedimentary rock* forms from the remains of once-living plants and animals.

Clastic Sedimentary Rock

Clastic sedimentary rock is made of fragments of rocks cemented together by a mineral such as calcite or quartz. **Figure 2** shows how clastic sedimentary rock is classified according to the size of the fragments from which the rock is made. Clastic sedimentary rocks can have coarse-grained, medium-grained, or fine-grained textures.

Chemical Sedimentary Rock

Chemical sedimentary rock forms from solutions of dissolved minerals and water. As rainwater slowly makes its way to the ocean, it dissolves some of the rock material it passes through. Some of this dissolved material eventually crystallizes and forms the minerals that make up chemical sedimentary rock. Halite, one type of chemical sedimentary rock, is made of sodium chloride, NaCl, or table salt. Halite forms when sodium ions and chlorine ions in shallow bodies of water become so concentrated that halite crystallizes from solution.

Reading Check How does a chemical sedimentary rock such as halite form? (*See the Appendix for answers to Reading Checks.*)

strata layers of rock (singular, *stratum*)

CONNECTION TO Language Arts

WRITING SKILL **Salty Expressions** The word salt is used in many expressions in the English language. Some common examples include "the salt of the earth," "taken with a grain of salt," not worth his salt," "the salt of truth," "rubbing salt into a wound," and "old salt." Use the Internet or another source to research one these expressions. In your research, attempt to find the origin of the expression. Write a short paragraph that summarizes what you found.

Organic Sedimentary Rock

Most limestone forms from the remains, or *fossils*, of animals that once lived in the ocean. For example, some limestone is made of the skeletons of tiny organisms called *coral*. Coral are very small, but they live in huge colonies called *reefs*, shown in **Figure 3.** Over time, the skeletons of these sea animals, which are made of calcium carbonate, collect on the ocean floor. These animal remains eventually become cemented together to form *fossiliferous limestone* (FAH suhl IF uhr uhs LIEM STOHN).

Corals are not the only animals whose remains are found in fossiliferous limestone. The shells of mollusks, such as clams and oysters, commonly form fossiliferous limestone. An example of fossiliferous limestone that contains mollusks is shown in **Figure 4.**

Another type of organic sedimentary rock is *coal*. Coal forms underground when partially decomposed plant material is buried beneath sediment and is changed into coal by increasing heat and pressure. This process occurs over millions of years.

Figure 3 *Ocean animals called coral create huge deposits of limestone. As they die, their skeletons collect on the ocean floor.*

Figure 4 The Formation of Organic Sedimentary Rock

Marine organisms, such as brachiopods, get the calcium carbonate for their shells from ocean water. When these organisms die, their shells collect on the ocean floor and eventually form fossiliferous limestone (inset). Over time, huge rock formations that contain the remains of large numbers of organisms, such as brachiopods, form.

Sedimentary Rock Structures

Many features can tell you about the way sedimentary rock formed. The most important feature of sedimentary rock is stratification. **Stratification** is the process in which sedimentary rocks are arranged in layers. Strata differ from one another depending on the kind, size, and color of their sediment.

Sedimentary rocks sometimes record the motion of wind and water waves on lakes, oceans, rivers, and sand dunes in features called *ripple marks*, as shown in **Figure 5.** Structures called *mud cracks* form when fine-grained sediments at the bottom of a shallow body of water are exposed to the air and dry out. Mud cracks indicate the location of an ancient lake, stream, or ocean shoreline. Even raindrop impressions can be preserved in fine-grained sediments, as small pits with raised rims.

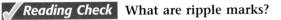 **Reading Check** What are ripple marks?

Figure 5 *These ripple marks were made by flowing water and were preserved when the sediments became sedimentary rock. Ripple marks can also form from the action of wind.*

stratification the process in which sedimentary rocks are arranged in layers

SECTION Review

Summary

- Sedimentary rock forms at or near the Earth's surface.
- Clastic sedimentary rock forms when rock or mineral fragments are cemented together.
- Chemical sedimentary rock forms from solutions of dissolved minerals and water.
- Organic limestone forms from the remains of plants and animals.
- Sedimentary structures include ripple marks, mud cracks, and raindrop impressions.

Using Key Terms

1. In your own words, write a definition for each of the following terms: *strata* and *stratification.*

Understanding Key Ideas

2. Which of the following is an organic sedimentary rock?
   a. chemical limestone
   b. shale
   c. fossiliferous limestone
   d. conglomerate

3. Explain the process by which clastic sedimentary rock forms.

4. Describe the three main categories of sedimentary rock.

Math Skills

5. A layer of a sedimentary rock is 2 m thick. How many years did it take for this layer to form if an average of 4 mm of sediment accumulated per year?

Critical Thinking

6. **Identifying Relationships** Rocks are classified based on texture and composition. Which of these two properties would be more important for classifying clastic sedimentary rock?

7. **Analyzing Processes** Why do you think raindrop impressions are more likely to be preserved in fine-grained sedimentary rock rather than in coarse-grained sedimentary rock?

SCiLINKS

NSTA
Developed and maintained by the National Science Teachers Association

For a variety of links related to this chapter, go to www.scilinks.org

Topic: Sedimentary Rock
SciLinks code: HSM1365

Metamorphic Rock

Have you ever watched a caterpillar change into a butterfly? Some caterpillars go through a biological process called metamorphosis in which they completely change their shape.

What You Will Learn

● Describe two ways a rock can undergo metamorphism.
● Explain how the mineral composition of rocks changes as the rocks undergo metamorphism.
● Describe the difference between foliated and nonfoliated metamorphic rock.
● Explain how metamorphic rock structures are related to deformation.

Vocabulary

foliated
nonfoliated

READING STRATEGY

Discussion Read this section silently. Write down questions that you have about this section. Discuss your questions in a small group.

Rocks can also go through a process called *metamorphism*. The word *metamorphism* comes from the Greek words *meta*, which means "changed," and *morphos*, which means "shape." Metamorphic rocks are rocks in which the structure, texture, or composition of the rock have changed. All three types of rock can be changed by heat, pressure, or a combination of both.

Origins of Metamorphic Rock

The texture or mineral composition of a rock can change when its surroundings change. If the temperature or pressure of the new environment is different from the one in which the rock formed, the rock will undergo metamorphism.

The temperature at which most metamorphism occurs ranges from 50°C to 1,000°C. However, the metamorphism of some rocks takes place at temperatures above 1,000°C. It seems that at these temperatures the rock would melt, but this is not true of metamorphic rock. It is the depth and pressure at which metamorphic rocks form that allows the rock to heat to this temperature and maintain its solid nature. Most metamorphic change takes place at depths greater than 2 km. But at depths greater than 16 km, the pressure can be 4,000 times greater than the pressure of the atmosphere at Earth's surface.

Large movements within the crust of the Earth cause additional pressure to be exerted on a rock during metamorphism. This pressure can cause the mineral grains in rock to align themselves in certain directions. The alignment of mineral grains into parallel bands is shown in the metamorphic rock in **Figure 1.**

Figure 1 *This metamorphic rock is an example of how mineral grains were aligned into distinct bands when the rock underwent metamorphism.*

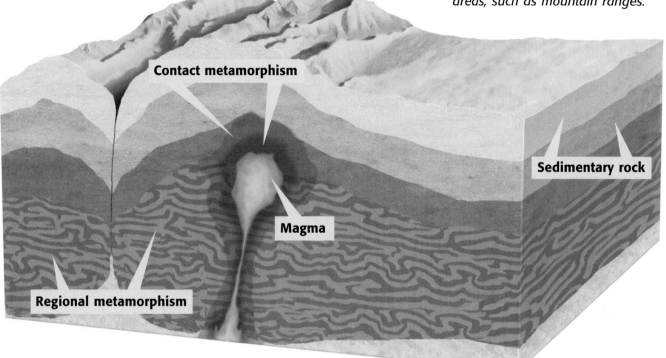

Contact metamorphism

Sedimentary rock

Magma

Regional metamorphism

Contact Metamorphism

One way rock can undergo metamorphism is by being heated by nearby magma. When magma moves through the crust, the magma heats the surrounding rock and changes it. Some minerals in the surrounding rock are changed into other minerals by this increase in temperature. The greatest change takes place where magma comes into direct contact with the surrounding rock. The effect of heat on rock gradually decreases as the rock's distance from the magma increases and as temperature decreases. *Contact metamorphism* occurs near igneous intrusions, as shown in **Figure 2.**

Regional Metamorphism

When pressure builds up in rock that is buried deep below other rock formations or when large pieces of the Earth's crust collide with each other, *regional metamorphism* occurs. The increased pressure and temperature causes rock to become deformed and chemically changed. Unlike contact metamorphism, which happens near bodies of magma, regional metamorphism occurs over thousands of cubic kilometers deep within Earth's crust. Rocks that have undergone regional metamorphism are found beneath most continental rock formations.

✓ Reading Check Explain how and where regional metamorphism takes place. (*See the Appendix for answers to Reading Checks.*)

Stretching Out

1. Sketch the crystals in granite rock on a **piece of paper** with a **black-ink pen.** Be sure to include the outline of the rock, and fill it in with different crystal shapes.

2. Flatten some **plastic play putty** over your drawing, and slowly peel it off.

3. After making sure that the outline of your granite has been transferred to the putty, squeeze and stretch the putty. What happened to the crystals in the granite? What happened to the granite?

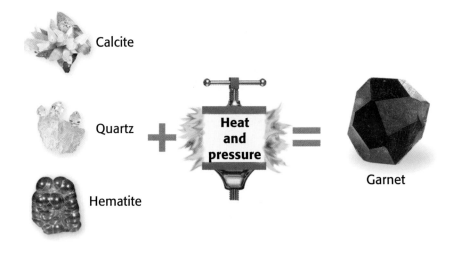

Figure 3 *The minerals calcite, quartz, and hematite combine and recrystallize to form the metamorphic mineral garnet.*

Calcite

Quartz

Hematite

+

Heat and pressure

=

Garnet

SCHOOL to HOME

Making a Rock Collection

With a parent or guardian, try to collect a sample of each class of rock described in this chapter. You may wish to collect rocks from road cuts or simply collect pebbles from your garden or driveway. Try to collect samples that show the composition and texture of each rock. Classify the rocks in your collection, and bring it to class. With other members of the class, discuss your rock samples and see if they are accurately identified.

ACTIVITY

Composition of Metamorphic Rock

Metamorphism occurs when temperature and pressure inside the Earth's crust change. Minerals that were present in the rock when it formed may not be stable in the new temperature and pressure conditions. The original minerals change into minerals that are more stable in these new conditions. Look at **Figure 3** to see an example of how this change happens.

Many of these new minerals form only in metamorphic rock. As shown in **Figure 4,** some metamorphic minerals form only at certain temperatures and pressures. These minerals, known as *index minerals,* are used to estimate the temperature, depth, and pressure at which a rock undergoes metamorphism. Index minerals include biotite mica, chlorite, garnet, kyanite, muscovite mica, sillimanite, and staurolite.

✓ Reading Check What is an index mineral?

Figure 4 *Scientists can understand a metamorphic rock's history by observing the minerals the rock contains. For example, a metamorphic rock that contains garnet formed at a greater depth and under greater heat and pressure than a rock that contains only chlorite.*

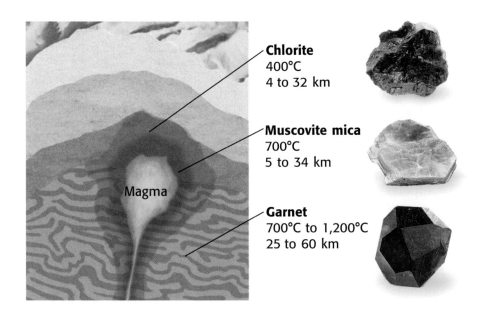

Magma

Chlorite
400°C
4 to 32 km

Muscovite mica
700°C
5 to 34 km

Garnet
700°C to 1,200°C
25 to 60 km

Textures of Metamorphic Rock

You have learned that texture helps scientists classify igneous and sedimentary rock. The same is true of metamorphic rock. All metamorphic rock has one of two textures—foliated or nonfoliated. Take a closer look at each of these types of metamorphic rock to find out how each type forms.

Foliated Metamorphic Rock

The texture of metamorphic rock in which the mineral grains are arranged in planes or bands is called **foliated.** Foliated metamorphic rock usually contains aligned grains of flat minerals, such as biotite mica or chlorite. Look at **Figure 5.** Shale is a sedimentary rock made of layers of clay minerals. When shale is exposed to slight heat and pressure, the clay minerals change into mica minerals. The shale becomes a foliated metamorphic rock called *slate*.

Metamorphic rocks can become other metamorphic rocks if the environment changes again. If slate is exposed to more heat and pressure, the slate can change into rock called *phyllite*. When phyllite is exposed to heat and pressure, it can change into *schist*.

If metamorphism continues, the arrangement of minerals in the rock changes. More heat and pressure cause minerals to separate into distinct bands in a metamorphic rock called *gneiss* (NIES).

foliated the texture of metamorphic rock in which the mineral grains are arranged in planes or bands

Sedimentary shale

Slate

Phyllite

Figure 5 *The effects of metamorphism depend on the heat and pressure applied to the rock. Here you can see what happens to shale, a sedimentary rock, when it is exposed to more and more heat and pressure.*

Schist

Gneiss

nonfoliated the texture of metamorphic rock in which the mineral grains are not arranged in planes or bands

Nonfoliated Metamorphic Rock

The texture of metamorphic rock in which the mineral grains are not arranged in planes or bands is called **nonfoliated.** Notice that the rocks shown in **Figure 6** do not have mineral grains that are aligned. This lack of aligned mineral grains is the reason these rocks are called *nonfoliated rocks.*

Nonfoliated rocks are commonly made of one or only a few minerals. During metamorphism, the crystals of these minerals may change in size or the mineral may change in composition in a process called *recrystallization*. The quartzite and marble shown in **Figure 6** are examples of sedimentary rocks that have recrystallized during metamorphism.

Quartz sandstone is a sedimentary rock made of quartz sand grains that have been cemented together. When quartz sandstone is exposed to the heat and pressure, the spaces between the sand grains disappear as the grains recrystallize to form quartzite. Quartzite has a shiny, glittery appearance. Like quartz sandstone, it is made of quartz. But during recrystallization, the mineral grains have grown larger than the original grains in the sandstone.

When limestone undergoes metamorphism, the same process that happened to the quartz happens to the calcite, and the limestone becomes marble. The calcite crystals in the marble are larger than the calcite grains in the original limestone.

Figure 6   **Two Examples of Nonfoliated Metamorphic Rock**

Marble and quartzite are nonfoliated metamorphic rocks. As you can see in the views through a microscope, the mineral crystals are not well aligned.

Marble

Quartzite

Metamorphic Rock Structures

Like igneous and sedimentary rock, metamorphic rock also has features that tell you about its history. In metamorphic rocks, these features are caused by deformation. *Deformation* is a change in the shape of a rock caused by a force placed on it. These forces may cause a rock to be squeezed or stretched.

Folds, or bends, in metamorphic rock are structures that indicate that a rock has been deformed. Some folds are not visible to the naked eye. But, as shown in **Figure 7,** some folds may be kilometers or even hundreds of kilometers in size.

✔️ **Reading Check** How are metamorphic rock structures related to deformation?

Figure 7 *These large folds occur in metamorphosed sedimentary rock along Saglet Fiord in Labrador, Canada.*

SECTION
Review

Summary

- Metamorphic rocks are rocks in which the structure, texture, or composition has changed.
- Two ways rocks can undergo metamorphism are by contact metamorphism and regional metamorphism.
- As rocks undergo metamorphism, the original minerals in a rock change into new minerals that are more stable in new pressure and temperature conditions.
- Foliated metamorphic rock has mineral crystals aligned in planes or bands, whereas nonfoliated rocks have unaligned mineral crystals.
- Metamorphic rock structures are caused by deformation.

Using Key Terms

1. In your own words, define the following terms: *foliated* and *nonfoliated.*

Understanding Key Ideas

2. Which of the following is not a type of foliated metamorphic rock?
   a. gneiss
   b. slate
   c. marble
   d. schist

3. Explain the difference between contact metamorphism and regional metamorphism.

4. Explain how index minerals allow a scientist to understand the history of a metamorphic rock.

Math Skills

5. For every 3.3 km a rock is buried, the pressure placed upon it increases 0.1 gigapascal (100 million pascals). If rock undergoing metamorphosis is buried at 16 km, what is the pressure placed on that rock? (Hint: The pressure at Earth's surface is .101 gigapascal.)

Critical Thinking

6. **Making Inferences** If you had two metamorphic rocks, one that has garnet crystals and the other that has chlorite crystals, which one could have formed at a deeper level in the Earth's crust? Explain your answer.

7. **Applying Concepts** Which do you think would be easier to break, a foliated rock, such as slate, or a nonfoliated rock, such as quartzite? Explain.

8. **Analyzing Processes** A mountain range is located at a boundary where two tectonic plates are colliding. Would most of the metamorphic rock in the mountain range be a product of contact metamorphism or regional metamorphism? Explain.

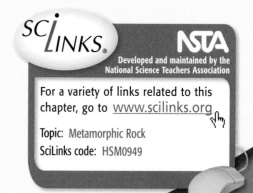

Skills Practice Lab

OBJECTIVES

Model the process of sedimentation.

Determine whether sedimentary rock layers are undisturbed.

MATERIALS

- clay
- dropper pipet
- gravel
- magnifying lens
- mixing bowl, 2 qt
- sand
- scissors
- soda bottle with a cap, plastic, 2 L
- soil, clay rich, if available
- water

SAFETY

Let's Get Sedimental

How do we determine if sedimentary rock layers are undisturbed? The best way to do this is to be sure that fine-grained sediments near the top of a layer lie above coarse-grained sediments near the bottom of the layer. This lab activity will show you how to read rock features that will help you distinguish individual sedimentary rock layers. Then, you can look for the features in real rock layers.

Procedure

1 In a mixing bowl, thoroughly mix the sand, gravel, and soil. Fill the soda bottle about one-third full of the mixture.

2 Add water to the soda bottle until the bottle is two-thirds full. Twist the cap back onto the bottle, and shake the bottle vigorously until all of the sediment is mixed in the rapidly moving water.

3 Place the bottle on a tabletop. Using the scissors, carefully cut the top off the bottle a few centimeters above the water, as shown. The open bottle will allow water to evaporate.

4 Immediately after you set the bottle on the tabletop, describe what you see from above and through the sides of the bottle.

5 Do not disturb the container. Allow the water to evaporate. (You may speed up the process by carefully using the dropper pipet to siphon off some of the clear water after you allow the container to sit for at least 24 hours.) You may also set the bottle in the sun or under a desk lamp to speed up evaporation.

6 After the sediment has dried and hardened, describe its surface.

7 Carefully lay the container on its side, and cut a wide, vertical strip of plastic down the length of the bottle to expose the sediments in the container. You may find it easier if you place pieces of clay on either side of the container to stabilize it. (If the bottle is clear along its length, this step may not be required.)

8 Brush away the loose material from the sediment, and gently blow on the surface until it is clean. Examine the surface, and record your observations.

Analyze the Results

1 **Identifying Patterns** Do you see anything through the side of the bottle that could help you determine if a sedimentary rock is undisturbed? Explain your answer.

2 **Identifying Patterns** Can you observe a pattern of deposition? If so, describe the pattern of deposition of sediment that you observe from top to bottom.

3 **Explaining Events** Explain how these features might be used to identify the top of a sedimentary layer in real rock and to decide if the layer has been disturbed.

4 **Identifying Patterns** Do you see any structures through the side of the bottle that might indicate which direction is up, such as a change in particle density or size?

5 **Identifying Patterns** Use the magnifying lens to examine the boundaries between the gravel, sand, and silt. Do the size of the particles and the type of sediment change dramatically in each layer?

Draw Conclusions

6 **Making Predictions** Imagine that a layer was deposited directly above the sediment in your bottle. Describe the composition of this new layer. Will it have the same composition as the mixture in steps 1–5 in the Procedure?

Applying Your Data

With your class or with a parent, visit an outcrop of sedimentary rock. Apply the information that you have learned in this lab to see if you can determine whether the sedimentary rock layers are disturbed or undisturbed.

Chapter Review

USING KEY TERMS

1 In your own words, write a definition for the term *rock cycle*.

Complete each of the following sentences by choosing the correct term from the word bank.

stratification   foliated
extrusive igneous rock   texture

2 The ___ of a rock is determined by the sizes, shapes, and positions of the minerals the rock contains.

3 ___ metamorphic rock contains minerals that are arranged in plates or bands.

4 The most characteristic property of sedimentary rock is ___.

5 ___ forms plains called *lava plateaus*.

UNDERSTANDING KEY IDEAS

Multiple Choice

6 Sedimentary rock is classified into all of the following main categories except

   a. clastic sedimentary rock.

   b. chemical sedimentary rock.

   c. nonfoliated sedimentary rock.

   d. organic sedimentary rock.

7 An igneous rock that cools very slowly has a ___ texture.

   a. foliated

   b. fine-grained

   c. nonfoliated

   d. coarse-grained

8 Igneous rock forms when

   a. minerals crystallize from a solution.

   b. sand grains are cemented together.

   c. magma cools and solidifies.

   d. mineral grains in a rock recrystallize.

9 A ___ is a common structure found in metamorphic rock.

   a. ripple mark   **c.** sill

   b. fold   **d.** layer

10 The process in which sediment is removed from its source and transported is called

   a. deposition.   **c.** weathering.

   b. erosion.   **d.** uplift.

11 Mafic rocks are

   a. light-colored rocks rich in calcium, iron, and magnesium.

   b. dark-colored rocks rich in aluminum, potassium, silica, and sodium.

   c. light-colored rocks rich in aluminum, potassium, silica, and sodium.

   d. dark-colored rocks rich in calcium, iron, and magnesium.

Short Answer

12 Explain how composition and texture are used by scientists to classify rocks.

13 Describe two ways a rock can undergo metamorphism.

14 Explain why some minerals only occur in metamorphic rocks.

15 Describe how each type of rock changes as it moves through the rock cycle.

16 Describe two ways rocks were used by early humans and ancient civilizations.

17 **Concept Mapping** Use the following terms to construct a concept map: *rocks, metamorphic, sedimentary, igneous, foliated, nonfoliated, organic, clastic, chemical, intrusive,* and *extrusive.*

18 **Making Inferences** If you were looking for fossils in the rocks around your home and the rock type that was closest to your home was metamorphic, do you think that you would find many fossils? Explain your answer.

19 **Applying Concepts** Imagine that you want to quarry, or mine, granite. You have all of the equipment, but you have two pieces of land to choose from. One area has a granite batholith underneath it. The other has a granite sill. If both intrusive bodies are at the same depth, which one would be the better choice for you to quarry? Explain your answer.

20 **Applying Concepts** The sedimentary rock coquina is made up of pieces of seashells. Which of the three kinds of sedimentary rock could coquina be? Explain your answer.

21 **Analyzing Processes** If a rock is buried deep inside the Earth, which geological processes cannot change the rock? Explain your answer.

The bar graph below shows the percentage of minerals by mass that compose a sample of granite. Use the graph below to answer the questions that follow.

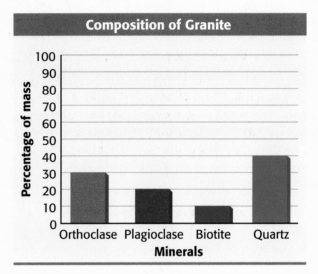

22 Your rock sample is made of four minerals. What percentage of each mineral makes up your sample?

23 Both plagioclase and orthoclase are feldspar minerals. What percentage of the minerals in your sample of granite are not feldspar minerals?

24 If your rock sample has a mass of 10 g, how many grams of quartz does it contain?

25 Use paper, a compass, and a protractor or a computer to make a pie chart. Show the percentage of each of the four minerals your sample of granite contains. (Look in the Appendix of this book for help on making a pie chart.)

Standardized Test Preparation

Read each of the passages below. Then, answer the questions that follow each passage.

Passage 1 The texture and composition of a rock can provide good clues about how and where the rock formed. Scientists use both texture and composition to understand the <u>origin</u> and history of rocks. For example, marble is a rock that is made when limestone is metamorphosed. Only limestone contains the mineral—calcite—that can change into marble. Therefore, wherever scientists find marble, they know the sediment that created the original limestone was deposited in a warm ocean or lake environment.

1. In the passage, what does the word *origin* mean?

   A size or appearance

   B age

   C location or surroundings

   D source or formation

2. Based on the passage, what can the reader conclude?

   F Marble is a sedimentary rock.

   G Limestone is created by sediments deposited in warm ocean or lake environments.

   H Marble is a rock that is made when sandstone has undergone metamorphism.

   I In identifying a rock, the texture of a rock is more important than the composition of the rock.

3. What is the main idea of the passage?

   A Scientists believe marble is the most important rock type to study.

   B Scientists study the composition and texture of a rock to determine how the rock formed and what happened after it formed.

   C Some sediments are deposited in warm oceans and lakes.

   D When limestone undergoes metamorphism, it creates marble.

Passage 2 Fulgurites are a rare type of natural glass found in areas that have quartz-rich sediments, such as beaches and deserts. A <u>tubular</u> fulgurite forms when a lightning bolt strikes material such as sand and melts the quartz into a liquid. The liquid quartz cools and solidifies quickly, and a thin, glassy tube is left behind. Fulgurites usually have a rough outer surface and a smooth inner surface. Underground, a fulgurite may be shaped like the roots of a tree. The fulgurite branches out with many arms that trace the zigzag path of the lightning bolt. Some fulgurites are as short as your little finger, but others stretch 20 m into the ground.

1. In the passage, what does the word *tubular* mean?

   A flat and sharp

   B round and long

   C funnel shaped

   D pyramid shaped

2. From the information in the passage, what can the reader conclude?

   F Fulgurites are formed above ground.

   G Sand contains a large amount of quartz.

   H Fulgurites are most often very small.

   I Fulgurites are easy to find in sandy places.

3. Which of the following statements best describes a fulgurite?

   A Fulgurites are frozen lightning bolts.

   B Fulgurites are rootlike rocks.

   C Fulgurites are glassy tubes found in deserts.

   D Fulgurites are natural glass tubes formed by lightning bolts.

Use the diagram below to answer the questions that follow.

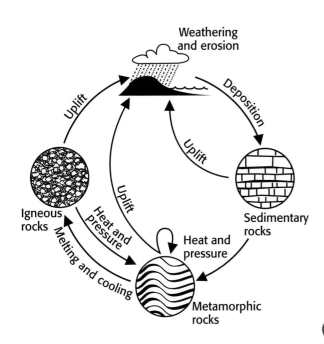

1. According to the rock cycle diagram, which of the following statements is true?

   A Only sedimentary rock gets weathered and eroded.

   B Sedimentary rocks are made from metamorphic, igneous, and sedimentary rock fragments and minerals.

   C Heat and pressure create igneous rocks.

   D Metamorphic rocks are created by melting and cooling.

2. A rock exists at the surface of the Earth. What would be the next step in the rock cycle?

   F cooling

   G weathering

   H melting

   I metamorphism

3. Which of the following processes brings rocks to Earth's surface, where they can be eroded?

   A burial

   B deposition

   C uplift

   D weathering

4. Which of the following is the best summary of the rock cycle?

   F Each type of rock gets melted. Then the magma turns into igneous, sedimentary, and metamorphic rock.

   G Magma cools to form igneous rock. Then, the igneous rock becomes sedimentary rock. Sedimentary rock is heated and forms metamorphic rock. Metamorphic rock melts to form magma.

   H All three rock types weather to create sedimentary rock. All three rock types melt to form magma. Magma forms igneous rock. All three types of rock form metamorphic rock because of heat and pressure.

   I Igneous rock is weathered to create sedimentary rock. Sedimentary rock is melted to form igneous rock. Metamorphic rock is weathered to form igneous rock.

Read each question below, and choose the best answer.

1. Eric has 25 rocks he has collected as a science project for class. Nine rocks are sedimentary, 10 are igneous, and 6 are metamorphic. If Eric chooses a rock at random, what is the probability that he will choose an igneous rock?

   A 1/2

   B 2/5

   C 3/8

   D 1/15

2. At a mineral and fossil show, Elizabeth bought two quartz crystals that cost $2.00 each and four trilobite fossils that cost $3.50 each. Which equation can be used to describe c, the total cost of her purchase?

   F $c = (2 \times 4) + (2.00 \times 3.50)$

   G $c = (2 \times 2.00) + (4 \times 3.50)$

   H $c = (4 \times 2.00) + (2 \times 3.50)$

   I $c = (2 + 2.00) + (4 + 3.50)$

Science in Action

Science, Technology, and Society

The Moai of Easter Island

Easter island is located in the Pacific Ocean more than 3,200 km from the coast of Chile. The island is home to mysterious statues that were carved from volcanic ash. The statues, called *moai,* have human heads and large torsos. The average moai weighs 14 tons and is more than 4.5 m tall, though some are as tall as 10 m! Altogether, 887 moai have been discovered. How old are the moai? Scientists believe that the moai were built between 500 and 1,000 years ago. What purpose did moai serve for their creators? The moai may have been religious symbols or gods.

Social Studies ACTiViTY

WRITING SKILL Research another ancient society or civilization, such as the ancient Egyptians, who are believed to have used stone to construct monuments to their gods or to important people. Report your findings in a short essay.

Scientific Discoveries

Shock Metamorphism

When a large asteroid, meteoroid, or comet collides with the Earth, extremely high temperatures and pressures are created in Earth's surface rock. These high pressures and temperatures cause minerals in the surface rock to shatter and recrystallize. The new minerals that result from this recrystallization cannot be created under any other conditions. This process is called *shock metamorphism.*

When large objects from space collide with the Earth, craters are formed by the impact. However, impact craters are not always easy to find on Earth. Scientists use shock metamorphism as a clue to locate ancient impact craters.

Language Arts ACTiViTY

WRITING SKILL The impact site caused by the asteroid strike in the Yucatán 65 million years ago has been named the Chicxulub (cheeks OO loob) structure. Research the origin of the name Chicxulub, and report your findings in a short paper.

Robert L. Folk

Petrologist For Dr. Robert Folk, the study of rock takes place on the microscopic level. Dr. Folk is searching for tiny life-forms he has named nannobacteria, or dwarf bacteria, in rock. *Nannobacteria* may also be spelled *nanobacteria*. Because nannobacteria are so incredibly small, only 0.05 to 0.2 μm in diameter, Folk must use an extremely powerful 100,000× microscope, called a *scanning electron microscope,* to see the shape of the bacteria in rock. Folk's research had already led him to discover that a certain type of Italian limestone is produced by bacteria. The bacteria were consuming the minerals, and the waste of the bacteria was forming the limestone. Further research led Folk to the discovery of the tiny nannobacteria. The spherical or oval-shaped nannobacteria appeared as chains and grapelike clusters. From his research, Folk hypothesized that nannobacteria are responsible for many inorganic reactions that occur in rock. Many scientists are skeptical of Folk's nannobacteria. Some skeptics believe that the tiny size of nannobacteria makes the bacteria simply too small to contain the chemistry of life. Others believe that nannobacteria actually represent structures that do not come from living things.

Math ACTiViTY

If a nannobacterium is 1/10 the length, 1/10 the width, and 1/10 the height of an ordinary bacterium, how many nannobacteria can fit within an ordinary bacterium? (Hint: Draw block diagrams of both a nannobacterium and an ordinary bacterium.)

To learn more about these Science in Action topics, visit **go.hrw.com** and type in the keyword **HZ5RCKF.**

Current Science

Check out Current Science® articles related to this chapter by visiting **go.hrw.com**. Just type in the keyword **HZ5CS04.**

The Rock and Fossil Record

The Big Idea
Studying the rock and fossil record helps us understand Earth's history and the history of life on Earth.

About the

This extremely well preserved crocodile fossil has been out of water for 49 million years. Its skeleton was collected in an abandoned mine pit in Messel, Germany.

PRE-READING ACTIVITY

FOLDNOTES **Layered Book** Before you read the chapter, create the FoldNote entitled "Layered Book" described in the **Study Skills** section of the Appendix. Label the tabs of the layered book with "Earth's history," "Relative dating," "Absolute dating," "Fossils," and "Geologic time." As you read the chapter, write information you learn about each category under the appropriate tab.

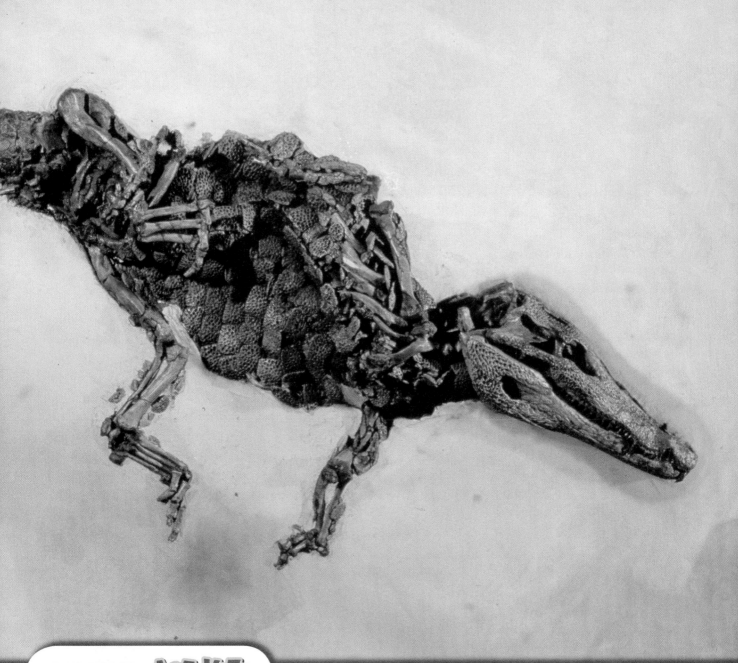

START-UP ACTIVITY

Making Fossils

How do scientists learn from fossils? In this activity, you will study "fossils" and identify the object that made each.

Procedure

1. You and three or four of your classmates will be given **several pieces** of **modeling clay** and a **paper sack** containing a few **small objects.**

2. Press each object firmly into a piece of clay. Try to leave a "fossil" imprint showing as much detail as possible.

3. After you have made an imprint of each object, exchange your model fossils with another group.

4. On a **sheet of paper,** describe the fossils you have received. List as many details as possible. What patterns and textures do you observe?

5. Work as a group to identify each fossil, and check your results. Were you right?

Analysis

1. What kinds of details were important in identifying your fossils? What kinds of details were not preserved in the imprints? For example, can you tell the materials from which the objects are made or their color?

2. Explain how scientists follow similar methods when studying fossils.

Earth's Story and Those Who First Listened

How do mountains form? How is new rock created? How old is the Earth? Have you ever asked these questions? Nearly 250 years ago, a Scottish farmer and scientist named James Hutton did.

Searching for answers to his questions, Hutton spent more than 30 years studying rock formations in Scotland and England. His observations led to the foundation of modern geology.

The Principle of Uniformitarianism

In 1788, James Hutton collected his notes and wrote *Theory of the Earth*. In *Theory of the Earth,* he stated that the key to understanding Earth's history was all around us. In other words, processes that we observe today—such as erosion and deposition—remain uniform, or do not change, over time. This assumption is now called uniformitarianism. **Uniformitarianism** is the idea that the same geologic processes shaping the Earth today have been at work throughout Earth's history. **Figure 1** shows how Hutton developed the idea of uniformitarianism.

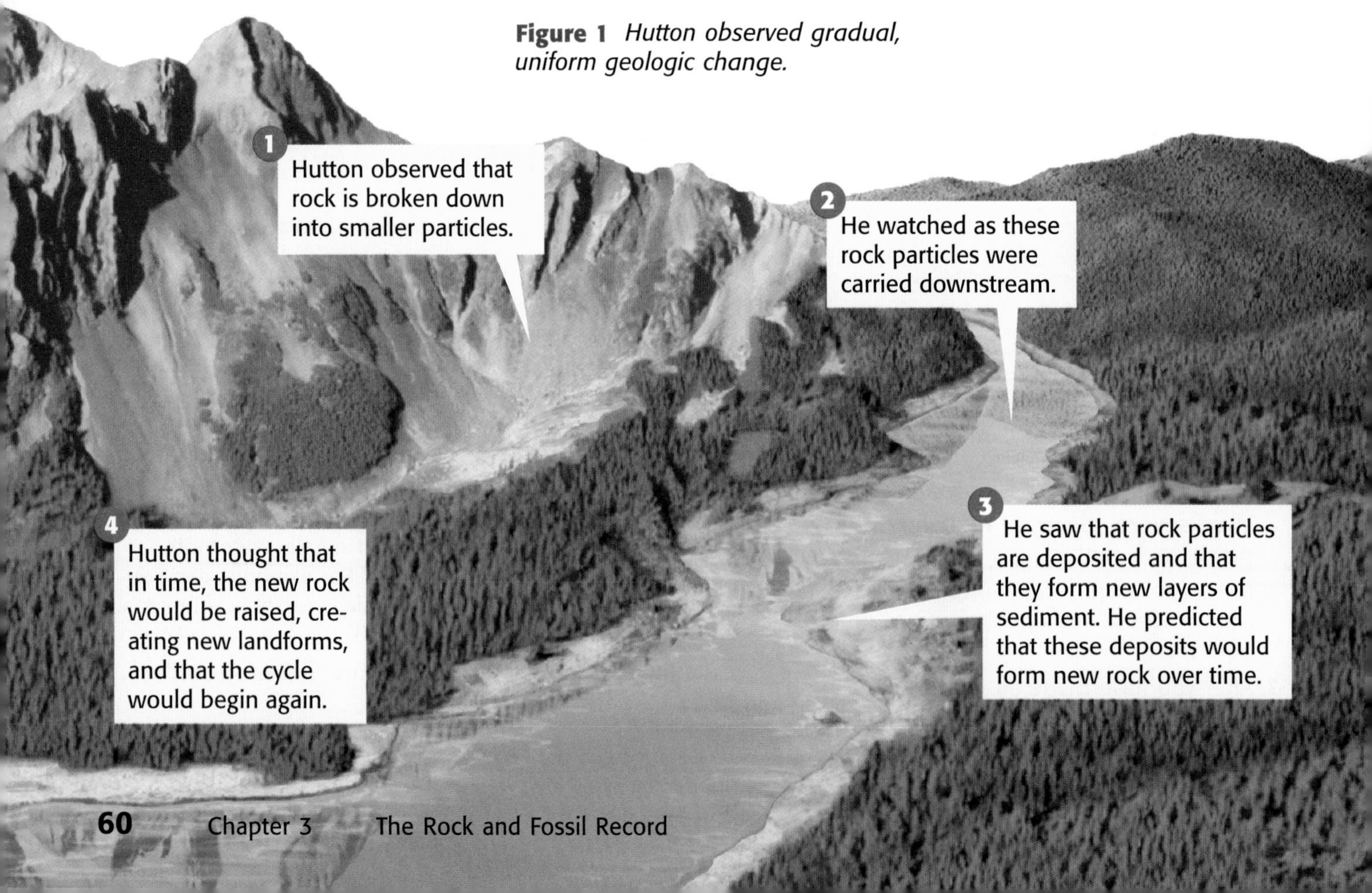

What You Will Learn

- Compare uniformitarianism and catastrophism.
- Describe how the science of geology has changed over the past 200 years.
- Explain the role of paleontology in the study of Earth's history.

Vocabulary

uniformitarianism
catastrophism
paleontology

READING STRATEGY

Reading Organizer As you read this section, make a table comparing uniformitarianism and catastrophism.

Figure 1 *Hutton observed gradual, uniform geologic change.*

1 Hutton observed that rock is broken down into smaller particles.

2 He watched as these rock particles were carried downstream.

3 He saw that rock particles are deposited and that they form new layers of sediment. He predicted that these deposits would form new rock over time.

4 Hutton thought that in time, the new rock would be raised, creating new landforms, and that the cycle would begin again.

Figure 2 *This photograph shows Siccar Point on the coast of Scotland. Siccar Point is one of the places where Hutton observed results of geologic processes that would lead him to form his principle of uniformitarianism.*

Uniformitarianism Versus Catastrophism

Hutton's theories sparked a scientific debate by suggesting that Earth was much older than previously thought. In Hutton's time, most people thought that Earth was only a few thousand years old. A few thousand years was not nearly enough time for the gradual geologic processes that Hutton described to have shaped our planet. The rocks that he observed at Siccar Point, shown in **Figure 2,** were deposited and folded, indicating a long geological history. To explain Earth's history, most scientists supported catastrophism. **Catastrophism** is the principle that states that all geologic change occurs suddenly. Supporters of catastrophism thought that Earth's features, such as its mountains, canyons, and seas, formed during rare, sudden events called *catastrophes*. These unpredictable events caused rapid geologic change over large areas—sometimes even globally.

✔ Reading Check According to catastrophists, what was the rate of geologic change? (*See the Appendix for answers to Reading Checks.*)

A Victory for Uniformitarianism

Despite Hutton's work, catastrophism remained geology's guiding principle for decades. Only after the work of British geologist Charles Lyell did people seriously consider uniformitarianism as geology's guiding principle.

From 1830 to 1833, Lyell published three volumes, collectively titled *Principles of Geology,* in which he reintroduced uniformitarianism. Armed with Hutton's notes and new evidence of his own, Lyell successfully challenged the principle of catastrophism. Lyell saw no reason to doubt that major geologic change happened at the same rate in the past as it happens in the present—gradually.

uniformitarianism a principle that states that geologic processes that occurred in the past can be explained by current geologic processes

catastrophism a principle that states that geologic change occurs suddenly

CONNECTION TO Biology

WRITING SKILL **Darwin and Lyell** The theory of evolution was developed soon after Lyell introduced his ideas, which was no coincidence. Lyell and Charles Darwin were good friends, and their talks greatly influenced Darwin's theories. Similar to uniformitarianism, Darwin's theory of evolution proposes that changes in species occur gradually over long periods of time. Write a short essay comparing uniformitarianism and evolution.

Modern Geology—A Happy Medium

During the late 20th century, scientists such as Stephen J. Gould challenged Lyell's uniformitarianism. They believed that catastrophes do, at times, play an important role in shaping Earth's history.

Today, scientists realize that neither uniformitarianism nor catastrophism accounts for all geologic change throughout Earth's history. Although most geologic change is gradual and uniform, catastrophes that cause geologic change have occurred during Earth's long history. For example, huge craters have been found where asteroids and comets are thought to have struck Earth in the past. Some scientists think one such asteroid strike, approximately 65 million years ago, may have caused the dinosaurs to become extinct. **Figure 3** is an imaginary re-creation of the asteroid strike that is thought to have caused the extinction of the dinosaurs. The impact of this asteroid is thought to have thrown debris into the atmosphere. The debris spread around the entire planet and rained down on Earth for decades. This global debris cloud may have blocked the sun's rays, causing major changes in the global climate that doomed the dinosaurs.

Reading Check How can a catastrophe affect life on Earth?

Figure 3 *Today, scientists think that sudden events are responsible for some changes during Earth's past. An asteroid hitting Earth, for example, may have led to the extinction of the dinosaurs about 65 million years ago.*

Paleontology—The Study of Past Life

The history of the Earth would be incomplete without a knowledge of the organisms that have inhabited our planet and the conditions under which they lived. The science involved with the study of past life is called **paleontology.** Scientists who study this life are called *paleontologists*. The data paleontologists use are fossils. Fossils are the remains of organisms preserved by geologic processes. Some paleontologists specialize in the study of particular organisms. Invertebrate paleontologists study animals without backbones, whereas vertebrate paleontologists, such as the scientist in **Figure 4,** study animals with backbones. Paleobotanists study fossils of plants. Other paleontologists reconstruct past ecosystems, study the traces left behind by animals, and piece together the conditions under which fossils were formed. As you see, the study of past life is as varied and complex as Earth's history itself.

Figure 4 *Edwin Colbert was a 20th-century vertebrate paleontologist who made important contributions to the study of dinosaurs.*

paleontology the scientific study of fossils

SECTION Review

Summary

- Uniformitarianism assumes that geologic change is gradual. Catastrophism is based on the idea that geologic change is sudden.
- Modern geology is based on the idea that gradual geologic change is interrupted by catastrophes.
- Using fossils to study past life is called *paleontology*.

Using Key Terms

1. Use each of the following terms in a separate sentence: *uniformitarianism, catastrophism,* and *paleontology.*

Understanding Key Ideas

2. Which of the following words describes change according to the principle of uniformitarianism?
   a. sudden
   b. rare
   c. global
   d. gradual

3. What is the difference between uniformitarianism and catastrophism?

4. Describe how the science of geology has changed.

5. Give one example of catastrophic global change.

6. Describe the work of three types of paleontologists.

Math Skills

7. An impact crater left by an asteroid strike has a radius of 85 km. What is the area of the crater? (Hint: The area of a circle is πr^2.)

Critical Thinking

8. **Analyzing Ideas** Why is uniformitarianism considered to be the foundation of modern geology?

9. **Applying Concepts** Give an example of a type of recent catastrophe.

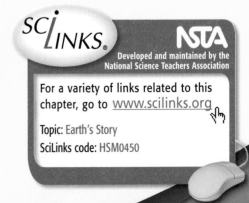

Relative Dating: Which Came First?

Imagine that you are a detective investigating a crime scene. What is the first thing you would do?

What You Will Learn

● Explain how relative dating is used in geology.
● Explain the principle of superposition.
● Describe how the geologic column is used in relative dating.
● Identify two events and two features that disrupt rock layers.
● Explain how physical features are used to determine relative ages.

Vocabulary

relative dating
superposition
geologic column
unconformity

READING STRATEGY

Reading Organizer As you read this section, create an outline of the section. Use the headings from the section in your outline.

You might begin by dusting the scene for fingerprints or by searching for witnesses. As a detective, you must figure out the sequence of events that took place before you reached the crime scene.

Geologists have a similar goal when investigating the Earth. They try to determine the order in which events have happened during Earth's history. But instead of relying on fingerprints and witnesses, geologists rely on rocks and fossils to help them in their investigation. Determining whether an object or event is older or younger than other objects or events is called **relative dating.**

The Principle of Superposition

Suppose that you have an older brother who takes a lot of photographs of your family and piles them in a box. Over the years, he keeps adding new photographs to the top of the stack. Think about the family history recorded in those photos. Where are the oldest photographs—the ones taken when you were a baby? Where are the most recent photographs—those taken last week?

Layers of sedimentary rock, such as the ones shown in **Figure 1,** are like stacked photographs. As you move from top to bottom, the layers are older. The principle that states that younger rocks lie above older rocks in undisturbed sequences is called **superposition.**

Figure 1 *Rock layers are like photos stacked over time—the younger ones lie above the older ones.*

Disturbing Forces

Not all rock sequences are arranged with the oldest layers on the bottom and the youngest layers on top. Some rock sequences are disturbed by forces within the Earth. These forces can push other rocks into a sequence, tilt or fold rock layers, and break sequences into movable parts. Sometimes, geologists even find rock sequences that are upside down! The disruptions of rock sequences pose a challenge to geologists trying to determine the relative ages of rocks. Fortunately, geologists can get help from a very valuable tool—the geologic column.

The Geologic Column

To make their job easier, geologists combine data from all the known undisturbed rock sequences around the world. From this information, geologists create the geologic column, as illustrated in **Figure 2.** The **geologic column** is an ideal sequence of rock layers that contains all the known fossils and rock formations on Earth, arranged from oldest to youngest.

Geologists rely on the geologic column to interpret rock sequences. Geologists also use the geologic column to identify the layers in puzzling rock sequences.

✔ **Reading Check** List two ways in which geologists use the geologic column. (*See the Appendix for answers to Reading Checks.*)

relative dating any method of determining whether an event or object is older or younger than other events or objects

superposition a principle that states that younger rocks lie above older rocks if the layers have not been disturbed

geologic column an arrangement of rock layers in which the oldest rocks are at the bottom

Figure 2 Constructing the Geologic Column

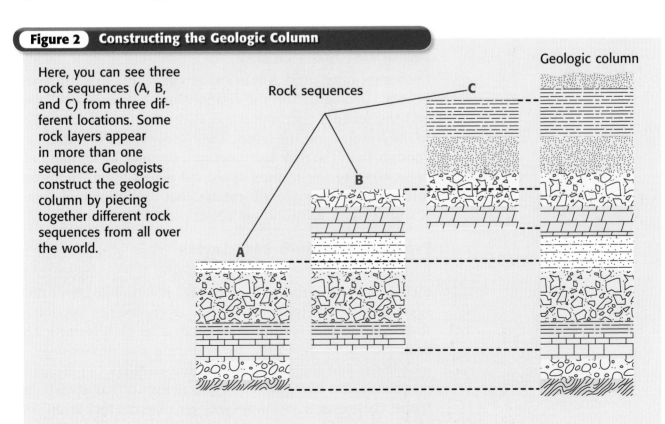

Here, you can see three rock sequences (A, B, and C) from three different locations. Some rock layers appear in more than one sequence. Geologists construct the geologic column by piecing together different rock sequences from all over the world.

Rock sequences

Geologic column

Figure 3 How Rock Layers Become Disturbed

Fault A *fault* is a break in the Earth's crust along which blocks of the crust slide relative to one another.

Intrusion An *intrusion* is molten rock from the Earth's interior that squeezes into existing rock and cools.

Folding *Folding* occurs when rock layers bend and buckle from Earth's internal forces.

Tilting *Tilting* occurs when internal forces in the Earth slant rock layers.

Disturbed Rock Layers

Geologists often find features that cut across existing layers of rock. Geologists use the relationships between rock layers and the features that cut across them to assign relative ages to the features and the layers. They know that the features are younger than the rock layers because the rock layers had to be present before the features could cut across them. Faults and intrusions are examples of features that cut across rock layers. A fault and an intrusion are illustrated in **Figure 3.**

Events That Disturb Rock Layers

Geologists assume that the way sediment is deposited to form rock layers—in horizontal layers—has not changed over time. According to this principle, if rock layers are not horizontal, something must have disturbed them after they formed. This principle allows geologists to determine the relative ages of rock layers and the events that disturbed them.

Folding and tilting are two types of events that disturb rock layers. These events are always younger than the rock layers they affect. The results of folding and tilting are shown in **Figure 3.**

Gaps in the Record—Unconformities

Faults, intrusions, and the effects of folding and tilting can make dating rock layers a challenge. Sometimes, layers of rock are missing altogether, creating a gap in the geologic record. To think of this another way, let's say that you stack your newspapers every day after reading them. Now, let's suppose you want to look at a paper you read 10 days ago. You know that the paper should be 10 papers deep in the stack. But when you look, the paper is not there. What happened? Perhaps you forgot to put the paper in the stack. Now, imagine a missing rock layer instead of a missing newspaper.

Missing Evidence

Missing rock layers create breaks in rock-layer sequences called unconformities. An **unconformity** is a surface that represents a missing part of the geologic column. Unconformities also represent missing time—time that was not recorded in layers of rock. When geologists find an unconformity, they must question whether the "missing layer" was never present or whether it was somehow removed. **Figure 4** shows how *nondeposition,* or the stoppage of deposition when a supply of sediment is cut off, and *erosion* create unconformities.

unconformity a break in the geologic record created when rock layers are eroded or when sediment is not deposited for a long period of time

Reading Check Define the term unconformity.

Figure 4 How Unconformities Are Created

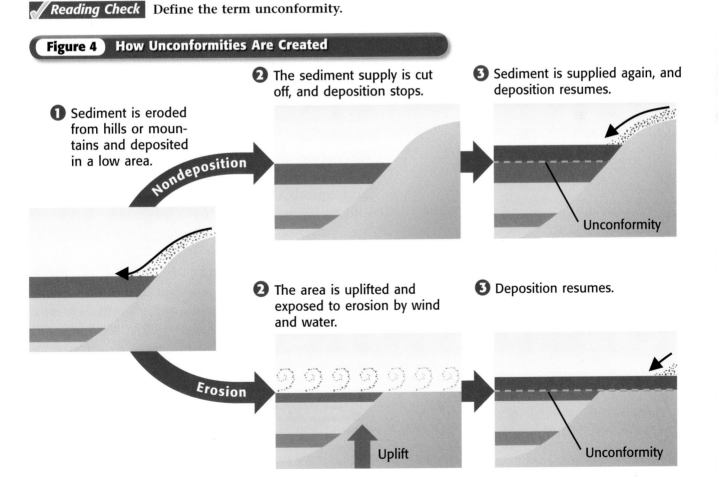

1 Sediment is eroded from hills or mountains and deposited in a low area.

Nondeposition

2 The sediment supply is cut off, and deposition stops.

3 Sediment is supplied again, and deposition resumes.

Unconformity

Erosion

2 The area is uplifted and exposed to erosion by wind and water.

Uplift

3 Deposition resumes.

Unconformity

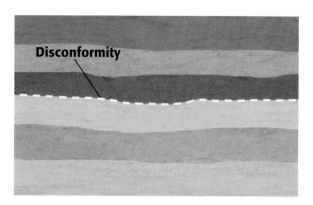

Figure 5 *A disconformity exists where part of a sequence of parallel rock layers is missing.*

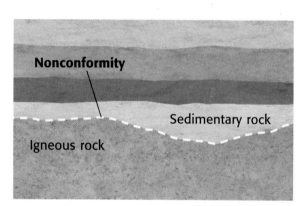

Figure 6 *A nonconformity exists where sedimentary rock layers lie on top of an eroded surface of nonlayered igneous or metamorphic rock.*

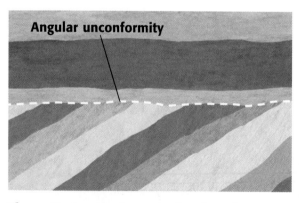

Figure 7 *An angular unconformity exists between horizontal rock layers and rock layers that are tilted or folded.*

Types of Unconformities

Most unconformities form by both erosion and nondeposition. But other factors can complicate matters. To simplify the study of unconformities, geologists place them into three major categories: disconformities, nonconformities, and angular unconformities. The three diagrams at left illustrate these three categories.

Disconformities

The most common type of unconformity is a disconformity, which is illustrated in **Figure 5.** *Disconformities* are found where part of a sequence of parallel rock layers is missing. A disconformity can form in the following way. A sequence of rock layers is uplifted. Younger layers at the top of the sequence are removed by erosion, and the eroded material is deposited elsewhere. At some future time, deposition resumes, and sediment buries the old erosion surface. The disconformity that results shows where erosion has taken place and rock layers are missing. A disconformity represents thousands to many millions of years of missing time.

Nonconformities

A nonconformity is illustrated in **Figure 6.** *Nonconformities* are found where horizontal sedimentary rock layers lie on top of an eroded surface of older intrusive igneous or metamorphic rock. Intrusive igneous and metamorphic rocks form deep within the Earth. When these rocks are raised to Earth's surface, they are eroded. Deposition causes the erosion surface to be buried. Nonconformities represent millions of years of missing time.

Angular Unconformities

An angular unconformity is shown in **Figure 7.** *Angular unconformities* are found between horizontal layers of sedimentary rock and layers of rock that have been tilted or folded. The tilted or folded layers were eroded before horizontal layers formed above them. Angular unconformities represent millions of years of missing time.

✔ Reading Check Describe each of the three major categories of unconformities.

Rock-Layer Puzzles

Geologists often find rock-layer sequences that have been affected by more than one of the events and features mentioned in this section. For example, as shown in **Figure 8,** intrusions may squeeze into rock layers that contain an unconformity. Determining the order of events that led to such a sequence is like piecing together a jigsaw puzzle. Geologists must use their knowledge of the events that disturb or remove rock-layer sequences to help piece together the history of Earth as told by the rock record.

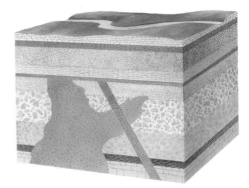

Figure 8 *Rock-layer sequences are often disturbed by more than one rock-disturbing feature.*

SECTION Review

Summary

- Geologists use relative dating to determine the order in which events happen.

- The principle of super-position states that in undisturbed rock sequences, younger layers lie above older layers.

- Folding and tilting are two events that disturb rock layers. Faults and intrusions are two features that disturb rock layers.

- The known rock and fossil record is indicated by the geologic column.

- Geologists examine the relationships between rock layers and the structures that cut across them in order to determine relative ages.

Using Key Terms

1. In your own words, write a definition for each of the following terms: *relative dating, superposition,* and *geologic column.*

Understanding Key Ideas

2. Molten rock that squeezes into existing rock and cools is called a(n)
   a. fold.
   b. fault.
   c. intrusion.
   d. unconformity.

3. List two events and two features that can disturb rock-layer sequences.

4. Explain how physical features are used to determine relative ages.

Critical Thinking

5. **Analyzing Concepts** Is there a place on Earth that has all the layers of the geologic column? Explain.

6. **Analyzing Ideas** Disconformities are hard to recognize because all of the layers are horizontal. How does a geologist know when he or she is looking at a disconformity?

Interpreting Graphics

Use the illustration below to answer the question that follows.

7. If the top rock layer were eroded and deposition later resumed, what type of unconformity would mark the boundary between older rock layers and the newly deposited rock layers?

Developed and maintained by the National Science Teachers Association

For a variety of links related to this chapter, go to www.scilinks.org

Topic: Relative Dating
SciLinks code: HSM1288

Absolute Dating: A Measure of Time

Have you ever heard the expression "turning back the clock"? With the discovery of the natural decay of uranium in 1896, French physicist Henri Becquerel provided a means of doing just that. Scientists could use radioactive elements as clocks to measure geologic time.

The process of establishing the age of an object by determining the number of years it has existed is called **absolute dating.** In this section, you will learn about radiometric dating, which is the most common method of absolute dating.

Radioactive Decay

To determine the absolute ages of fossils and rocks, scientists analyze isotopes of radioactive elements. Atoms of the same element that have the same number of protons but have different numbers of neutrons are called **isotopes.** Most isotopes are stable, meaning that they stay in their original form. But some isotopes are unstable. Scientists call unstable isotopes *radioactive.* Radioactive isotopes tend to break down into stable isotopes of the same or other elements in a process called **radioactive decay. Figure 1** shows an example of how radioactive decay occurs. Because radioactive decay occurs at a steady rate, scientists can use the relative amounts of stable and unstable isotopes present in an object to determine the object's age.

What You Will Learn

● Describe how radioactive decay occurs.
● Explain how radioactive decay relates to radiometric dating.
● Identify four types of radiometric dating.
● Determine the best type of radiometric dating to use to date an object.

Vocabulary

absolute dating
isotope
radioactive decay
radiometric dating
half-life

READING STRATEGY

Reading Organizer As you read this section, make a concept map by using the terms above.

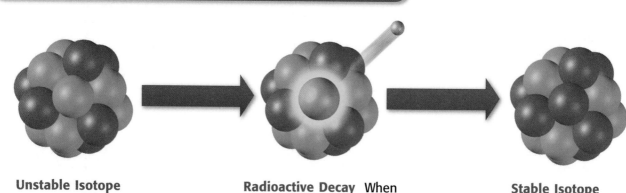

Figure 1 Radioactive Decay

Unstable Isotope
6 protons, 8 neutrons

Radioactive Decay When some unstable isotopes decay, a neutron is converted into a proton. In the process, an electron is released.

Stable Isotope
7 protons, 7 neutrons

Dating Rocks—How Does It Work?

In the process of radioactive decay, an unstable radioactive isotope of one element breaks down into a stable isotope. The stable isotope may be of the same element or, more commonly, a different element. The unstable radioactive isotope is called the *parent isotope.* The stable isotope produced by the radioactive decay of the parent isotope is called the *daughter isotope.* The radioactive decay of a parent isotope into a stable daughter isotope can occur in a single step or a series of steps. In either case, the rate of decay is constant. Therefore, to date rock, scientists compare the amount of parent material with the amount of daughter material. The more daughter material there is, the older the rock is.

Radiometric Dating

If you know the rate of decay for a radioactive element in a rock, you can figure out the absolute age of the rock. Determining the absolute age of a sample, based on the ratio of parent material to daughter material, is called **radiometric dating.** For example, let's say that a rock sample contains an isotope with a half-life of 10,000 years. A **half-life** is the time that it takes one-half of a radioactive sample to decay. So, for this rock sample, in 10,000 years, half the parent material will have decayed and become daughter material. You analyze the sample and find equal amounts of parent material and daughter material. This means that half the original radioactive isotope has decayed and that the sample must be about 10,000 years old.

What if one-fourth of your sample is parent material and three-fourths is daughter material? You would know that it took 10,000 years for half the original sample to decay and another 10,000 years for half of what remained to decay. The age of your sample would be 2 × 10,000, or 20,000, years. **Figure 2** shows how this steady decay happens.

✔ **Reading Check** What is a half-life? (*See the Appendix for answers to Reading Checks.*)

absolute dating any method of measuring the age of an event or object in years

isotope an atom that has the same number of protons (or the same atomic number) as other atoms of the same element do but that has a different number of neutrons (and thus a different atomic mass)

radioactive decay the process in which a radioactive isotope tends to break down into a stable isotope of the same element or another element

radiometric dating a method of determining the age of an object by estimating the relative percentages of a radioactive (parent) isotope and a stable (daughter) isotope

half-life the time needed for half of a sample of a radioactive substance to undergo radioactive decay

Figure 2 *After every half-life, the amount of parent material decreases by one-half.*

1/1
0 years

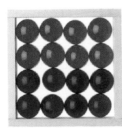
1/2
10,000 years

1/4
20,000 years

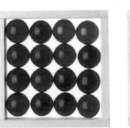
1/8
30,000 years

1/16
40,000 years

Types of Radiometric Dating

Imagine traveling back through the centuries to a time before Columbus arrived in America. You are standing along the bluffs of what will one day be called the Mississippi River. You see dozens of people building large mounds. Who are these people, and what are they building?

The people you saw in your time travel were Native Americans, and the structures they were building were burial mounds. The area you imagined is now an archaeological site called Effigy Mounds National Monument. **Figure 3** shows one of these mounds.

According to archaeologists, people lived at Effigy Mounds from 2,500 years ago to 600 years ago. How do archaeologists know these dates? They have dated bones and other objects in the mounds by using radiometric dating. Scientists use different radiometric-dating techniques based on the estimated age of an object. As you read on, think about how the half-life of an isotope relates to the age of the object being dated. Which technique would you use to date the burial mounds?

Figure 3 This burial mound at Effigy Mounds resembles a snake.

Potassium-Argon Method

One isotope that is used for radiometric dating is potassium-40. Potassium-40 has a half-life of 1.3 billion years, and it decays to argon and calcium. Geologists measure argon as the daughter material. This method is used mainly to date rocks older than 100,000 years.

Uranium-Lead Method

Uranium-238 is a radioactive isotope that decays in a series of steps to lead-206. The half-life of uranium-238 is 4.5 billion years. The older the rock is, the more daughter material (lead-206) there will be in the rock. Uranium-lead dating can be used for rocks more than 10 million years old. Younger rocks do not contain enough daughter material to be accurately measured by this method.

Rubidium-Strontium Method

Through radioactive decay, the unstable parent isotope rubidium-87 forms the stable daughter isotope strontium-87. The half-life of rubidium-87 is 49 billion years. This method is used to date rocks older than 10 million years.

Reading Check What is the daughter isotope of rubidium-87?

Carbon-14 Method

The element carbon is normally found in three forms, the stable isotopes carbon-12 and carbon-13 and the radioactive isotope carbon-14. These carbon isotopes combine with oxygen to form the gas carbon dioxide, which is taken in by plants during photosynthesis. As long as a plant is alive, new carbon dioxide with a constant carbon-14 to carbon-12 ratio is continually taken in. Animals that eat plants contain the same ratio of carbon isotopes.

Once a plant or an animal dies, however, no new carbon is taken in. The amount of carbon-14 begins to decrease as the plant or animal decays, and the ratio of carbon-14 to carbon-12 decreases. This decrease can be measured in a laboratory, such as the one shown in **Figure 4.** Because the half-life of carbon-14 is only 5,730 years, this dating method is used mainly for dating things that lived within the last 50,000 years.

Figure 4 *Some samples containing carbon must be cleaned and burned before their age can be determined.*

SECTION Review

Summary

- During radioactive decay, an unstable isotope decays at a constant rate and becomes a stable isotope of the same or a different element.

- Radiometric dating, based on the ratio of parent to daughter material, is used to determine the absolute age of a sample.

- Methods of radiometric dating include potassium-argon, uranium-lead, rubidium-strontium, and carbon-14 dating.

Using Key Terms

1. Use each of the following terms in a separate sentence: *absolute dating, isotope,* and *half-life.*

Understanding Key Ideas

2. Rubidium-87 has a half-life of
   a. 5,730 years.
   b. 4.5 billion years.
   c. 49 billion years.
   d. 1.3 billion years.

3. Explain how radioactive decay occurs.

4. How does radioactive decay relate to radiometric dating?

5. List four types of radiometric dating.

Math Skills

6. A radioactive isotope has a half-life of 1.3 billion years. After 3.9 billion years, how much of the parent material will be left?

Critical Thinking

7. **Analyzing Methods** Explain why radioactive decay must be constant in order for radiometric dating to be accurate.

8. **Applying Concepts** Which radiometric-dating method would be most appropriate for dating artifacts found at Effigy Mounds? Explain.

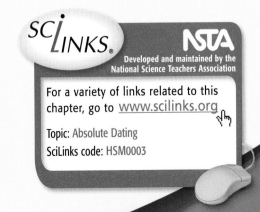

SCiLINKS.

NSTA
Developed and maintained by the
National Science Teachers Association

For a variety of links related to this chapter, go to www.scilinks.org

Topic: Absolute Dating
SciLinks code: HSM0003

73

Looking at Fossils

Descending from the top of a ridge in the badlands of Argentina, your expedition team suddenly stops. You look down and realize that you are walking on eggshells—dinosaur eggshells!

A paleontologist named Luis Chiappe had this experience. He had found an enormous dinosaur nesting ground.

Fossilized Organisms

The remains or physical evidence of an organism preserved by geologic processes is called a **fossil.** Fossils are most often preserved in sedimentary rock. But as you will see, other materials can also preserve evidence of past life.

Fossils in Rocks

When an organism dies, it either immediately begins to decay or is consumed by other organisms. Sometimes, however, organisms are quickly buried by sediment when they die. The sediment slows down decay. Hard parts of organisms, such as shells and bones, are more resistant to decay than soft tissues are. So, when sediments become rock, the hard parts of animals are much more commonly preserved than are soft tissues.

Fossils in Amber

Imagine that an insect is caught in soft, sticky tree sap. Suppose that the insect gets covered by more sap, which quickly hardens and preserves the insect inside. Hardened tree sap is called *amber*. Some of our best insect fossils are found in amber, as shown in **Figure 1.** Frogs and lizards have also been found in amber.

✓ Reading Check Describe how organisms are preserved in amber. (*See the Appendix for answers to Reading Checks.*)

What You Will Learn

● Describe five ways that different types of fossils form.
● List three types of fossils that are not part of organisms.
● Explain how fossils can be used to determine the history of changes in environments and organisms.
● Explain how index fossils can be used to date rock layers.

Vocabulary

fossil
trace fossil
mold
cast
index fossil

READING STRATEGY

Reading Organizer As you read this section, create an outline of the section. Use the headings from this section in your outline.

Figure 1 *These insects are preserved in amber.*

Figure 2 *Scientist Vladimir Eisner studies the upper molars of a 20,000-year-old woolly mammoth found in Siberia, Russia. The almost perfectly preserved male mammoth was excavated from a block of ice in October 1999.*

Petrifaction

Another way that organisms are preserved is by petrifaction. *Petrifaction* is a process in which minerals replace an organism's tissues. One form of petrifaction is called permineralization. *Permineralization* is a process in which the pore space in an organism's hard tissue—for example, bone or wood—is filled up with mineral. Another form of petrifaction is called *replacement,* a process in which the organism's tissues are completely replaced by minerals. For example, in some specimens of petrified wood, all of the wood has been replaced by minerals.

fossil the trace or remains of an organism that lived long ago, most commonly preserved in sedimentary rock

Fossils in Asphalt

There are places where asphalt wells up at the Earth's surface in thick, sticky pools. The La Brea asphalt deposits in Los Angeles, California, for example, are at least 38,000 years old. These pools of thick, sticky asphalt have trapped and preserved many kinds of organisms for the past 38,000 years. From these fossils, scientists have learned about the past environment in southern California.

Frozen Fossils

In October 1999, scientists removed a 20,000-year-old woolly mammoth frozen in the Siberian tundra. The remains of this mammoth are shown in **Figure 2.** Woolly mammoths, relatives of modern elephants, became extinct approximately 10,000 years ago. Because cold temperatures slow down decay, many types of frozen fossils are preserved from the last ice age. Scientists hope to find out more about the mammoth and the environment in which it lived.

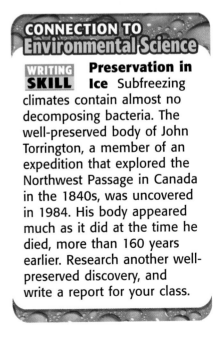

CONNECTION TO Environmental Science

WRITING SKILL **Preservation in Ice** Subfreezing climates contain almost no decomposing bacteria. The well-preserved body of John Torrington, a member of an expedition that explored the Northwest Passage in Canada in the 1840s, was uncovered in 1984. His body appeared much as it did at the time he died, more than 160 years earlier. Research another well-preserved discovery, and write a report for your class.

Figure 3 These dinosaur tracks are located in Arizona. They leave a trace of a dinosaur that had longer legs than humans do.

trace fossil a fossilized mark that is formed in soft sediment by the movement of an animal

mold a mark or cavity made in a sedimentary surface by a shell or other body

cast a type of fossil that forms when sediments fill in the cavity left by a decomposed organism

Other Types of Fossils

Besides their hard parts—and in rare cases their soft parts—do organisms leave behind any other clues about their existence? What other evidence of past life do paleontologists look for?

Trace Fossils

Any naturally preserved evidence of animal activity is called a **trace fossil.** Tracks like the ones shown in **Figure 3** are a fascinating example of a trace fossil. These fossils form when animal footprints fill with sediment and are preserved in rock. Tracks reveal a lot about the animal that made them, including how big it was and how fast it was moving. Parallel trackways showing dinosaurs moving in the same direction have led paleontologists to hypothesize that dinosaurs moved in herds.

Burrows are another trace fossil. Burrows are shelters made by animals, such as clams, that bury in sediment. Like tracks, burrows are preserved when they are filled in with sediment and buried quickly. A *coprolite* (KAHP roh LIET), a third type of trace fossil, is preserved animal dung.

Molds and Casts

Molds and casts are two more examples of fossils. A cavity in rock where a plant or animal was buried is called a **mold.** A **cast** is an object created when sediment fills a mold and becomes rock. A cast shows what the outside of the organism looked like. **Figure 4** shows two types of molds from the same organism—and internal mold and an external mold.

Reading Check How are a cast and a mold different?

Figure 4 This photograph shows two molds from an ammonite. The image on the left is the internal mold of the ammonite, which formed when sediment filled the ammonite's shell, which later dissolved away. The image on the right is the external mold of the ammonite, which preserves the external features of the shell.

Figure 5 *This scientist has found marine fossils on mountaintops in the Yoho National Park in Canada. The fossil of* Marrella, *shown above, tells the scientist that these rocks were pushed up from below sea level millions of years ago.*

Using Fossils to Interpret the Past

Think about your favorite outdoor place. Now, imagine that you are a paleontologist at the same site 65 million years from now. What types of fossils would you dig up? Based on the fossils you found, how would you reconstruct this place?

The Information in the Fossil Record

The fossil record offers only a rough sketch of the history of life on Earth. Some parts of this history are more complete than others. For example, scientists know more about organisms that had hard body parts than about organisms that had soft body parts. Scientists also know more about organisms that lived in environments that favored fossilization. The fossil record is incomplete because most organisms never became fossils. And of course, many fossils have yet to be discovered.

History of Environmental Changes

Would you expect to find marine fossils on the mountaintop shown in **Figure 5**? The presence of marine fossils means that the rocks of these mountaintops in Canada formed in a totally different environment—at the bottom of an ocean.

The fossil record reveals a history of environmental change. For example, marine fossils help scientists reconstruct ancient coastlines and the deepening and shallowing of ancient seas. Using the fossils of plants and land animals, scientists can reconstruct past climates. They can tell whether the climate in an area was cooler or wetter than it is at present.

Quick Lab

Make a Fossil

1. Find a **common object,** such as a shell, a button, or a pencil, to use to make a mold. Keep the object hidden from your classmates.

2. To create a mold, press the items down into **modeling clay** in a **shallow pan or tray.**

3. Trade your tray with a classmate's tray, and try to identify the item that made the mold.

4. Describe how a cast could be formed from your mold.

Fossil Hunt

Go on a fossil hunt with a parent or guardian. Find out what kinds of rocks in your local area might contain fossils. Take pictures or draw sketches of your trip and any fossils that you find.

index fossil a fossil that is found in the rock layers of only one geologic age and that is used to establish the age of the rock layers

History of Changing Organisms

By studying the relationships between fossils, scientists can interpret how life has changed over time. For example, older rock layers contain organisms that often differ from the organisms found in younger rock layers.

Only a small fraction of the organisms that have existed in Earth's history have been fossilized. Because the fossil record is incomplete, it does not provide paleontologists with a continuous record of change. Instead, they look for similarities between fossils, or between fossilized organisms and their closest living relatives, and try to fill in the blanks in the fossil record.

✓ **Reading Check** How do paleontologists fill in missing information about changes in organisms in the fossil record?

Using Fossils to Date Rocks

Scientists have found that particular types of fossils appear only in certain layers of rock. By dating the rock layers above and below these fossils, scientists can determine the time span in which the organisms that formed the fossils lived. If a type of organism existed for only a short period of time, its fossils would show up in a limited range of rock layers. These types of fossils are called index fossils. **Index fossils** are fossils of organisms that lived during a relatively short, well-defined geologic time span.

Ammonites

To be considered an index fossil, a fossil must be found in rock layers throughout the world. One example of an index fossil is the fossil of a genus of ammonites (AM uh NIETS) called *Tropites*, shown in **Figure 6.** *Tropites* was a marine mollusk similar to a modern squid. It lived in a coiled shell. *Tropites* lived between 230 million and 208 million years ago and is an index fossil for that period of time.

Figure 6 Tropites *is a genus of coiled ammonites.* Tropites *existed for only about 20 million years, which makes this genus a good index fossil.*

Trilobites

Fossils of a genus of trilobites (TRIE loh BIETS) called *Phacops* are another example of an index fossil. Trilobites are extinct. Their closest living relative is the horseshoe crab. Through the dating of rock, paleontologists have determined that *Phacops* lived approximately 400 million years ago. So, when scientists find *Phacops* in rock layers anywhere on Earth, they assume that these rock layers are also approximately 400 million years old. An example of a *Phacops* fossil is shown in **Figure 7.**

✓ Reading Check Explain how fossils of *Phacops* can be used to establish the age of rock layers.

Figure 7 *Paleontologists assume that any rock layer containing a fossil of the trilobite* Phacops *is about 400 million years old.*

SECTION Review

Summary

- Fossils are the remains or physical evidence of an organism preserved by geologic processes.

- Fossils can be preserved in rock, amber, asphalt, and ice and by petrifaction.

- Trace fossils are any naturally preserved evidence of animal activity. Tracks, burrows, and coprolites are examples of trace fossils.

- Scientists study fossils to determine how environments and organisms have changed over time.

- An index fossil is a fossil of an organism that lived during a relatively short, well-defined time span. Index fossils can be used to establish the age of rock layers.

Using Key Terms

Complete each of the following sentences by choosing the correct term from the word bank.

cast	index fossils
mold	trace fossils

1. A ___ is a cavity in rock where a plant or animal was buried.

2. ___ can be used to establish the age of rock layers.

Understanding Key Ideas

3. Fossils are most often preserved in
   - **a.** ice.
   - **b.** amber.
   - **c.** asphalt.
   - **d.** rock.

4. Describe three types of trace fossils.

5. Explain how an index fossil can be used to date rock.

6. Explain why the fossil record contains an incomplete record of the history of life on Earth.

7. Explain how fossils can be used to determine the history of changes in environments and organisms.

Math Skills

8. If a scientist finds the remains of a plant between a rock layer that contains 400 million–year-old *Phacops* fossils and a rock layer that contains 230 million–year-old *Tropites* fossils, how old could the plant fossil be?

Critical Thinking

9. **Making Inferences** If you find rock layers containing fish fossils in a desert, what can you infer about the history of the desert?

10. **Identifying Bias** Because information in the fossil record is incomplete, scientists are left with certain biases concerning fossil preservation. Explain two of these biases.

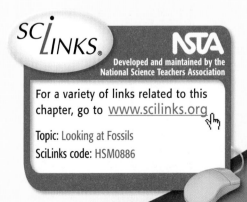

SCI LINKS®

NSTA
Developed and maintained by the
National Science Teachers Association

For a variety of links related to this chapter, go to www.scilinks.org

Topic: Looking at Fossils
SciLinks code: HSM0886

Time Marches On

How old is the Earth? Well, if the Earth celebrated its birthday every million years, there would be 4,600 candles on its birthday cake! Humans have been around only long enough to light the last candle on the cake.

Try to think of the Earth's history in "fast-forward." If you could watch the Earth change from this perspective, you would see mountains rise up like wrinkles in fabric and quickly wear away. You would see life-forms appear and then go extinct. In this section, you will learn that geologists must "fast-forward" the Earth's history when they write or talk about it. You will also learn about some incredible events in the history of life on Earth.

Geologic Time

Shown in **Figure 1** is the rock wall at the Dinosaur Quarry Visitor Center in Dinosaur National Monument, Utah. Contained within this wall are approximately 1,500 fossil bones that have been excavated by paleontologists. These are the remains of dinosaurs that inhabited the area about 150 million years ago. Granted, 150 million years seems to be an incredibly long period of time. However, in terms of the Earth's history, 150 million years is little more than 3% of the time our planet has existed. It is a little less than 4% of the time represented by the Earth's oldest known rocks.

What You Will Learn

● Explain how geologic time is recorded in rock layers.
● Identify important dates on the geologic time scale.
● Explain how environmental changes resulted in the extinction of some species.

Vocabulary

geologic time scale	period
eon	epoch
era	extinction

READING STRATEGY

Brainstorming The key idea of this section is the geologic time scale. Brainstorm words and phrases related to the geologic time scale.

Figure 1 *Bones of dinosaurs that lived about 150 million years ago are exposed in the quarry wall at Dinosaur National Monument in Utah.*

Figure 2 *Well-preserved plant and animal fossils are common in the Green River formation. Clockwise from the upper right are a fossil leaf, a dragonfly, a fish, and a turtle.*

The Rock Record and Geologic Time

One of the best places in North America to see the Earth's history recorded in rock layers is in Grand Canyon National Park. The Colorado River has cut the canyon nearly 2 km deep in some places. Over the course of 6 million years, the river has eroded countless layers of rock. These layers represent almost half, or nearly 2 billion years, of Earth's history.

✔ **Reading Check** How much geologic time is represented by the rock layers in the Grand Canyon? (*See the Appendix for answers to Reading Checks.*)

The Fossil Record and Geologic Time

Figure 2 shows sedimentary rocks that belong to the Green River formation. These rocks, which are found in parts of Wyoming, Utah, and Colorado, are thousands of meters thick. These rocks were once part of a system of ancient lakes that existed for a period of millions of years. Fossils of plants and animals are common in these rocks and are very well preserved. Burial in the fine-grained lake-bed sediments preserved even the most delicate structures.

For another activity related to this chapter, go to **go.hrw.com** and type in the keyword **HZ5FOSW**.

Phanerozoic Eon

(542 million years ago to the present)
The rock and fossil record represents mainly the Phanerozoic eon, which is the eon in which we live.

Proterozoic Eon

(2.5 billion years ago to 542 million years ago)
The first organisms with well-developed cells appeared during this eon.

Archean Eon

(3.8 billion years ago to 2.5 billion years ago)
The earliest known rocks on Earth formed during this eon.

Hadean Eon

(4.6 billion years ago to 3.8 billion years ago)
The only rocks that scientists have found from this eon are meteorites and rocks from the moon.

Geologic Time Scale

Era	Period	Epoch	Millions of years ago
Cenozoic	Quaternary	Holocene	0.01
		Pleistocene	1.8
	Tertiary	Pliocene	5.3
		Miocene	23
		Oligocene	33.9
		Eocene	55.8
		Paleocene	65.5
Mesozoic	Cretaceous		146
	Jurassic		200
	Triassic		251
Paleozoic	Permian		299
	Pennsylvanian		318
	Mississippian		359
	Devonian		416
	Silurian		444
	Ordovician		488
	Cambrian		542

PHANEROZOIC EON

PROTEROZOIC EON — 2,500

ARCHEAN EON — 3,800

HADEAN EON — 4,600

Figure 3 *The geologic time scale accounts for Earth's entire history. It is divided into four major parts called* eons. *Dates given for intervals on the geologic time scale are estimates.*

The Geologic Time Scale

The geologic column represents the billions of years that have passed since the first rocks formed on Earth. Altogether, geologists study 4.6 billion years of Earth's history! To make their job easier, geologists have created the geologic time scale. The **geologic time scale,** which is shown in **Figure 3,** is a scale that divides Earth's 4.6 billion–year history into distinct intervals of time.

Reading Check Define the term *geologic time scale.*

Divisions of Time

Geologists have divided Earth's history into sections of time, as shown on the geologic time scale in **Figure 3.** The largest divisions of geologic time are **eons** (EE AHNZ). There are four eons—the Hadean eon, the Archean eon, the Proterozoic eon, and the Phanerozoic eon. The Phanerozoic eon is divided into three **eras,** which are the second-largest divisions of geologic time. The three eras are further divided into **periods,** which are the third-largest divisions of geologic time. Periods are divided into **epochs** (EP uhks), which are the fourth-largest divisions of geologic time.

The boundaries between geologic time intervals represent shorter intervals in which visible changes took place on Earth. Some changes are marked by the disappearance of index fossil species, while others are recognized only by detailed paleontological studies.

The Appearance and Disappearance of Species

At certain times during Earth's history, the number of species has increased or decreased dramatically. An increase in the number of species often comes as a result of either a relatively sudden increase or decrease in competition among species. *Hallucigenia,* shown in **Figure 4,** appeared during the Cambrian period, when the number of marine species greatly increased. On the other hand, the number of species decreases dramatically over a relatively short period of time during a mass extinction event. **Extinction** is the death of every member of a species. Gradual events, such as global climate change and changes in ocean currents, can cause mass extinctions. A combination of these events can also cause mass extinctions.

geologic time scale the standard method used to divide the Earth's long natural history into manageable parts

eon the largest division of geologic time

era a unit of geologic time that includes two or more periods

period a unit of geologic time into which eras are divided

epoch a subdivision of a geologic period

extinction the death of every member of a species

Figure 4 Hallucigenia, *named for its "bizarre and dreamlike quality," was one of numerous marine organisms to make its appearance during the early Cambrian period.*

Figure 5 *Jungles were present during the Paleozoic era, but there were no birds singing in the trees and no monkeys swinging from the branches. Birds and mammals didn't evolve until much later.*

The Paleozoic Era—Old Life

The Paleozoic era lasted from about 542 million to 251 million years ago. It is the first era well represented by fossils.

Marine life flourished at the beginning of the Paleozoic era. The oceans became home to a diversity of life. However, there were few land organisms. By the middle of the Paleozoic, all modern groups of land plants had appeared. By the end of the era, amphibians and reptiles lived on the land, and insects were abundant. **Figure 5** shows what the Earth might have looked like late in the Paleozoic era. The Paleozoic era came to an end with the largest mass extinction in Earth's history. Some scientists believe that ocean changes were a likely cause of this extinction, which killed nearly 90% of all marine species.

The Mesozoic Era—The Age of Reptiles

The Mesozoic era began about 251 million years ago. The Mesozoic is known as the *Age of Reptiles* because reptiles, such as the dinosaurs shown in **Figure 6,** inhabited the land.

During this time, reptiles dominated. Small mammals appeared about the same time as dinosaurs, and birds appeared late in the Mesozoic era. Many scientists think that birds evolved directly from a type of dinosaur. At the end of the Mesozoic era, about 15% to 20% of all species on Earth, including the dinosaurs, became extinct. Global climate change may have been the cause.

✔ **Reading Check** Why is the Mesozoic known as the *Age of Reptiles*?

Figure 6 *Imagine walking in the desert and bumping into these fierce creatures! It's a good thing humans didn't evolve in the Mesozoic era, which was dominated by dinosaurs.*

The Cenozoic Era—The Age of Mammals

The Cenozoic era, as shown in **Figure 7,** began about 65.5 million years ago and continues to the present. This era is known as the *Age of Mammals.* During the Mesozoic era, mammals had to compete with dinosaurs and other animals for food and habitat. After the mass extinction at the end of the Mesozoic era, mammals flourished. Unique traits, such as regulating body temperature internally and bearing young that develop inside the mother, may have helped mammals survive the environmental changes that probably caused the extinction of the dinosaurs.

Figure 7 *Thousands of species of mammals evolved during the Cenozoic era. This scene shows species from the early Cenozoic era that are now extinct.*

SECTION Review

Summary

- The geologic time scale divides Earth's 4.6 billion–year history into distinct intervals of time. Divisions of geologic time include eons, eras, periods, and epochs.

- The boundaries between geologic time intervals represent visible changes that have taken place on Earth.

- The rock and fossil record represents mainly the Phanerozoic eon, which is the eon in which we live.

- At certain times in Earth's history, the number of life-forms has increased or decreased dramatically.

Using Key Terms

1. Use each of the following terms in the same sentence: *era, period,* and *epoch.*

Understanding Key Ideas

2. The unit of geologic time that began 65.5 million years ago and continues to the present is the

   a. Holocene epoch.
   b. Cenozoic era.
   c. Phanerozoic eon.
   d. Quaternary period.

3. What are the major time intervals represented by the geologic time scale?

4. Explain how geologic time is recorded in rock layers.

5. What kinds of environmental changes cause mass extinctions?

Critical Thinking

6. **Making Inferences** What future event might mark the end of the Cenozoic era?

7. **Identifying Relationships** How might a decrease in competition between species lead to the sudden appearance of many new species?

Interpreting Graphics

8. Look at the illustration below. On the Earth-history clock shown, 1 h equals 383 million years, and 1 min equals 6.4 million years. In millions of years, how much more time is represented by the Proterozoic eon than by the Phanerozoic eon?

Phanerozoic eon

Hadean eon

Proterozoic eon

Archean eon

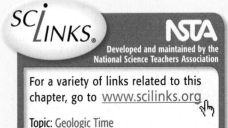

Developed and maintained by the National Science Teachers Association

For a variety of links related to this chapter, go to www.scilinks.org

Topic: Geologic Time
SciLinks code: HSM0668

Model-Making Lab

OBJECTIVES

Make a model of a geologic column.

Interpret the geologic history represented by the geologic column you have made.

MATERIALS

- paper, white
- pencil
- pencils or crayons, assorted colors
- ruler, metric
- scissors
- tape, transparent

SAFETY

How Do You Stack Up?

According to the principle of superposition, in undisturbed sequences of sedimentary rock, the oldest layers are on the bottom. Geologists use this principle to determine the relative age of the rocks in a small area. In this activity, you will model what geologists do by drawing sections of different rock outcrops. Then, you will create a part of the geologic column, showing the geologic history of the area that contains all of the outcrops.

Procedure

1 Use a metric ruler and a pencil to draw four boxes on a blank piece of paper. Each box should be 3 cm wide and at least 6 cm tall. (You can trace the boxes shown on the next page.)

2 With colored pencils, copy the illustrations of the four outcrops on the next page. Copy one illustration in each of the four boxes. Use colors and patterns similar to those shown.

3 Pay close attention to the contact between layers—straight or wavy. Straight lines represent bedding planes, where deposition was continuous. Wavy lines represent unconformities, where rock layers may be missing. The top of each outcrop is incomplete, so it should be a jagged line. (Assume that the bottom of the lowest layer is a bedding plane.)

4 Use a black crayon or pencil to add the symbols representing fossils to the layers in your drawings. Pay attention to the shapes of the fossils and the layers that they are in.

5 Write the outcrop number on the back of each section.

6 Carefully cut the outcrops out of the paper, and lay the individual outcrops next to each other on your desk or table.

7 Find layers that have the same rocks and contain the same fossils. Move each outcrop up or down to line up similar layers next to each other.

8 If unconformities appear in any of the outcrops, there may be rock layers missing. You may need to examine other sections to find out what fits between the layers above and below the unconformities. Leave room for these layers by cutting the outcrops along the unconformities (wavy lines).

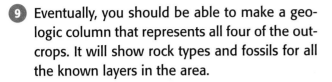

9. Eventually, you should be able to make a geologic column that represents all four of the outcrops. It will show rock types and fossils for all the known layers in the area.

10. Tape the pieces of paper together in a pattern that represents the complete geologic column.

Analyze the Results

1. **Examining Data** How many layers are in the part of the geologic column that you modeled?

2. **Examining Data** Which is the oldest layer in your column? Which rock layer is the youngest? How do you know? Describe these layers in terms of rock type or the fossils they contain.

3. **Classifying** List the fossils in your column from oldest to youngest. Label the youngest and oldest fossils.

4. **Analyzing Data** Look at the unconformity in outcrop 2. Which rock layers are partially or completely missing? How do you know?

Draw Conclusions

5. **Drawing Conclusions** Which (if any) fossils can be used as index fossils for a single layer? Why are these fossils considered index fossils? What method(s) would be required to determine the absolute age of these fossils?

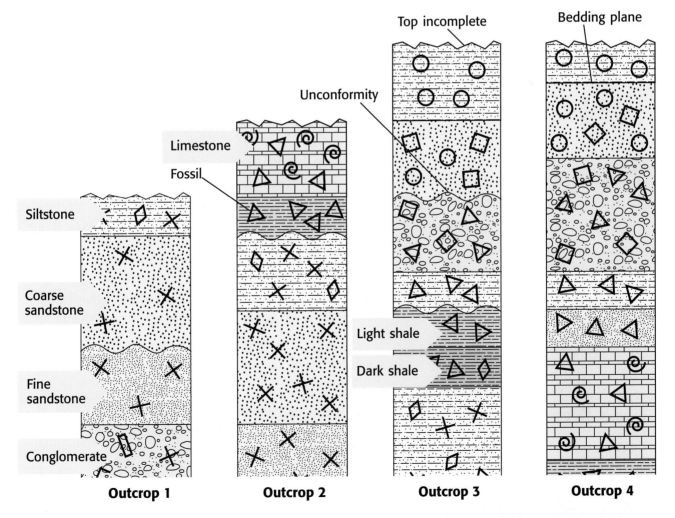

Outcrop 1

Outcrop 2

Outcrop 3

Outcrop 4

Siltstone

Coarse sandstone

Fine sandstone

Conglomerate

Limestone

Fossil

Unconformity

Top incomplete

Bedding plane

Light shale

Dark shale

Chapter Review

USING KEY TERMS

1 In your own words, write a definition for each of the following terms: *superposition, geologic column,* and *geologic time scale.*

For each pair of terms, explain how the meanings of the terms differ.

2 *uniformitarianism* and *catastrophism*

3 *relative dating* and *absolute dating*

4 *trace fossil* and *index fossil*

UNDERSTANDING KEY IDEAS

Multiple Choice

5 Which of the following does not describe catastrophic change?

a. widespread

b. sudden

c. rare

d. gradual

6 Scientists assign relative ages by using

a. absolute dating.

b. the principle of superposition.

c. radioactive half-lives.

d. carbon-14 dating.

7 Which of the following is a trace fossil?

a. an insect preserved in amber

b. a mammoth frozen in ice

c. wood replaced by minerals

d. a dinosaur trackway

8 The largest divisions of geologic time are called

a. periods.

b. eras.

c. eons.

d. epochs.

9 Rock layers cut by a fault formed

a. after the fault.

b. before the fault.

c. at the same time as the fault.

d. There is not enough information to determine the answer.

10 Of the following isotopes, which is stable?

a. uranium-238

b. potassium-40

c. carbon-12

d. carbon-14

11 A surface that represents a missing part of the geologic column is called a(n)

a. intrusion.

b. fault.

c. unconformity.

d. fold.

12 Which method of radiometric dating is used mainly to date the remains of organisms that lived within the last 50,000 years?

a. carbon-14 dating

b. potassium-argon dating

c. uranium-lead dating

d. rubidium-strontium dating

Short Answer

13 Describe three processes by which fossils form.

14 Identify the role of uniformitarianism in Earth science.

15 Explain how radioactive decay occurs.

16 Describe two ways in which scientists use fossils to determine environmental change.

17 Explain the role of paleontology in the study of Earth's history.

18 **Concept Mapping** Use the following terms to create a concept map: *age, half-life, absolute dating, radioactive decay, radiometric dating, relative dating, superposition, geologic column,* and *isotopes.*

19 **Applying Concepts** Identify how changes in environmental conditions can affect the survival of a species. Give two examples.

20 **Identifying Relationships** Why do paleontologists know more about hard-bodied organisms than about soft-bodied organisms?

21 **Analyzing Processes** Why isn't a 100 million–year-old fossilized tree made of wood?

INTERPRETING GRAPHICS

Use the diagram below to answer the questions that follow.

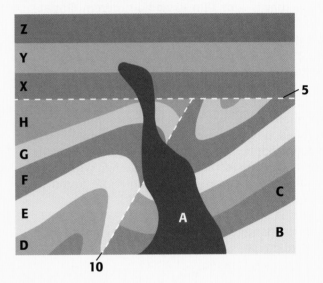

22 Is intrusion **A** younger or older than layer **X**? Explain.

23 What feature is marked by **5**?

24 Is intrusion **A** younger or older than fault **10**? Explain.

25 Other than the intrusion and faulting, what event happened in layers **B, C, D, E, F, G,** and **H**? Number this event, the intrusion, and the faulting in the order that they happened.

READING

Read each of the passages below. Then, answer the questions that follow each passage.

Passage 1 Three hundred million years ago, the region that is now Illinois had a different climate than it does today. Swamps and shallow bays covered much of the area. No fewer than 500 species of plants and animals lived in this environment. Today, the remains of these organisms are found beautifully preserved within nodules. Nodules are round or oblong structures usually composed of cemented sediments that sometimes contain the fossilized hard parts of plants and animals. The Illinois nodules are <u>exceptional</u> because the soft parts of organisms are found together with hard parts. For this reason, these nodules are found in fossil collections around the world.

1. In the passage, what is the meaning of the word *exceptional*?

  A beautiful

  B extraordinary

  C average

  D large

2. According to the passage, which of the following statements about nodules is correct?

  F Nodules are rarely round or oblong.

  G Nodules are usually composed of cemented sediment.

  H Nodules are not found in present-day Illinois.

  I Nodules always contain fossils.

3. Which of the following is a fact in the passage?

  A The Illinois nodules are not well known outside of Illinois.

  B Illinois has had the same climate throughout Earth's history.

  C Both the hard and soft parts of organisms are preserved in the Illinois nodules.

  D Fewer than 500 species of plants and animals have been found in Illinois nodules.

Passage 2 In 1995, paleontologist Paul Sereno and his team were working in an unexplored region of Morocco when they made an <u>astounding</u> find—an enormous dinosaur skull! The skull measured approximately 1.6 m in length, which is about the height of a refrigerator. Given the size of the skull, Sereno concluded that the skeleton of the animal it came from must have been about 14 m long—about as big as a school bus. The dinosaur was even larger than *Tyrannosaurus rex*! The newly discovered 90 million–year-old predator most likely chased other dinosaurs by running on large, powerful hind legs, and its bladelike teeth meant certain death for its prey.

1. In the passage, what does the word *astounding* mean?

  A important

  B new

  C incredible

  D one of a kind

2. Which of the following is evidence that the dinosaur described in the passage was a predator?

  F It had bladelike teeth.

  G It had a large skeleton.

  H It was found with the bones of a smaller animal nearby.

  I It is 90 million years old.

3. What types of information do you think that fossil teeth provide about an organism?

  A the color of its skin

  B the types of food it ate

  C the speed that it ran

  D the mating habits it had

Use the graph below to answer the questions that follow.

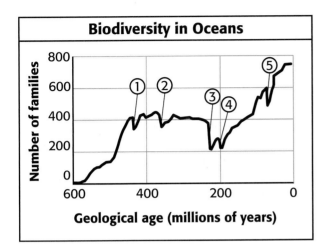

Biodiversity in Oceans

1. At which point in Earth's history did the greatest mass-extinction event take place?

   A at point 1, the Ordovician-Silurian boundary

   B at point 3, the Permian-Triassic boundary

   C at point 4, the Triassic-Jurassic boundary

   D at point 5, the Cretaceous-Tertiary boundary

2. Immediately following the Cretaceous-Tertiary extinction, represented by point 5, approximately how many families of marine organisms remained in the Earth's oceans?

   F 200 marine families

   G 300 marine families

   H 500 marine families

   I 700 marine families

3. Approximately how many million years ago did the Ordovician-Silurian mass-extinction event, represented by point 1, take place?

   A 200 million years ago

   B 250 million years ago

   C 350 million years ago

   D 420 million years ago

Read each question below, and choose the best answer.

1. Carbon-14 is a radioactive isotope with a half-life of 5,730 years. How much carbon-14 would remain in a sample that is 11,460 years old?

   A 12.5%

   B 25%

   C 50%

   D 100%

2. If a sample contains an isotope with a half-life of 10,000 years, how old would the sample be if 1/8 of the original isotope remained in the sample?

   F 20,000 years

   G 30,000 years

   H 40,000 years

   I 50,000 years

3. If a sample contains an isotope with a half-life of 5,000 years, how old would the sample be if 1/4 of the original isotope remained in the sample?

   A 10,000 years

   B 20,000 years

   C 30,000 years

   D 40,000 years

4. If Earth history spans 4.6 billion years and the Phanerozoic eon was 543 million years, what percentage of Earth history does the Phanerozoic eon represent?

   F about 6%

   G about 12%

   H about 18%

   I about 24%

5. Humans live in the Holocene epoch. If the Holocene epoch has lasted approximately 10,000 years, what percentage of the Quaternary period, which began 1.8 million years ago, is represented by the Holocene?

   A about 0.0055%

   B about 0.055%

   C about 0.55%

   D about 5.5%

Science in Action

Scientific Debate

Feathered Dinosaurs

One day in 1996, a Chinese farmer broke open a rock he found in the bed of an ancient dry lake. What he found inside the rock became one of the most exciting paleontological discoveries of the 20th century. Preserved inside were the remains of a dinosaur. The dinosaur had a large head; powerful jaws; sharp, jagged teeth; and, most important of all, a row of featherlike structures along the backbone. Scientists named the dinosaur *Sinosauropteryx,* or "Chinese dragon wing." *Sinosauropteryx* and the remains of other "feathered" dinosaurs recently discovered in China have led some scientists to hypothesize that feathers evolved through theropod (three-toed) dinosaurs. Other paleontologists disagree. They believe the structures along the backbone of these dinosaurs are not feathers but the remains of elongated spines, like those that run down the head and back of an iguana.

Science, Technology, and Society

DNA and a Mammoth Discovery

In recent years, scientists have unearthed several mammoths that had been frozen in ice in Siberia and other remote northern locations. Bones, fur, food in the stomach, and even dung have all been found in good condition. Some scientists hoped that DNA extracted from the mammoths might lead to the cloning of this animal, which became extinct about 10,000 years ago. But the DNA might not be able to be duplicated by scientists. However, DNA samples may nevertheless help scientists understand why mammoths became extinct. One theory about why mammoths became extinct is that they were killed off by disease. Using DNA taken from fossilized mammoth bone, hair, or dung, scientists can check to see if it contains the DNA of a disease-causing pathogen that led to the extinction of the mammoths.

Language Arts ACTiViTY

Paleontologists often give dinosaurs names that describe something unusual about the animal's head, body, feet, or size. These names have Greek or Latin roots. Research the names of some dinosaurs, and find out what the names mean. Create a list of dinosaur names and their meanings.

Math ACTiViTY

The male Siberian mammoth reached a height of about 3 m at the shoulder. Females reached a height of about 2.5 m at the shoulder. What is the ratio of the maximum height of a female Siberian mammoth to the height of a male Siberian mammoth?

Lizzie May

Amateur Paleontologist For Lizzie May, summer vacations have meant trips into the Alaskan wilderness with her stepfather, geologist/paleontologist Kevin May. The purpose of these trips has not been for fun. Instead, Kevin and Lizzie have been exploring the Alaskan wilderness for the remains of ancient life—dinosaurs, in particular.

At age 18, Lizzie May has gained the reputation of being Alaska's most famous teenage paleontologist. It is a reputation that is well deserved. To date, Lizzie has collected hundreds of dinosaur bones and located important sites of dinosaur, bird, and mammal tracks. In her honor and as a result of her hard work in the field, scientists named the skeleton of a dinosaur discovered by the Mays "Lizzie." "Lizzie" is a duck-bill dinosaur, or hadrosaur, that lived approximately 90 million years ago. "Lizzie" is the oldest dinosaur ever found in Alaska and one of the earliest known duckbill dinosaurs in North America.

The Mays have made other, equally exciting discoveries. On one summer trip, Kevin and Lizzie located six dinosaur and bird track sites that dated back 97 million to 144 million years. On another trip, the Mays found a fossil marine reptile more than 200 million years old—an ichthyosaur—that had to be removed with the help of a military helicopter. You have to wonder what other exciting adventures are in store for Lizzie and Kevin!

Social Studies ACTiViTY

WRITING SKILL Lizzie May is not the only young person to have made a mark in dinosaur paleontology. Using the Internet or another source, research people such as Bucky Derflinger, Johnny Maurice, Brad Riney, and Wendy Sloboda, who as young people made contributions to the field of dinosaur study. Write a short essay summarizing your findings.

To learn more about these Science in Action topics, visit **go.hrw.com** and type in the keyword **HZ5FOSF**.

Check out Current Science® articles related to this chapter by visiting **go.hrw.com**. Just type in the keyword **HZ5CS06**.

The Big Idea

Plate tectonics accounts for important features of Earth's surface and major geologic events.

About the  PHOTO

The San Andreas fault stretches across the California landscape like a giant wound. The fault, which is 1,000 km long, breaks the Earth's crust from Northern California to Mexico. Because the North American plate and Pacific plate are slipping past one another along the fault, many earthquakes happen.

PRE-READING ACTIVITY

 **FOLDNOTES** **Key-Term Fold** Before you read the chapter, create the FoldNote entitled "Key-Term Fold" described in the **Study Skills** section of the Appendix. Write a key term from the chapter on each tab of the key-term fold. Under each tab, write the definition of the key term.

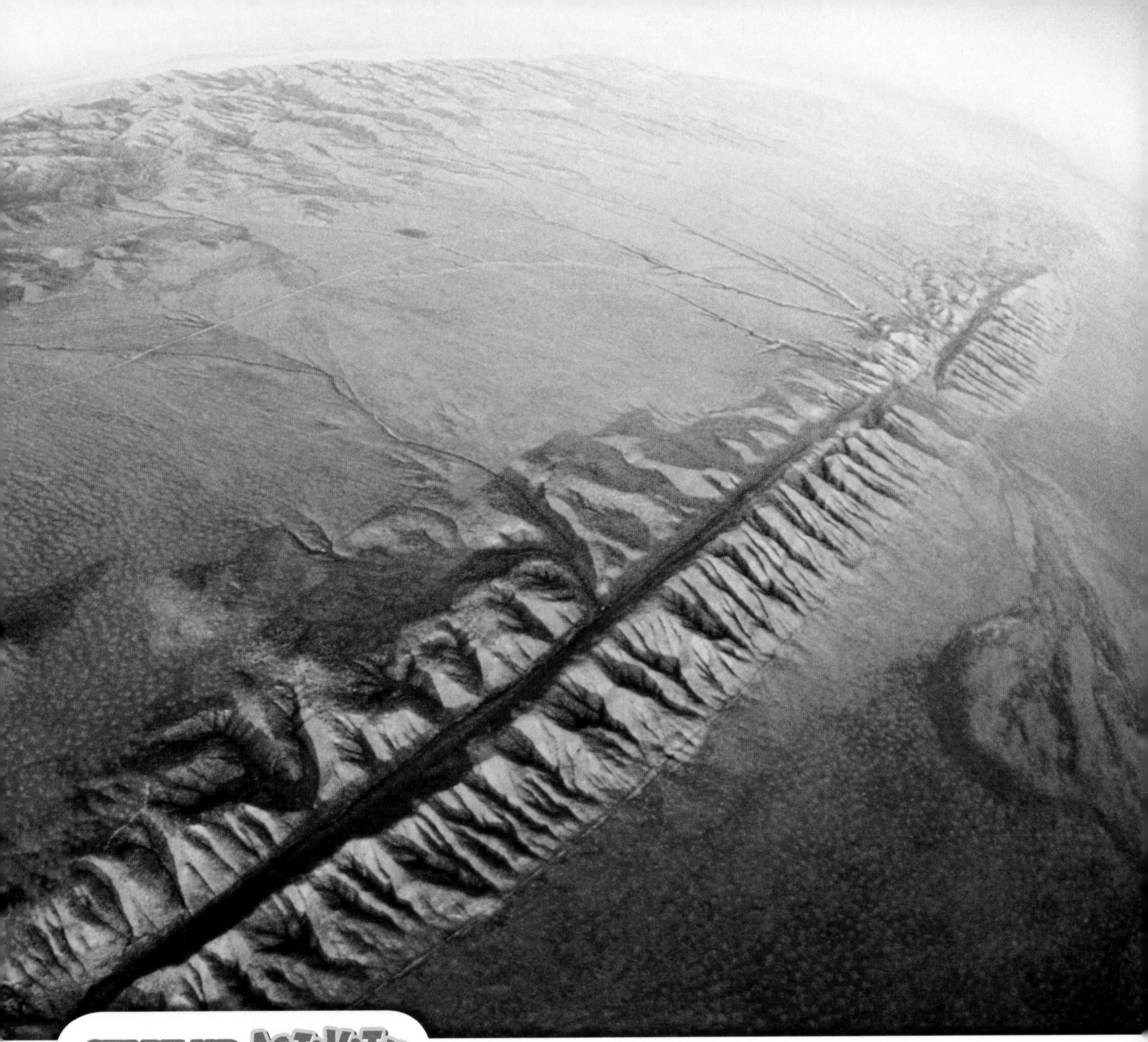

Continental Collisions

As you can see, continents not only move but can also crash into each other. In this activity, you will model the collision of two continents.

Procedure

1. Obtain **two stacks of paper** that are each about 1 cm thick.

2. Place the two stacks of paper on a **flat surface,** such as a desk.

3. Very slowly, push the stacks of paper together so that they collide. Continue to push the stacks until the paper in one of the stacks folds over.

Analysis

1. What happens to the stacks of paper when they collide with each other?

2. Are all of the pieces of paper pushed upward? If not, what happens to the pieces that are not pushed upward?

3. What type of landform will most likely result from this continental collision?

Inside the Earth

If you tried to dig to the center of the Earth, what do you think you would find? Would the Earth be solid or hollow? Would it be made of the same material throughout?

Actually, the Earth is made of several layers. Each layer is made of different materials that have different properties. Scientists think about physical layers in two ways—by their chemical composition and by their physical properties.

The Composition of the Earth

The Earth is divided into three layers—the crust, the mantle, and the core—based on the compounds that make up each layer. A *compound* is a substance composed of two or more elements. The less dense compounds make up the crust and mantle, and the densest compounds make up the core. The layers form because heavier elements are pulled toward the center of the Earth by gravity, and elements of lesser mass are found farther from the center.

The Crust

The outermost layer of the Earth is the **crust.** The crust is 5 to 100 km thick. It is the thinnest layer of the Earth.

As **Figure 1** shows, there are two types of crust—continental and oceanic. Both continental crust and oceanic crust are made mainly of the elements oxygen, silicon, and aluminum. However, the denser oceanic crust has almost twice as much iron, calcium, and magnesium, which form minerals that are denser than those in the continental crust.

What You Will Learn

● Identify the layers of the Earth by their chemical composition.
● Identify the layers of the Earth by their physical properties.
● Describe a tectonic plate.
● Explain how scientists know about the structure of Earth's interior.

Vocabulary

crust   asthenosphere
mantle   mesosphere
core   tectonic plate
lithosphere

READING STRATEGY

Reading Organizer As you read this section, create an outline of the section. Use the headings from the section in your outline.

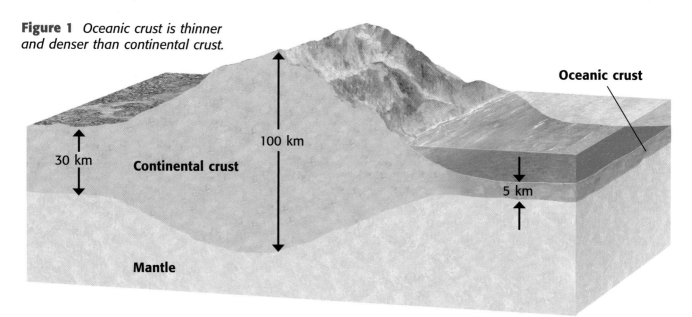

Figure 1 *Oceanic crust is thinner and denser than continental crust.*

Oceanic crust

100 km

30 km **Continental crust**

5 km

Mantle

The Mantle

The layer of the Earth between the crust and the core is the **mantle.** The mantle is much thicker than the crust and contains most of the Earth's mass.

No one has ever visited the mantle. The crust is too thick to drill through to reach the mantle. Scientists must draw conclusions about the composition and other physical properties of the mantle from observations made on the Earth's surface. In some places, mantle rock pushes to the surface, which allows scientists to study the rock directly.

As you can see in **Figure 2,** another place scientists look for clues about the mantle is the ocean floor. Magma from the mantle flows out of active volcanoes on the ocean floor. These underwater volcanoes have given scientists many clues about the composition of the mantle. Because the mantle has more magnesium and less aluminum and silicon than the crust does, the mantle is denser than the crust.

The Core

The layer of the Earth that extends from below the mantle to the center of the Earth is the **core.** Scientists think that the Earth's core is made mostly of iron and contains smaller amounts of nickel but almost no oxygen, silicon, aluminum, or magnesium. As shown in **Figure 3,** the core makes up roughly one-third of the Earth's mass.

✓ **Reading Check** Briefly describe the layers that make up the Earth. (*See the Appendix for answers to Reading Checks.*)

Figure 2 *Volcanic vents on the ocean floor, such as this vent off the coast of Hawaii, allow magma to rise up through the crust from the mantle.*

crust the thin and solid outermost layer of the Earth above the mantle

mantle the layer of rock between the Earth's crust and core

core the central part of the Earth below the mantle

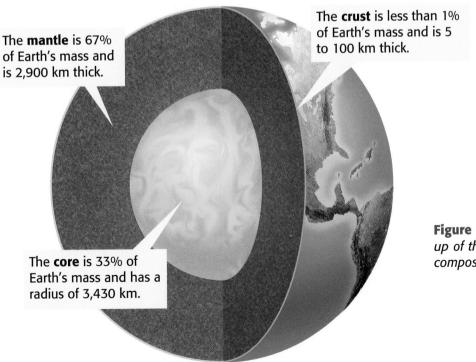

The **mantle** is 67% of Earth's mass and is 2,900 km thick.

The **crust** is less than 1% of Earth's mass and is 5 to 100 km thick.

The **core** is 33% of Earth's mass and has a radius of 3,430 km.

Figure 3 *The Earth is made up of three layers based on the composition of each layer.*

Imagine that you are building a model of the Earth that will have a radius of 1 m. You find out that the average radius of the Earth is 6,380 km and that the thickness of the lithosphere is about 150 km. What percentage of the Earth's radius is the lithosphere? How thick (in centimeters) would you make the lithosphere in your model?

The Physical Structure of the Earth

Another way to look at the Earth is to examine the physical properties of its layers. The Earth is divided into five physical layers—the lithosphere, asthenosphere, mesosphere, outer core, and inner core. As shown in the figure below, each layer has its own set of physical properties.

Reading Check What are the five physical layers of the Earth?

Lithosphere The outermost, rigid layer of the Earth is the **lithosphere.** The lithosphere is made of two parts—the crust and the rigid upper part of the mantle. The lithosphere is divided into pieces called *tectonic plates*.

Asthenosphere The **asthenosphere** is a plastic layer of the mantle on which pieces of the lithosphere move. The asthenosphere is made of solid rock that flows very slowly.

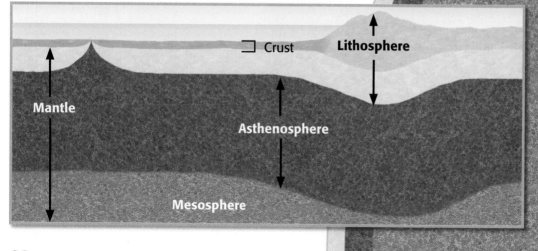

Crust

Lithosphere

Mantle

Asthenosphere

Mesosphere

lithosphere the solid, outer layer of the Earth that consists of the crust and the rigid upper part of the mantle

asthenosphere the soft layer of the mantle on which the tectonic plates move

mesosphere the strong, lower part of the mantle between the asthenosphere and the outer core

Mesosphere Beneath the asthenosphere is the strong, lower part of the mantle called the **mesosphere.** The mesosphere extends from the bottom of the asthenosphere to the Earth's core.

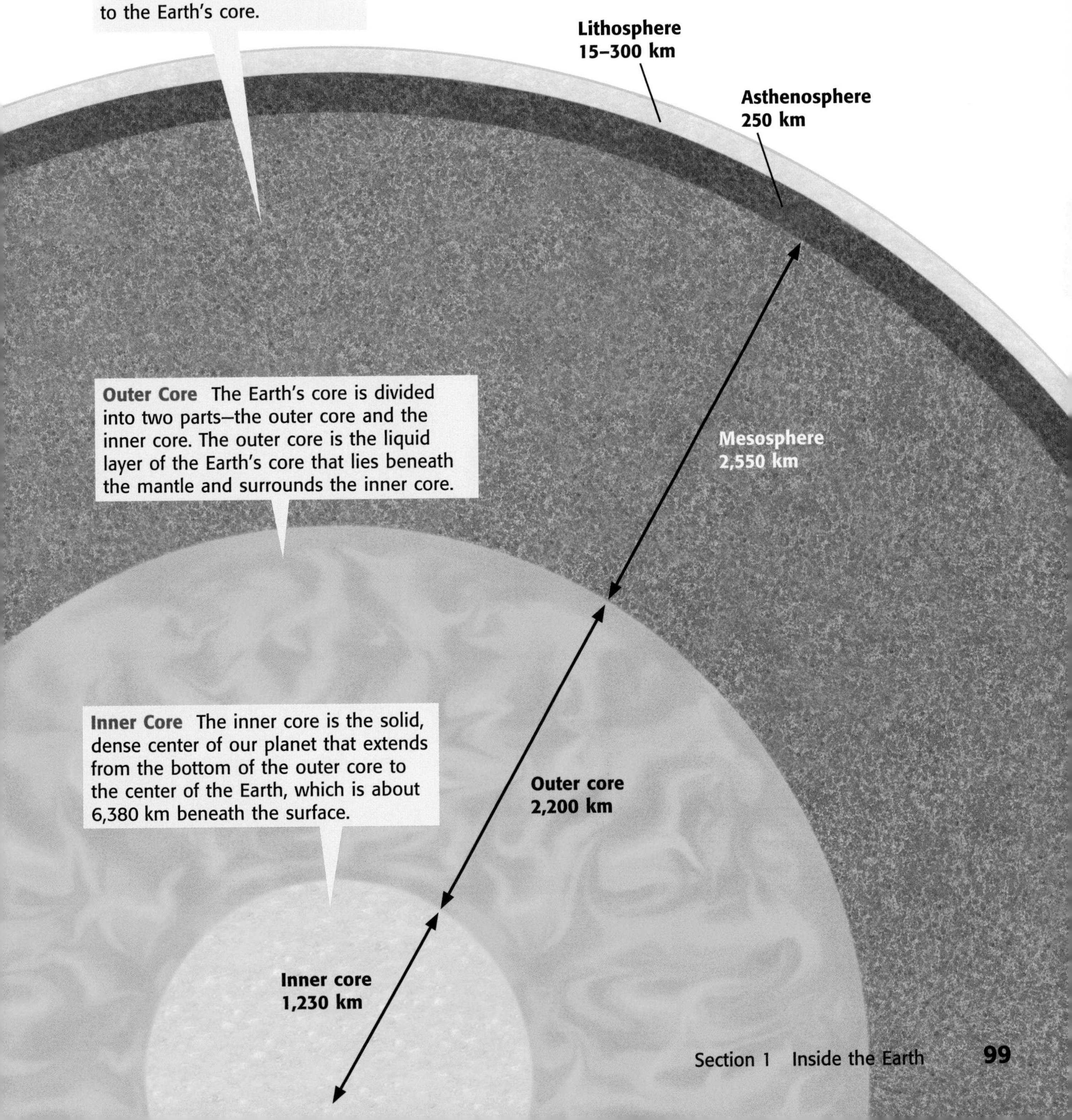

Lithosphere
15–300 km

Asthenosphere
250 km

Mesosphere
2,550 km

Outer Core The Earth's core is divided into two parts—the outer core and the inner core. The outer core is the liquid layer of the Earth's core that lies beneath the mantle and surrounds the inner core.

Inner Core The inner core is the solid, dense center of our planet that extends from the bottom of the outer core to the center of the Earth, which is about 6,380 km beneath the surface.

Outer core
2,200 km

Inner core
1,230 km

Tectonic Plates

Pieces of the lithosphere that move around on top of the asthenosphere are called **tectonic plates**. But what exactly does a tectonic plate look like? How big are tectonic plates? How and why do they move around? To answer these questions, begin by thinking of the lithosphere as a giant jigsaw puzzle.

A Giant Jigsaw Puzzle

All of the tectonic plates have names, some of which you may already know. Some of the major tectonic plates are named on the map in **Figure 4.** Notice that each tectonic plate fits together with the tectonic plates that surround it. The lithosphere is like a jigsaw puzzle, and the tectonic plates are like the pieces of a jigsaw puzzle.

Notice that not all tectonic plates are the same. For example, compare the size of the South American plate with that of the Cocos plate. Tectonic plates differ in other ways, too. For example, the South American plate has an entire continent on it and has oceanic crust, but the Cocos plate has only oceanic crust. Some tectonic plates, such as the South American plate, include both continental and oceanic crust.

tectonic plate a block of lithosphere that consists of the crust and the rigid, outermost part of the mantle

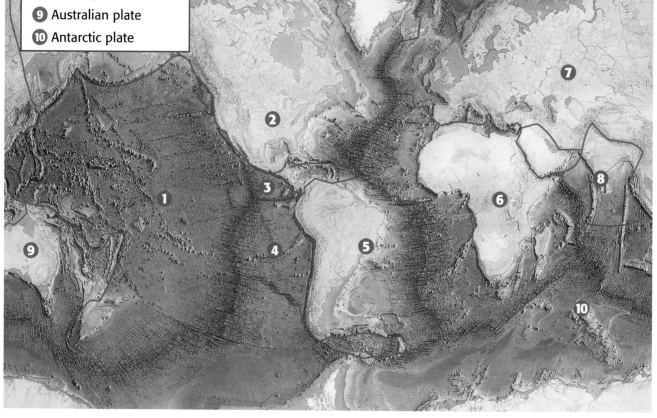

Major Tectonic Plates

1 Pacific plate
2 North American plate
3 Cocos plate
4 Nazca plate
5 South American plate
6 African plate
7 Eurasian plate
8 Indian plate
9 Australian plate
10 Antarctic plate

Figure 4 *Tectonic plates fit together like the pieces of a giant jigsaw puzzle.*

Figure 5 The South American Plate

This image shows what you might see if you could lift the South American plate out of its position between other tectonic plates.

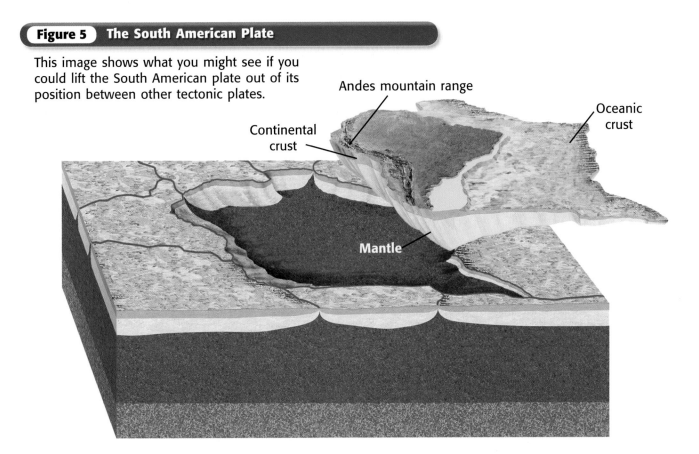

Andes mountain range

Oceanic crust

Continental crust

Mantle

A Tectonic Plate Close-Up

What would a tectonic plate look like if you could lift it out of its place? **Figure 5** shows what the South American plate might look like if you could. Notice that this tectonic plate not only consists of the upper part of the mantle but also consists of both oceanic crust and continental crust. The thickest part of the South American plate is the continental crust. The thinnest part of this plate is in the mid-Atlantic Ocean.

Like Ice Cubes in a Bowl of Punch

Think about ice cubes floating in a bowl of punch. If there are enough cubes, they will cover the surface of the punch and bump into one another. Parts of the ice cubes are below the surface of the punch and displace the punch. Large pieces of ice displace more punch than small pieces of ice. Tectonic plates "float" on the asthenosphere in a similar way. The plates cover the surface of the asthenosphere, and they touch one another and move around. The lithosphere displaces the asthenosphere. Thick tectonic plates, such as those made of continental crust, displace more asthenosphere than do thin plates, such as those made of oceanic lithosphere.

Reading Check Why do tectonic plates made of continental lithosphere displace more asthenosphere than tectonic plates made of oceanic lithosphere do?

Tectonic Ice Cubes

1. Take the bottom half of a clear, **2 L soda bottle** that has been cut in half. Make sure that the label has been removed.

2. Fill the bottle with **water** to about 1 cm below the top edge of the bottle.

3. Get **three pieces of irregularly shaped ice** that are small, medium, and large.

4. Float the ice in the water, and note how much of each piece is below the surface of the water.

5. Do all pieces of ice float mostly below the surface? Which piece is mostly below the surface? Why?

Mapping the Earth's Interior

How do scientists know things about the deepest parts of the Earth, where no one has ever been? Scientists have never even drilled through the crust, which is only a thin skin on the surface of the Earth. So, how do we know so much about the mantle and the core?

Would you be surprised to know that some of the answers come from earthquakes? When an earthquake happens, vibrations called *seismic waves* are produced. Seismic waves travel at different speeds through the Earth. Their speed depends on the density and composition of material that they pass through. For example, a seismic wave traveling through a solid will go faster than a seismic wave traveling through a liquid.

When an earthquake happens, machines called *seismographs* measure the times at which seismic waves arrive at different distances from an earthquake. Seismologists can then use these distances and travel times to calculate the density and thickness of each physical layer of the Earth. **Figure 6** shows how seismic waves travel through the Earth.

✓ *Reading Check* What are some properties of seismic waves?

Figure 6 *By measuring changes in the speed of seismic waves that travel through Earth's interior, seismologists have learned that the Earth is made of different layers.*

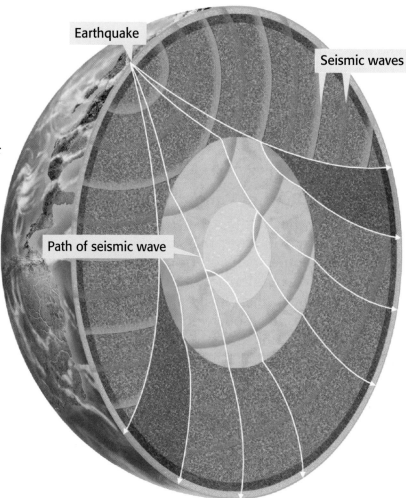

Earthquake

Seismic waves

Path of seismic wave

Summary

- The Earth is made up of three layers—the crust, the mantle, and the core—based on chemical composition. Less dense compounds make up the crust and mantle. Denser compounds make up the core.

- The Earth is made up of five main physical layers: the lithosphere, the asthenosphere, the mesosphere, the outer core, and the inner core.

- Tectonic plates are large pieces of the lithosphere that move around on the Earth's surface.

- The crust in some tectonic plates is mainly continental. Other plates have only oceanic crust. Still other plates include both continental and oceanic crust.

- Thick tectonic plates, such as those in which the crust is mainly continental, displace more asthenosphere than do thin plates, such as those in which the crust is mainly oceanic.

- Knowledge about the layers of the Earth comes from the study of seismic waves caused by earthquakes.

Using Key Terms

For each pair of terms, explain how the meanings of the terms differ.

1. *crust* and *mantle*

2. *lithosphere* and *asthenosphere*

Understanding Key Ideas

3. The part of the Earth that is molten is the
   a. crust.
   b. mantle.
   c. outer core.
   d. inner core.

4. The part of the Earth on which the tectonic plates move is the
   a. lithosphere.
   b. asthenosphere.
   c. mesosphere.
   d. crust.

5. Identify the layers of the Earth by their chemical composition.

6. Identify the layers of the Earth by their physical properties.

7. Describe a tectonic plate.

8. Explain how scientists know about the structure of the Earth's interior.

Interpreting Graphics

9. According to the wave speeds shown in the table below, which two physical layers of the Earth are densest?

Speed of Seismic Waves in Earth's Interior	
Physical layer	**Wave speed**
Lithosphere	7 to 8 km/s
Asthenosphere	7 to 11 km/s
Mesosphere	11 to 13 km/s
Outer core	8 to 10 km/s
Inner core	11 to 12 km/s

Critical Thinking

10. **Making Comparisons** Explain the difference between the crust and the lithosphere.

11. **Analyzing Ideas** Why does a seismic wave travel faster through solid rock than through water?

Restless Continents

Have you ever looked at a map of the world and noticed how the coastlines of continents on opposite sides of the oceans appear to fit together like the pieces of a puzzle? Is it just coincidence that the coastlines fit together well? Is it possible that the continents were actually together sometime in the past?

What You Will Learn

● Describe Wegener's hypothesis of continental drift.

● Explain how sea-floor spreading provides a way for continents to move.

● Describe how new oceanic lithosphere forms at mid-ocean ridges.

● Explain how magnetic reversals provide evidence for sea-floor spreading.

Vocabulary

continental drift
sea-floor spreading

READING STRATEGY

Paired Summarizing Read this section silently. In pairs, take turns summarizing the material. Stop to discuss ideas that seem confusing.

Wegener's Continental Drift Hypothesis

One scientist who looked at the pieces of this puzzle was Alfred Wegener (VAY guh nuhr). In the early 1900s, he wrote about his hypothesis of *continental drift*. **Continental drift** is the hypothesis that states that the continents once formed a single landmass, broke up, and drifted to their present locations. This hypothesis seemed to explain a lot of puzzling observations, including the observation of how well continents fit together.

Continental drift also explained why fossils of the same plant and animal species are found on continents that are on different sides of the Atlantic Ocean. Many of these ancient species could not have crossed the Atlantic Ocean. As you can see in **Figure 1,** without continental drift, this pattern of fossils would be hard to explain. In addition to fossils, similar types of rock and evidence of the same ancient climatic conditions were found on several continents.

✓ **Reading Check** How did fossils provide evidence for Wegener's hypothesis of continental drift? (*See the Appendix for answers to Reading Checks.*)

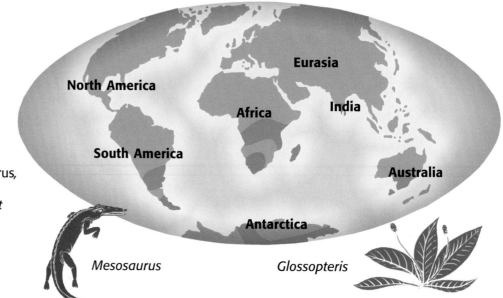

Figure 1 *Fossils of* Mesosaurus, *a small, aquatic reptile, and* Glossopteris, *an ancient plant species, have been found on several continents.*

Mesosaurus   *Glossopteris*

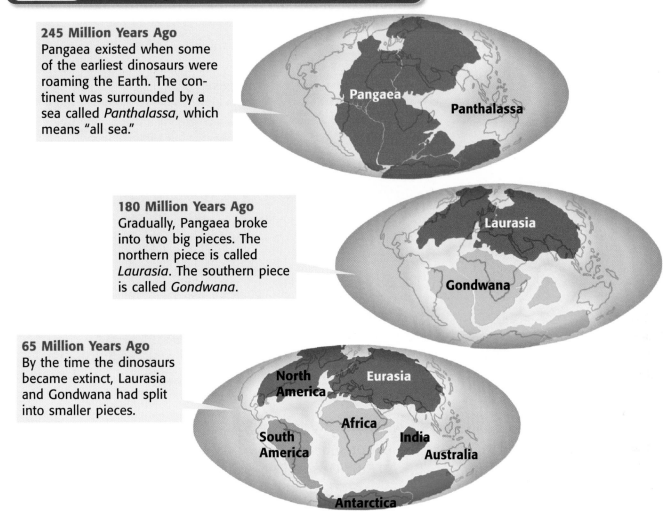

Figure 2 The Drifting Continents

245 Million Years Ago
Pangaea existed when some of the earliest dinosaurs were roaming the Earth. The continent was surrounded by a sea called *Panthalassa*, which means "all sea."

Pangaea
Panthalassa

180 Million Years Ago
Gradually, Pangaea broke into two big pieces. The northern piece is called *Laurasia*. The southern piece is called *Gondwana*.

Laurasia
Gondwana

65 Million Years Ago
By the time the dinosaurs became extinct, Laurasia and Gondwana had split into smaller pieces.

North America
Eurasia
Africa
South America
India
Australia
Antarctica

The Breakup of Pangaea

Wegener made many observations before proposing his hypothesis of continental drift. He thought that all of the present continents were once joined in a single, huge continent. Wegener called this continent *Pangaea* (pan JEE uh), which is Greek for "all earth." We now know from the hypothesis of plate tectonics that Pangaea existed about 245 million years ago. We also know that Pangaea further split into two huge continents—Laurasia and Gondwana—about 180 million years ago. As shown in **Figure 2,** these two continents split again and formed the continents we know today.

continental drift the hypothesis that states that the continents once formed a single landmass, broke up, and drifted to their present locations

Sea-Floor Spreading

When Wegener put forth his hypothesis of continental drift, many scientists would not accept his hypothesis. From the calculated strength of the rocks, it did not seem possible for the crust to move in this way. During Wegener's life, no one knew the answer. It wasn't until many years later that evidence provided some clues to the forces that moved the continents.

Figure 3 Sea-Floor Spreading

Sea-floor spreading creates new oceanic lithosphere at mid-ocean ridges.

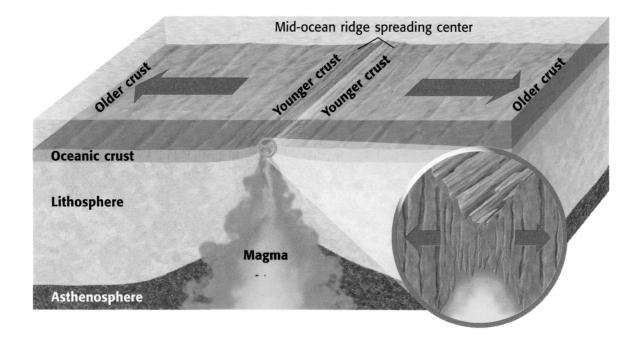

Mid-ocean ridge spreading center

Older crust

Younger crust

Younger crust

Older crust

Oceanic crust

Lithosphere

Magma

Asthenosphere

sea-floor spreading the process by which new oceanic lithosphere forms as magma rises toward the surface and solidifies

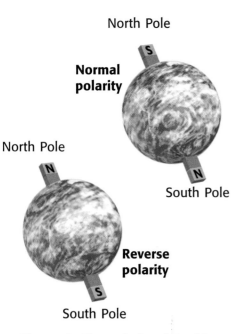

North Pole

Normal polarity

S

N

South Pole

North Pole

N

Reverse polarity

S

South Pole

Figure 4 *The polarity of Earth's magnetic field changes over time.*

Mid-Ocean Ridges and Sea-Floor Spreading

A chain of submerged mountains runs through the center of the Atlantic Ocean. The chain is part of a worldwide system of mid-ocean ridges. Mid-ocean ridges are underwater mountain chains that run through Earth's ocean basins.

Mid-ocean ridges are places where sea-floor spreading takes place. **Sea-floor spreading** is the process by which new oceanic lithosphere forms as magma rises toward the surface and solidifies. As the tectonic plates move away from each other, the sea floor spreads apart and magma fills in the gap. As this new crust forms, the older crust gets pushed away from the mid-ocean ridge. As **Figure 3** shows, the older crust is farther away from the mid-ocean ridge than the younger crust is.

Evidence for Sea-Floor Spreading: Magnetic Reversals

Some of the most important evidence of sea-floor spreading comes from magnetic reversals recorded in the ocean floor. Throughout Earth's history, the north and south magnetic poles have changed places many times. When the poles change places, the polarity of Earth's magnetic poles changes, as shown in **Figure 4.** When Earth's magnetic poles change places, this change is called a *magnetic reversal.*

Magnetic Reversals and Sea-Floor Spreading

The molten rock at the mid-ocean ridges contains tiny grains of magnetic minerals. These mineral grains contain iron and are like compasses. They align with the magnetic field of the Earth. When the molten rock cools, the record of these tiny compasses remains in the rock. This record is then carried slowly away from the spreading center of the ridge as sea-floor spreading occurs.

As you can see in **Figure 5,** when the Earth's magnetic field reverses, the magnetic mineral grains align in the opposite direction. The new rock records the direction of the Earth's magnetic field. As the sea floor spreads away from a mid-ocean ridge, it carries with it a record of magnetic reversals. This record of magnetic reversals was the final proof that sea-floor spreading does occur.

✓ Reading Check How is a record of magnetic reversals recorded in molten rock at mid-ocean ridges?

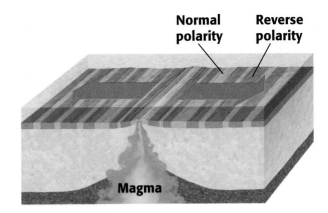

Figure 5 *Magnetic reversals in oceanic crust are shown as bands of light blue and dark blue oceanic crust. Light blue bands indicate normal polarity, and dark blue bands indicate reverse polarity.*

SECTION
Review

Summary

- Wegener hypothesized that continents drift apart from one another and have done so in the past.
- The process by which new oceanic lithosphere forms at mid-ocean ridges is called sea-floor spreading.
- As tectonic plates separate, the sea floor spreads apart and magma fills in the gap.
- Magnetic reversals are recorded over time in oceanic crust.

Using Key Terms

1. In your own words, write a definition for each of the following terms: *continental drift* and *sea-floor spreading.*

Understanding Key Ideas

2. At mid-ocean ridges,
   a. the crust is older.
   b. sea-floor spreading occurs.
   c. oceanic lithosphere is destroyed.
   d. tectonic plates are colliding.

3. Explain how oceanic lithosphere forms at mid-ocean ridges.

4. What is magnetic reversal?

Math Skills

5. If a piece of sea floor has moved 50 km in 5 million years, what is the yearly rate of sea-floor motion?

Critical Thinking

6. **Identifying Relationships** Explain how magnetic reversals provide evidence for sea-floor spreading.

7. **Applying Concepts** Why do bands indicating magnetic reversals appear to be of similar width on both sides of a mid-ocean ridge?

8. **Applying Concepts** Why do you think that old rocks are rare on the ocean floor?

SCILINKS.

NSTA
Developed and maintained by the
National Science Teachers Association

For a variety of links related to this chapter, go to www.scilinks.org

Topic: Tectonic Plates
SciLinks code: HSM1497

The Theory of Plate Tectonics

It takes an incredible amount of force to move a tectonic plate! But where does this force come from?

As scientists' understanding of mid-ocean ridges and magnetic reversals grew, scientists formed a theory to explain how tectonic plates move. **Plate tectonics** is the theory that the Earth's lithosphere is divided into tectonic plates that move around on top of the asthenosphere. In this section, you will learn what causes tectonic plates to move. But first you will learn about the different types of tectonic plate boundaries.

Tectonic Plate Boundaries

A boundary is a place where tectonic plates touch. All tectonic plates share boundaries with other tectonic plates. These boundaries are divided into three types: convergent, divergent, and transform. The type of boundary depends on how the tectonic plates move relative to one another. Tectonic plates can collide, separate, or slide past each other. Earthquakes can occur at all three types of plate boundaries. The figure below shows examples of tectonic plate boundaries.

What You Will Learn

● Describe the three types of tectonic plate boundaries.
● Describe the three forces thought to move tectonic plates.
● Explain how scientists measure the rate at which tectonic plates move.

Vocabulary

plate tectonics
convergent boundary
divergent boundary
transform boundary

READING STRATEGY

Brainstorming The key idea of this section is plate tectonics. Brainstorm words and phrases related to plate tectonics.

Continental-Continental Collisions
When two tectonic plates with continental crust collide, they buckle and thicken, which pushes the continental crust upward.

Convergent boundaries

Subduction zone

Continental lithosphere

Subduction zone

Continental-Oceanic Collisions When a plate with oceanic crust collides with a plate with continental crust, the denser oceanic crust sinks into the asthenosphere. This convergent boundary has a special name: the *subduction zone*. Old ocean crust gets pushed into the asthenosphere, where it is remelted and recycled.

Oceanic-Oceanic Collisions When two tectonic plates with oceanic lithosphere collide, one of the plates with oceanic lithosphere is subducted, or sinks, under the other plate.

Convergent Boundaries

When two tectonic plates collide, the boundary between them is a **convergent boundary.** What happens at a convergent boundary depends on the kind of crust at the leading edge of each tectonic plate. The three types of convergent boundaries are continental-continental boundaries, continental-oceanic boundaries, and oceanic-oceanic boundaries.

Divergent Boundaries

When two tectonic plates separate, the boundary between them is called a **divergent boundary.** New sea floor forms at divergent boundaries. Mid-ocean ridges are the most common type of divergent boundary.

Transform Boundaries

When two tectonic plates slide past each other horizontally, the boundary between them is a **transform boundary.** The San Andreas Fault in California is a good example of a transform boundary. This fault marks the place where the Pacific and North American plates are sliding past each other.

Reading Check Define the term *transform boundary*. (*See the Appendix for answers to Reading Checks*.)

plate tectonics the theory that explains how large pieces of the Earth's outermost layer, called *tectonic plates,* move and change shape

convergent boundary the boundary formed by the collision of two lithospheric plates

divergent boundary the boundary between two tectonic plates that are moving away from each other

transform boundary the boundary between tectonic plates that are sliding past each other horizontally

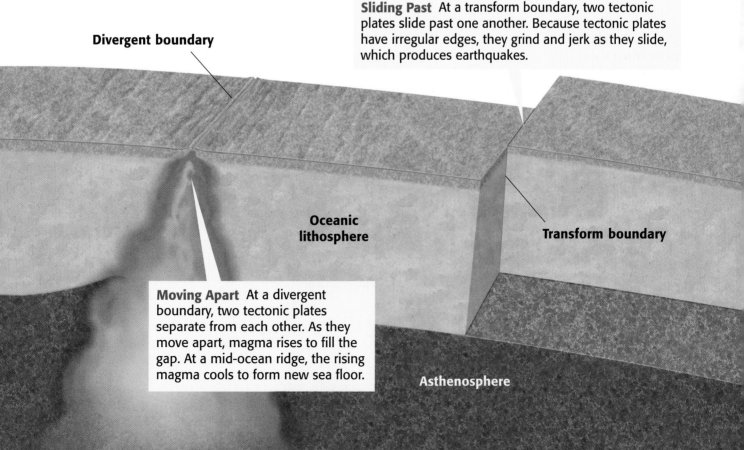

Divergent boundary

Sliding Past At a transform boundary, two tectonic plates slide past one another. Because tectonic plates have irregular edges, they grind and jerk as they slide, which produces earthquakes.

Oceanic lithosphere

Transform boundary

Moving Apart At a divergent boundary, two tectonic plates separate from each other. As they move apart, magma rises to fill the gap. At a mid-ocean ridge, the rising magma cools to form new sea floor.

Asthenosphere

Possible Causes of Tectonic Plate Motion

You have learned that plate tectonics is the theory that the lithosphere is divided into tectonic plates that move around on top of the asthenosphere. What causes the motion of tectonic plates? Remember that the solid rock of the asthenosphere flows very slowly. This movement occurs because of changes in density within the asthenosphere. These density changes are caused by the outward flow of thermal energy from deep within the Earth. When rock is heated, it expands, becomes less dense, and tends to rise to the surface of the Earth. As the rock gets near the surface, the rock cools, becomes more dense, and tends to sink. **Figure 1** shows three possible causes of tectonic plate motion.

✔ **Reading Check** What causes changes in density in the asthenosphere?

Figure 1 **Three Possible Driving Forces of Plate Tectonics**

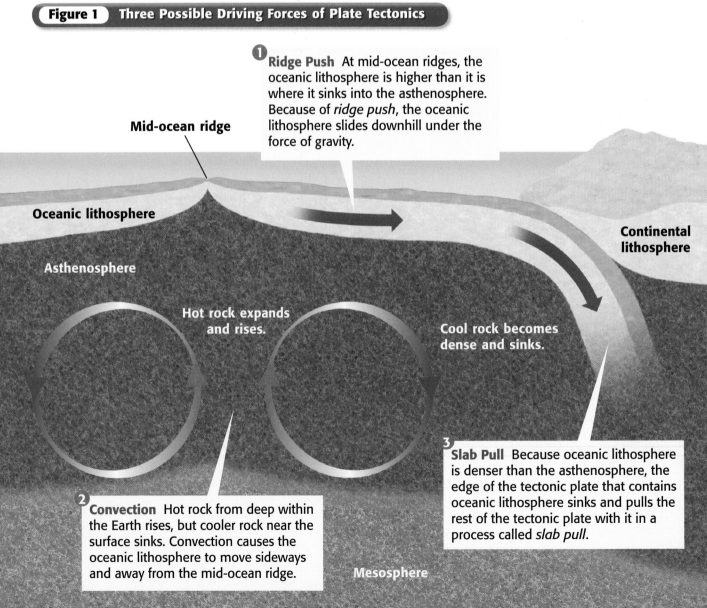

❶ Ridge Push At mid-ocean ridges, the oceanic lithosphere is higher than it is where it sinks into the asthenosphere. Because of *ridge push*, the oceanic lithosphere slides downhill under the force of gravity.

Mid-ocean ridge

Oceanic lithosphere

Continental lithosphere

Asthenosphere

Hot rock expands and rises.

Cool rock becomes dense and sinks.

❸ Slab Pull Because oceanic lithosphere is denser than the asthenosphere, the edge of the tectonic plate that contains oceanic lithosphere sinks and pulls the rest of the tectonic plate with it in a process called *slab pull*.

❷ Convection Hot rock from deep within the Earth rises, but cooler rock near the surface sinks. Convection causes the oceanic lithosphere to move sideways and away from the mid-ocean ridge.

Mesosphere

Tracking Tectonic Plate Motion

How fast do tectonic plates move? The answer to this question depends on many factors, such as the type and shape of the tectonic plate and the way that the tectonic plate interacts with the tectonic plates that surround it. Tectonic plate movements are so slow and gradual that you can't see or feel them—the movement is measured in centimeters per year.

The Global Positioning System

Scientists use a system of satellites called the *global positioning system* (GPS), shown in **Figure 2,** to measure the rate of tectonic plate movement. Radio signals are continuously beamed from satellites to GPS ground stations, which record the exact distance between the satellites and the ground station. Over time, these distances change slightly. By recording the time it takes for the GPS ground stations to move a given distance, scientists can measure the speed at which each tectonic plate moves.

GPS satellite

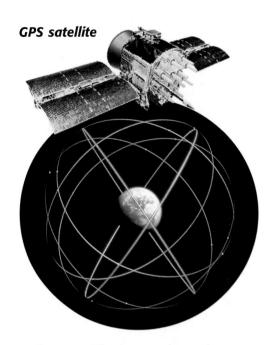

Figure 2 *The image above shows the orbits of the GPS satellites.*

SECTION Review

Summary

- Boundaries between tectonic plates are classified as convergent, divergent, or transform.

- Ridge push, convection, and slab pull are three possible driving forces of plate tectonics.

- Scientists use data from a system of satellites called the global positioning system to measure the rate of motion of tectonic plates.

Using Key Terms

1. In your own words, write a definition for the term *plate tectonics*.

Understanding Key Ideas

2. The speed a tectonic plate moves per year is best measured in
   a. kilometers per year.
   b. centimeters per year.
   c. meters per year.
   d. millimeters per year.

3. Briefly describe three possible driving forces of tectonic plate movement.

4. Explain how scientists use GPS to measure the rate of tectonic plate movement.

Math Skills

5. If an orbiting satellite has a diameter of 60 cm, what is the total surface area of the satellite? (Hint: *surface area* $= 4\pi r^2$)

Critical Thinking

6. **Identifying Relationships** When convection takes place in the mantle, why does cool rock material sink and warm rock material rise?

7. **Analyzing Processes** Why does oceanic crust sink beneath continental crust at convergent boundaries?

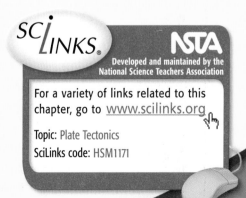

SCI*LINKS*®

Developed and maintained by the National Science Teachers Association

For a variety of links related to this chapter, go to www.scilinks.org

Topic: Plate Tectonics
SciLinks code: HSM1171

Deforming the Earth's Crust

Have you ever tried to bend something, only to have it break? Take long, uncooked pieces of spaghetti, and bend them very slowly but only a little. Now, bend them again, but this time, bend them much farther and faster. What happened?

How can a material bend at one time and break at another time? The answer is that the stress you put on the material was different each time. *Stress* is the amount of force per unit area on a given material. The same principle applies to the rocks in the Earth's crust. Different things happen to rock when different types of stress are applied.

Deformation

The process by which the shape of a rock changes because of stress is called *deformation*. In the example above, the spaghetti deformed in two different ways—by bending and by breaking. **Figure 1** illustrates this concept. The same thing happens in rock layers. Rock layers bend when stress is placed on them. But when enough stress is placed on rocks, they can reach their elastic limit and break.

Compression and Tension

The type of stress that occurs when an object is squeezed, such as when two tectonic plates collide, is called **compression.** When compression occurs at a convergent boundary, large mountain ranges can form.

Another form of stress is *tension.* **Tension** is stress that occurs when forces act to stretch an object. As you might guess, tension occurs at divergent plate boundaries, such as mid-ocean ridges, when two tectonic plates pull away from each other.

✔ **Reading Check** How do the forces of plate tectonics cause rock to deform? (*See the Appendix for answers to Reading Checks.*)

What You Will Learn

- Describe two types of stress that deform rocks.
- Describe three major types of folds.
- Explain the differences between the three major types of faults.
- Identify the most common types of mountains.
- Explain the difference between uplift and subsidence.

Vocabulary

compression	fault
tension	uplift
folding	subsidence

READING STRATEGY

Discussion Read this section silently. Write down questions that you have about this section. Discuss your questions in a small group.

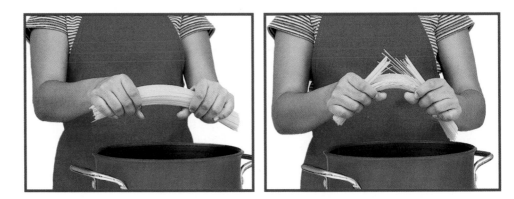

Figure 1 *When a small amount of stress is placed on uncooked spaghetti, the spaghetti bends. Additional stress causes the spaghetti to break.*

Figure 2   **Folding: When Rock Layers Bend Because of Stress**

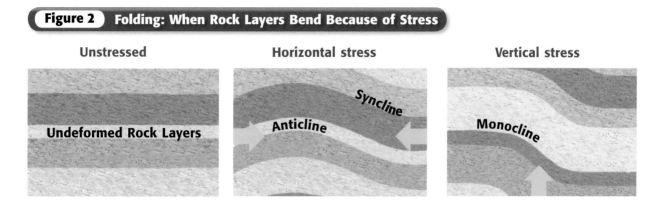

Unstressed   **Horizontal stress**   **Vertical stress**

Undeformed Rock Layers

Syncline

Anticline

Monocline

Folding

The bending of rock layers because of stress in the Earth's crust is called **folding.** Scientists assume that all rock layers started as horizontal layers. So, when scientists see a fold, they know that deformation has taken place.

Types of Folds

Depending on how the rock layers deform, different types of folds are made. **Figure 2** shows the two most common types of folds—*anticlines*, or upward-arching folds, and *synclines,* downward, troughlike folds. Another type of fold is a *monocline.* In a monocline, rock layers are folded so that both ends of the fold are horizontal. Imagine taking a stack of paper and laying it on a table. Think of the sheets of paper as different rock layers. Now put a book under one end of the stack. You can see that both ends of the sheets are horizontal, but all of the sheets are bent in the middle.

Folds can be large or small. The largest folds are measured in kilometers. Other folds are also obvious but are much smaller. These small folds can be measured in centimeters. **Figure 3** shows examples of large and small folds.

compression   stress that occurs when forces act to squeeze an object

tension   stress that occurs when forces act to stretch an object

folding   the bending of rock layers due to stress

Figure 3   The large photo shows mountain-sized folds in the Rocky Mountains. The small photo shows a rock that has folds smaller than a penknife.

Fault

Footwall   **Hanging wall**

Figure 4 *The position of a fault block determines whether it is a hanging wall or a footwall.*

fault a break in a body of rock along which one block slides relative to another

Faulting

Some rock layers break when stress is applied to them. The surface along which rocks break and slide past each other is called a **fault.** The blocks of crust on each side of the fault are called *fault blocks.*

When a fault is not vertical, understanding the difference between its two sides—the *hanging wall* and the *footwall*—is useful. **Figure 4** shows the difference between a hanging wall and a footwall. Two main types of faults can form. The type of fault that forms depends on how the hanging wall and footwall move in relationship to each other.

Normal Faults

A *normal fault* is shown in **Figure 5.** When a normal fault moves, it causes the hanging wall to move down relative to the footwall. Normal faults usually occur when tectonic forces cause tension that pulls rocks apart.

Reverse Faults

A *reverse fault* is shown in **Figure 5.** When a reverse fault moves, it causes the hanging wall to move up relative to the footwall. This movement is the reverse of a normal fault. Reverse faults usually happen when tectonic forces cause compression that pushes rocks together.

✓ Reading Check How does the hanging wall in a normal fault move in relation to a reverse fault?

Figure 5 **Normal and Reverse Faults**

Normal Fault When rocks are pulled apart because of tension, normal faults often form.

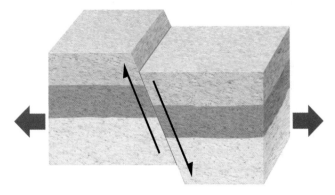

Reverse Fault When rocks are pushed together by compression, reverse faults often form.

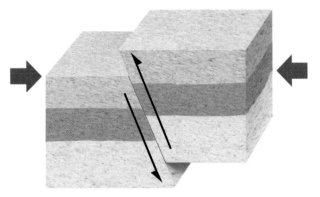

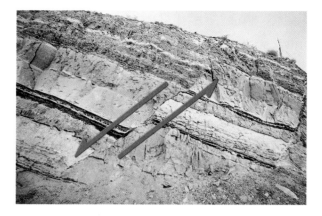

Figure 6 *The photo at left is a normal fault. The photo at right is a reverse fault.*

Telling the Difference Between Faults

It's easy to tell the difference between a normal fault and a reverse fault in drawings with arrows. But what types of faults are shown in **Figure 6**? You can certainly see the faults, but which one is a normal fault, and which one is a reverse fault? In the top left photo in **Figure 6,** one side has obviously moved relative to the other side. You can tell this fault is a normal fault by looking at the order of sedimentary rock layers. If you compare the two dark layers near the surface, you can see that the hanging wall has moved down relative to the footwall.

Strike-Slip Faults

A third major type of fault is called a *strike-slip fault.* An illustration of a strike-slip fault is shown in **Figure 7.** *Strike-slip faults* form when opposing forces cause rock to break and move horizontally. If you were standing on one side of a strike-slip fault looking across the fault when it moved, the ground on the other side would appear to move to your left or right. The San Andreas Fault in California is a spectacular example of a strike-slip fault.

Modeling Strike-Slip Faults

1. Use **modeling clay** to construct a box that is 6 in. × 6 in. × 4 in. Use different colors of clay to represent different horizontal layers.

2. Using **scissors,** cut the box down the middle. Place **two 4 in. × 6 in. index cards** inside the cut so that the two sides of the box slide freely.

3. Using gentle pressure, slide the two sides horizontally past one another.

4. How does this model illustrate the motion that occurs along a strike-slip fault?

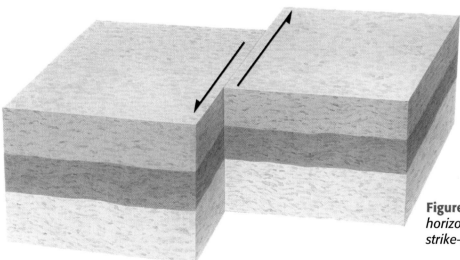

Figure 7 *When rocks are moved horizontally by opposing forces, strike-slip faults often form.*

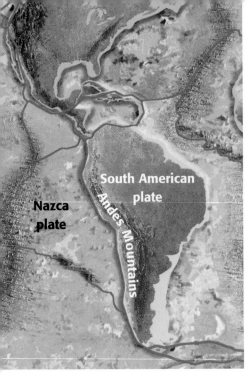

Figure 8 *The Andes Mountains formed on the edge of the South American plate where it converges with the Nazca plate.*

Plate Tectonics and Mountain Building

You have just learned about several ways the Earth's crust changes because of the forces of plate tectonics. When tectonic plates collide, land features that start as folds and faults can eventually become large mountain ranges. Mountains exist because tectonic plates are continually moving around and colliding with one another. As shown in **Figure 8,** the Andes Mountains formed above the subduction zone where two tectonic plates converge.

When tectonic plates undergo compression or tension, they can form mountains in several ways. Take a look at three of the most common types of mountains—folded mountains, fault-block mountains, and volcanic mountains.

Folded Mountains

The highest mountain ranges in the world are made up of folded mountains. These ranges form at convergent boundaries where continents have collided. *Folded mountains* form when rock layers are squeezed together and pushed upward. If you place a pile of paper on a table and push on opposite edges of the pile, you will see how folded mountains form.

An example of a folded mountain range that formed at a convergent boundary is shown in **Figure 9.** About 390 million years ago, the Appalachian Mountains formed when the landmasses that are now North America and Africa collided. Other examples of mountain ranges that consist of very large and complex folds are the Alps in central Europe, the Ural Mountains in Russia, and the Himalayas in Asia.

✔ *Reading Check* **Explain how folded mountains form.**

Figure 9 *The Appalachian Mountains were once as tall as the Himalaya Mountains but have been worn down by hundreds of millions of years of weathering and erosion.*

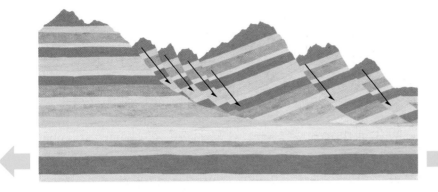

Figure 10 *When the crust is subjected to tension, the rock can break along a series of normal faults, which creates fault-block mountains.*

Fault-Block Mountains

When tectonic forces put enough tension on the Earth's crust, a large number of normal faults can result. *Fault-block mountains* form when this tension causes large blocks of the Earth's crust to drop down relative to other blocks. **Figure 10** shows one way that fault-block mountains form.

When sedimentary rock layers are tilted up by faulting, they can produce mountains that have sharp, jagged peaks. As shown in **Figure 11,** the Tetons in western Wyoming are a spectacular example of fault-block mountains.

Volcanic Mountains

Most of the world's major volcanic mountains are located at convergent boundaries where oceanic crust sinks into the asthenosphere at subduction zones. The rock that is melted in subduction zones forms magma, which rises to the Earth's surface and erupts to form *volcanic mountains*. Volcanic mountains can also form under the sea. Sometimes these mountains can rise above the ocean surface to become islands. The majority of tectonically active volcanic mountains on the Earth have formed around the tectonically active rim of the Pacific Ocean. The rim has become known as the *Ring of Fire*.

CONNECTION TO
Social Studies

WRITING SKILL **The Naming of the Appalachian Mountains** How did the Appalachian Mountains get their name? It is believed that the Appalachian Mountains were named by Spanish explorers in North America during the 16th century. It is thought that the name was taken from a Native American tribe called *Appalachee,* who lived in northern Florida. Research other geological features in the United States, including mountains and rivers, whose names are of Native American origin. Write the results of your research in a short essay.

Figure 11 *The Tetons formed as a result of tectonic forces that stretched the Earth's crust and caused it to break in a series of normal faults.*

For another activity related to this chapter, go to **go.hrw.com** and type in the keyword **HZ5TECW**.

uplift the rising of regions of the Earth's crust to higher elevations

subsidence the sinking of regions of the Earth's crust to lower elevations

Uplift and Subsidence

Vertical movements in the crust are divided into two types—uplift and subsidence. The rising of regions of Earth's crust to higher elevations is called **uplift.** Rocks that are uplifted may or may not be highly deformed. The sinking of regions of Earth's crust to lower elevations is known as **subsidence** (suhb SIED'ns). Unlike some uplifted rocks, rocks that subside do not undergo much deformation.

Uplifting of Depressed Rocks

The formation of mountains is one type of uplift. Uplift can also occur when large areas of land rise without deforming. One way areas rise without deforming is a process known as *rebound*. When the crust rebounds, it slowly springs back to its previous elevation. Uplift often happens when a weight is removed from the crust.

Subsidence of Cooler Rocks

Rocks that are hot take up more space than cooler rocks. For example, the lithosphere is relatively hot at mid-ocean ridges. The farther the lithosphere is from the ridge, the cooler and denser the lithosphere becomes. Because the oceanic lithosphere now takes up less volume, the ocean floor subsides.

Tectonic Letdown

Subsidence can also occur when the lithosphere becomes stretched in rift zones. A *rift zone* is a set of deep cracks that forms between two tectonic plates that are pulling away from each other. As tectonic plates pull apart, stress between the plates causes a series of faults to form along the rift zone. As shown in **Figure 12,** the blocks of crust in the center of the rift zone subside.

Figure 12 *The East African Rift, from Ethiopia to Kenya, is part of a divergent boundary, but you can see how the crust has subsided relative to the blocks at the edge of the rift zone.*

Summary

- Compression and tension are two forces of plate tectonics that can cause rock to deform.

- Folding occurs when rock layers bend because of stress.

- Faulting occurs when rock layers break because of stress and then move on either side of the break.

- Mountains are classified as either folded, fault-block, or volcanic depending on how they form.

- Mountain building is caused by the movement of tectonic plates. Folded mountains and volcanic mountains form at convergent boundaries. Fault-block mountains form at divergent boundaries.

- Uplift and subsidence are the two types of vertical movement in the Earth's crust. Uplift occurs when regions of the crust rise to higher elevations. Subsidence occurs when regions of the crust sink to lower elevations.

Using Key Terms

For each pair of key terms, explain how the meanings of the terms differ.

1. *compression* and *tension*

2. *uplift* and *subsidence*

Understanding Key Ideas

3. The type of fault in which the hanging wall moves up relative to the footwall is called a

   a. strike-slip fault.

   b. fault-block fault.

   c. normal fault.

   d. reverse fault.

4. Describe three types of folds.

5. Describe three types of faults.

6. Identify the most common types of mountains.

7. What is rebound?

8. What are rift zones, and how do they form?

Critical Thinking

9. **Predicting Consequences** If a fault occurs in an area where rock layers have been folded, which type of fault is it likely to be? Why?

10. **Identifying Relationships** Would you expect to see a folded mountain range at a mid-ocean ridge? Explain your answer.

Interpreting Graphics

Use the diagram below to answer the questions that follow.

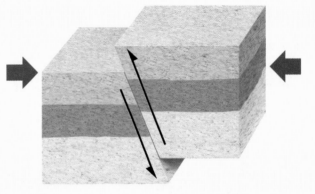

11. What type of fault is shown in the diagram?

12. At what kind of tectonic boundary would you most likely find this fault?

SCiLINKS®

NSTA
Developed and maintained by the National Science Teachers Association

For a variety of links related to this chapter, go to www.scilinks.org

Topic: Faults; Mountain Building
SciLinks code: HSM0566; HSM0999

Model-Making Lab

OBJECTIVES

Model convection currents to simulate plate tectonic movement.

Draw conclusions about the role of convection in plate tectonics.

MATERIALS

- craft sticks (2)
- food coloring
- gloves, heat-resistant
- hot plates, small (2)
- pan, aluminum, rectangular
- pencil
- ruler, metric
- thermometers (3)
- water, cold
- wooden blocks

SAFETY

Convection Connection

Some scientists think that convection currents within the Earth's mantle cause tectonic plates to move. Because these convection currents cannot be observed directly, scientists use models to simulate the process. In this activity, you will make your own model to simulate tectonic plate movement.

Ask a Question

1. How can I make a model of convection currents in the Earth's mantle?

Form a Hypothesis

2. Turn the question above into a statement in which you give your best guess about what factors will have the greatest effect on your convection model.

Test the Hypothesis

3. Place two hot plates side by side in the center of your lab table. Be sure that they are away from the edge of the table.

4. Place the pan on top of the hot plates. Slide the wooden blocks under the pan to support the ends. Make sure that the pan is level and secure.

5. Fill the pan with cold water. The water should be at least 4 cm deep. Turn on the hot plates, and put on your gloves.

6. After a minute or two, tiny bubbles will begin to rise in the water above the hot plates. Gently place two craft sticks on the water's surface.

7. Use the pencil to align the sticks parallel to the short ends of the pan. The sticks should be about 3 cm apart and near the center of the pan.

8. As soon as the sticks begin to move, place a drop of food coloring in the center of the pan. Observe what happens to the food coloring.

9 With the help of a partner, hold one thermometer bulb just under the water at the center of the pan. Hold the other two thermometers just under the water near the ends of the pan. Record the temperatures.

10 When you are finished, turn off the hot plates. After the water has cooled, carefully empty the water into a sink.

Analyze the Results

1 **Explaining Events** Based on your observations of the motion of the food coloring, how does the temperature of the water affect the direction in which the craft sticks move?

Draw Conclusions

2 **Drawing Conclusions** How does the motion of the craft sticks relate to the motion of the water?

3 **Applying Conclusions** How does this model relate to plate tectonics and the movement of the continents?

4 **Applying Conclusions** Based on your observations, what can you conclude about the role of convection in plate tectonics?

Applying Your Data

Suggest a substance other than water that might be used to model convection in the mantle. Consider using a substance that flows more slowly than water.

Chapter Review

USING KEY TERMS

1 Use the following terms in the same sentence: *crust, mantle,* and *core.*

Complete each of the following sentences by choosing the correct term from the word bank.

asthenosphere   uplift
tension   continental drift

2 The hypothesis that continents can drift apart and have done so in the past is known as ___.

3 The ___ is the soft layer of the mantle on which the tectonic plates move.

4 ___ is stress that occurs when forces act to stretch an object.

5 The rising of regions of the Earth's crust to higher elevations is called ___.

UNDERSTANDING KEY IDEAS

Multiple Choice

6 The strong, lower part of the mantle is a physical layer called the

a. lithosphere.

b. mesosphere.

c. asthenosphere.

d. outer core.

7 The type of tectonic plate boundary that forms from a collision between two tectonic plates is a

a. divergent plate boundary.

b. transform plate boundary.

c. convergent plate boundary.

d. normal plate boundary.

8 The bending of rock layers due to stress in the Earth's crust is known as

a. uplift.

b. folding.

c. faulting.

d. subsidence.

9 The type of fault in which the hanging wall moves up relative to the footwall is called a

a. strike-slip fault.

b. fault-block fault.

c. normal fault.

d. reverse fault.

10 The type of mountain that forms when rock layers are squeezed together and pushed upward is the

a. folded mountain.

b. fault-block mountain.

c. volcanic mountain.

d. strike-slip mountain.

11 Scientists' knowledge of the Earth's interior has come primarily from

a. studying magnetic reversals in oceanic crust.

b. using a system of satellites called the *global positioning system.*

c. studying seismic waves generated by earthquakes.

d. studying the pattern of fossils on different continents.

Short Answer

12 Explain how scientists use seismic waves to map the Earth's interior.

13 How do magnetic reversals provide evidence of sea-floor spreading?

14 Explain how sea-floor spreading provides a way for continents to move.

15 Describe two types of stress that deform rock.

16 What is the global positioning system (GPS), and how does GPS allow scientists to measure the rate of motion of tectonic plates?

CRITICAL THINKING

17 **Concept Mapping** Use the following terms to create a concept map: *sea-floor spreading, convergent boundary, divergent boundary, subduction zone, transform boundary,* and *tectonic plates.*

18 **Applying Concepts** Why does oceanic lithosphere sink at subduction zones but not at mid-ocean ridges?

19 **Identifying Relationships** New tectonic material continually forms at divergent boundaries. Tectonic plate material is also continually destroyed in subduction zones at convergent boundaries. Do you think that the total amount of lithosphere formed on the Earth is about equal to the amount destroyed? Why?

20 **Applying Concepts** Folded mountains usually form at the edge of a tectonic plate. How can you explain folded mountain ranges located in the middle of a tectonic plate?

INTERPRETING GRAPHICS

Imagine that you could travel to the center of the Earth. Use the diagram below to answer the questions that follow.

Composition	Structure
Crust (50 km)	Lithosphere (150 km)
Mantle (2,900 km)	Asthenosphere (250 km)
	Mesosphere (2,550 km)
Core (3,430 km)	Outer core (2,200 km)
	Inner core (1,228 km)

21 How far beneath the Earth's surface would you have to go before you were no longer passing through rock that had the composition of granite?

22 How far beneath the Earth's surface would you have to go to find liquid material in the Earth's core?

23 At what depth would you find mantle material but still be within the lithosphere?

24 How far beneath the Earth's surface would you have to go to find solid iron and nickel in the Earth's core?

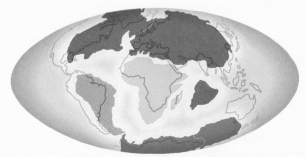

READING

Read each of the passages below. Then, answer the questions that follow each passage.

Passage 1 The Deep Sea Drilling Project was a program to retrieve and research rocks below the ocean to test the hypothesis of sea-floor spreading. For 15 years, scientists studying sea-floor spreading <u>conducted</u> research aboard the ship *Glomar Challenger*. Holes were drilled in the sea floor from the ship. Long, cylindrical lengths of rock, called *cores,* were obtained from the drill holes. By examining fossils in the cores, scientists discovered that rock closest to mid-ocean ridges was the youngest. The farther from the ridge the holes were drilled, the older the rock in the cores was. This evidence supported the idea that sea-floor spreading creates new lithosphere at mid-ocean ridges.

1. In the passage, what does *conducted* mean?

A directed

B led

C carried on

D guided

2. Why were cores drilled in the sea floor from the *Glomar Challenger*?

F to determine the depth of the crust

G to find minerals in the sea-floor rock

H to examine fossils in the sea-floor rock

I to find oil and gas in the sea-floor rock

3. Which of the following statements is a fact according to the passage?

A Rock closest to mid-ocean ridges is older than rock at a distance from mid-ocean ridges.

B One purpose of scientific research on the *Glomar Challenger* was to gather evidence for sea-floor spreading.

C Fossils examined by scientists came directly from the sea floor.

D Evidence gathered by scientists did not support sea-floor spreading.

Passage 2 The Himalayas are a range of mountains that is 2,400 km long and that <u>arcs</u> across Pakistan, India, Tibet, Nepal, Sikkim, and Bhutan. The Himalayas are the highest mountains on Earth. Nine mountains, including Mount Everest, the highest mountain on Earth, are more than 8,000 m tall. The formation of the Himalaya Mountains began about 80 million years ago. A tectonic plate carrying the Indian subcontinent collided with the Eurasian plate. The Indian plate was driven beneath the Eurasian plate. This collision caused the uplift of the Eurasian plate and the formation of the Himalayas. This process is continuing today.

1. In the passage, what does the word *arcs* mean?

A forms a circle

B forms a plane

C forms a curve

D forms a straight line

2. According to the passage, which geologic process formed the Himalaya Mountains?

F divergence

G subsidence

H strike-slip faulting

I convergence

3. Which of the following statements is a fact according to the passage?

A The nine tallest mountains on Earth are located in the Himalaya Mountains.

B The Himalaya Mountains are located within six countries.

C The Himalaya Mountains are the longest mountain range on Earth.

D The Himalaya Mountains formed more than 80 million years ago.

The illustration below shows the relative velocities (in centimeters per year) and directions in which tectonic plates are separating and colliding. Arrows that point away from one another indicate plate separation. Arrows that point toward one another indicate plate collision. Use the illustration below to answer the questions that follow.

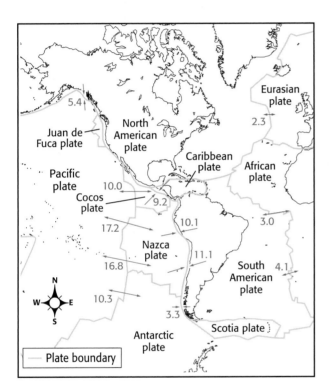

1. Between which two tectonic plates does spreading appear to be the fastest?

  A the Australian plate and the Pacific plate

  B the Antarctic plate and the Pacific plate

  C the Nazca plate and the Pacific plate

  D the Cocos plate and the Pacific plate

2. Where do you think mountain building is taking place?

  F between the African plate and the South American plate

  G between the Nazca plate and the South American plate

  H between the North American plate and the Eurasian plate

  I between the African plate and the North American plate

Read each question below, and choose the best answer.

1. The mesosphere is 2,550 km thick, and the asthenosphere is 250 km thick. If you assume that the lithosphere is 150 km thick and that the crust is 50 km thick, how thick is the mantle?

  A 2,950 km

  B 2,900 km

  C 2,800 km

  D 2,550 km

2. If a seismic wave travels through the mantle at an average velocity of 8 km/s, how many seconds will the wave take to travel through the mantle?

  F 318.75 s

  G 350.0 s

  H 362.5 s

  I 368.75 s

3. If the crust in a certain area is subsiding at the rate of 2 cm per year and has an elevation of 1,000 m, what elevation will the crust have in 10,000 years?

  A 500 m

  B 800 m

  C 1,200 m

  D 2,000 m

4. Assume that a very small oceanic plate is located between a mid-ocean ridge and a subduction zone. At the ridge, the plate is growing at a rate of 5 km every 1 million years. At the subduction zone, the plate is being destroyed at a rate of 10 km every 1 million years. If the oceanic plate is 100 km across, how long will it take the plate to disappear?

  F 100 million years

  G 50 million years

  H 20 million years

  I 5 million years

Science in Action

Science, Technology, and Society

Using Satellites to Track Plate Motion

When you think of laser beams firing, you may think of science fiction movies. However, scientists use laser beams to determine the rate and direction of motion of tectonic plates. From ground stations on Earth, laser beams are fired at several small satellites orbiting 5,900 km above Earth. From the satellites, the laser beams are reflected back to ground stations. Differences in the time it takes signals to be reflected from targets are measured over a period of time. From these differences, scientists can determine the rate and direction of plate motion.

Social Studies ACTIVITY

WRITING SKILL Research a society that lives at an active plate boundary. Find out how the people live with dangers such as volcanoes and earthquakes. Include your findings in a short report.

This scientist is using a laser to test one of the satellites that will be used to track plate motion.

Scientific Discoveries

Megaplumes

Eruptions of boiling water from the sea floor form giant, spiral disks that twist through the oceans. Do you think it's impossible? Oceanographers have discovered these disks at eight locations at mid-ocean ridges over the past 20 years. These disks, which may be tens of kilometers across, are called *megaplumes*. Megaplumes are like blenders. They mix hot water with cold water in the oceans. Megaplumes can rise hundreds of meters from the ocean floor to the upper layers of the ocean. They carry gases and minerals and provide extra energy and food to animals in the upper layers of the ocean.

Language Arts ACTIVITY

WRITING SKILL Did you ever wonder about the origin of the name *Himalaya*? Research the origin of the name *Himalaya*, and write a short report about what you find.

Alfred Wegener

Continental Drift Alfred Wegener's greatest contribution to science was the hypothesis of continental drift. This hypothesis states that continents drift apart from one another and have done so in the past. To support his hypothesis, Wegener used geologic, fossil, and glacial evidence gathered on both sides of the Atlantic Ocean. For example, Wegener recognized similarities between rock layers in North America and Europe and between rock layers in South America and Africa. He believed that these similarities could be explained only if these geologic features were once part of the same continent.

Although continental drift explained many of his observations, Wegener could not find scientific evidence to develop a complete explanation of how continents move. Most scientists were skeptical of Wegener's hypothesis and dismissed it as foolishness. It was not until the 1950s and 1960s that the discoveries of magnetic reversals and sea-floor spreading provided evidence of continental drift.

Math ACTiViTY

The distance between South America and Africa is 7,200 km. As new crust is created at the mid-ocean ridge, South America and Africa are moving away from each other at a rate of about 3.5 cm per year. How many millions of years ago were South America and Africa joined?

To learn more about these Science in Action topics, visit **go.hrw.com** and type in the keyword **HZ5TECF**.

Current Science

Check out Current Science® articles related to this chapter by visiting **go.hrw.com**. Just type in the keyword **HZ5CS07**.

Earthquakes

The Big Idea Earthquakes result from sudden motions along breaks in Earth's crust and can affect landforms and societies.

About the

On January 17, 1995, an earthquake of magnitude 7.0 shook the area in and around Kobe, Japan. Though the earthquake lasted for less than a minute, more than 5,000 people lost their lives and another 300,000 people were left homeless. More than 200,000 buildings were damaged or destroyed. Large sections of the elevated Hanshin Expressway, shown in the photo, toppled when the columns supporting the expressway failed. The expressway passed over ground that was soft and wet, where the shaking was stronger and longer lasting.

 **PRE-READING ACTIVITY**

Graphic Organizer **Spider Map** Before you read the chapter, create the graphic organizer entitled "Spider Map" described in the **Study Skills** section of the Appendix. Label the circle "Earthquakes." Create a leg for each of the sections in this chapter. As you read the chapter, fill in the map with details about the material presented in each section of the chapter.

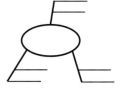

START-UP ACTIVITY

Bend, Break, or Shake

In this activity, you will test different materials in a model earthquake setting.

Procedure

1. Gather a **small wooden stick,** a **wire clothes hanger,** and a **plastic clothes hanger.**

2. Draw a straight line on a **sheet of paper.** Use a **protractor** to measure and draw the following angles from the line: 20°, 45°, and 90°.

3. Put on your **safety goggles.** Using the angles that you drew as a guide, try bending each item 20° and then releasing it. What happens? Does it break? If it bends, does it return to its original shape?

4. Repeat step 3, but bend each item 45°. Repeat the test again, but bend each item 90°.

Analysis

1. How do the different materials' responses to bending compare?

2. Where earthquakes happen, engineers use building materials that are flexible but that do not break or stay bent. Which materials from this experiment would you want building materials to behave like? Explain your answer.

What Are Earthquakes?

Have you ever felt the earth move under your feet? Many people have. Every day, somewhere within this planet, an earthquake is happening.

The word *earthquake* defines itself fairly well. But there is more to earthquakes than just the shaking of the ground. An entire branch of Earth science, called **seismology** (siez MAHL uh jee), is devoted to studying earthquakes. Earthquakes are complex, and they present many questions for *seismologists,* the scientists who study earthquakes.

Where Do Earthquakes Occur?

Most earthquakes take place near the edges of tectonic plates. *Tectonic plates* are giant pieces of Earth's thin, outermost layer. Tectonic plates move around on top of a layer of plastic rock. **Figure 1** shows the Earth's tectonic plates and the locations of recent major earthquakes.

Tectonic plates move in different directions and at different speeds. Two plates can push toward or pull away from each other. They can also slip slowly past each other. As a result of these movements, numerous features called faults exist in the Earth's crust. A *fault* is a break in the Earth's crust along which blocks of the crust slide relative to one another. Earthquakes occur along faults because of this sliding.

What You Will Learn

- Explain where earthquakes take place.
- Explain what causes earthquakes.
- Identify three different types of faults that occur at plate boundaries.
- Describe how energy from earthquakes travels through the Earth.

Vocabulary

seismology	P waves
deformation	S waves
elastic rebound	
seismic waves	

READING STRATEGY

Paired Summarizing Read this section silently. In pairs, take turns summarizing the material. Stop to discuss ideas that seem confusing.

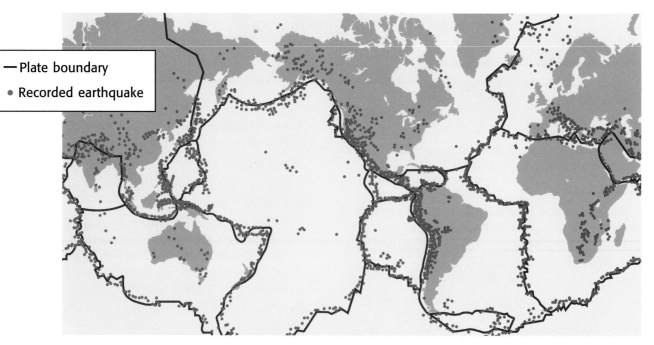

— Plate boundary
• Recorded earthquake

Figure 1 *The largest and most active earthquake zone lies along the plate boundaries surrounding the Pacific Ocean.*

What Causes Earthquakes?

As tectonic plates push, pull, or slip past each other, stress increases along faults near the plates' edges. In response to this stress, rock in the plates deforms. **Deformation** is the change in the shape of rock in response to stress. Rock along a fault deforms in mainly two ways. It deforms in a plastic manner, like a piece of molded clay, or in an elastic manner, like a rubber band. *Plastic deformation,* which is shown in **Figure 2,** does not lead to earthquakes.

Elastic deformation, however, does lead to earthquakes. Rock can stretch farther without breaking than steel can, but rock will break at some point. Think of elastically deformed rock as a stretched rubber band. You can stretch a rubber band only so far before it breaks. When the rubber band breaks, it releases energy. Then, the broken pieces return to their unstretched shape.

Figure 2 *This road cut is adjacent to the San Andreas Fault in southern California. The rocks in the cut have undergone deformation because of the continuous motion of the fault.*

Elastic Rebound

The sudden return of elastically deformed rock to its original shape is called **elastic rebound.** Elastic rebound is like the return of the broken rubber-band pieces to their unstretched shape. Elastic rebound occurs when more stress is applied to rock than the rock can withstand. During elastic rebound, energy is released. Some of this energy travels as seismic waves. These seismic waves cause an earthquake, as shown in **Figure 3.**

✓ *Reading Check* How does elastic rebound relate to earthquakes? (*See the Appendix for answers to Reading Checks.*)

seismology the study of earthquakes

deformation the bending, tilting, and breaking of the Earth's crust; the change in the shape of rock in response to stress

elastic rebound the sudden return of elastically deformed rock to its undeformed shape

---

Figure 3 **Elastic Rebound and Earthquakes**

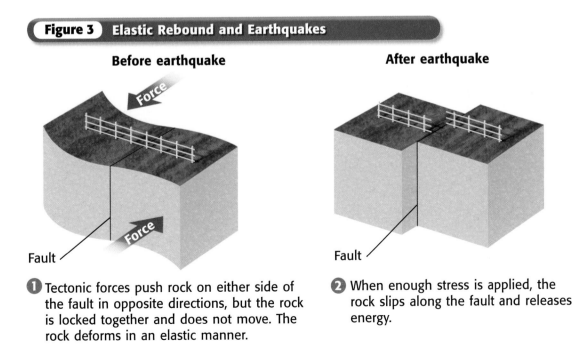

Before earthquake

After earthquake

❶ Tectonic forces push rock on either side of the fault in opposite directions, but the rock is locked together and does not move. The rock deforms in an elastic manner.

❷ When enough stress is applied, the rock slips along the fault and releases energy.

Faults at Tectonic Plate Boundaries

A specific type of plate motion takes place at different tectonic plate boundaries. Each type of motion creates a particular kind of fault that can produce earthquakes. Examine **Table 1** and the diagram below to learn more about plate motion.

Table 1 Plate Motion and Fault Types	
Plate motion	**Major fault type**
Transform	strike-slip fault
Convergent	reverse fault
Divergent	normal fault

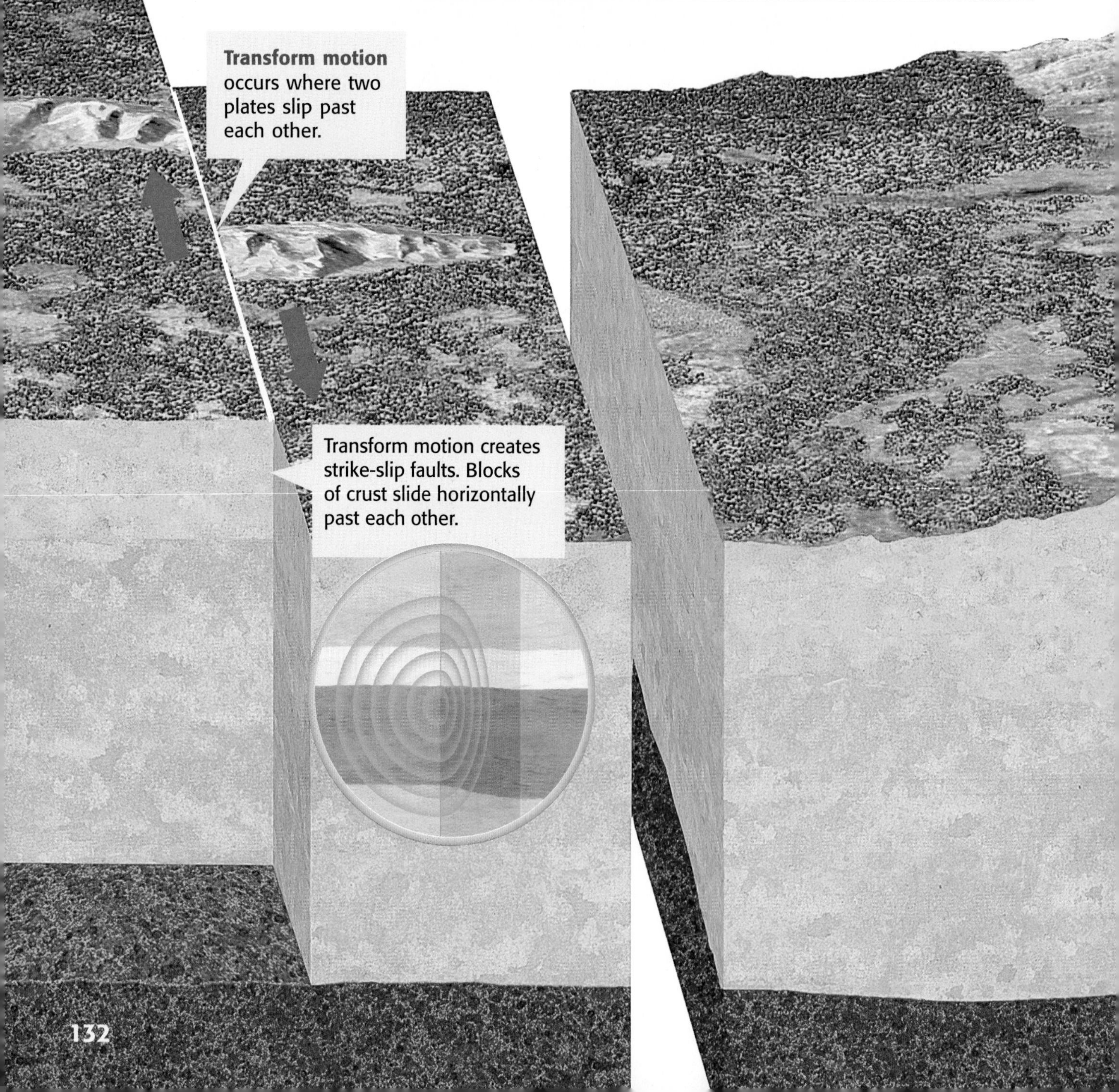

Transform motion occurs where two plates slip past each other.

Transform motion creates strike-slip faults. Blocks of crust slide horizontally past each other.

Earthquake Zones

Earthquakes can happen both near Earth's surface or far below it. Most earthquakes happen in the earthquake zones along tectonic plate boundaries. Earthquake zones are places where a large number of faults are located. The San Andreas Fault Zone in California is an example of an earthquake zone. But not all faults are located at tectonic plate boundaries. Sometimes, earthquakes happen along faults in the middle of tectonic plates.

Reading Check Where are earthquake zones located?

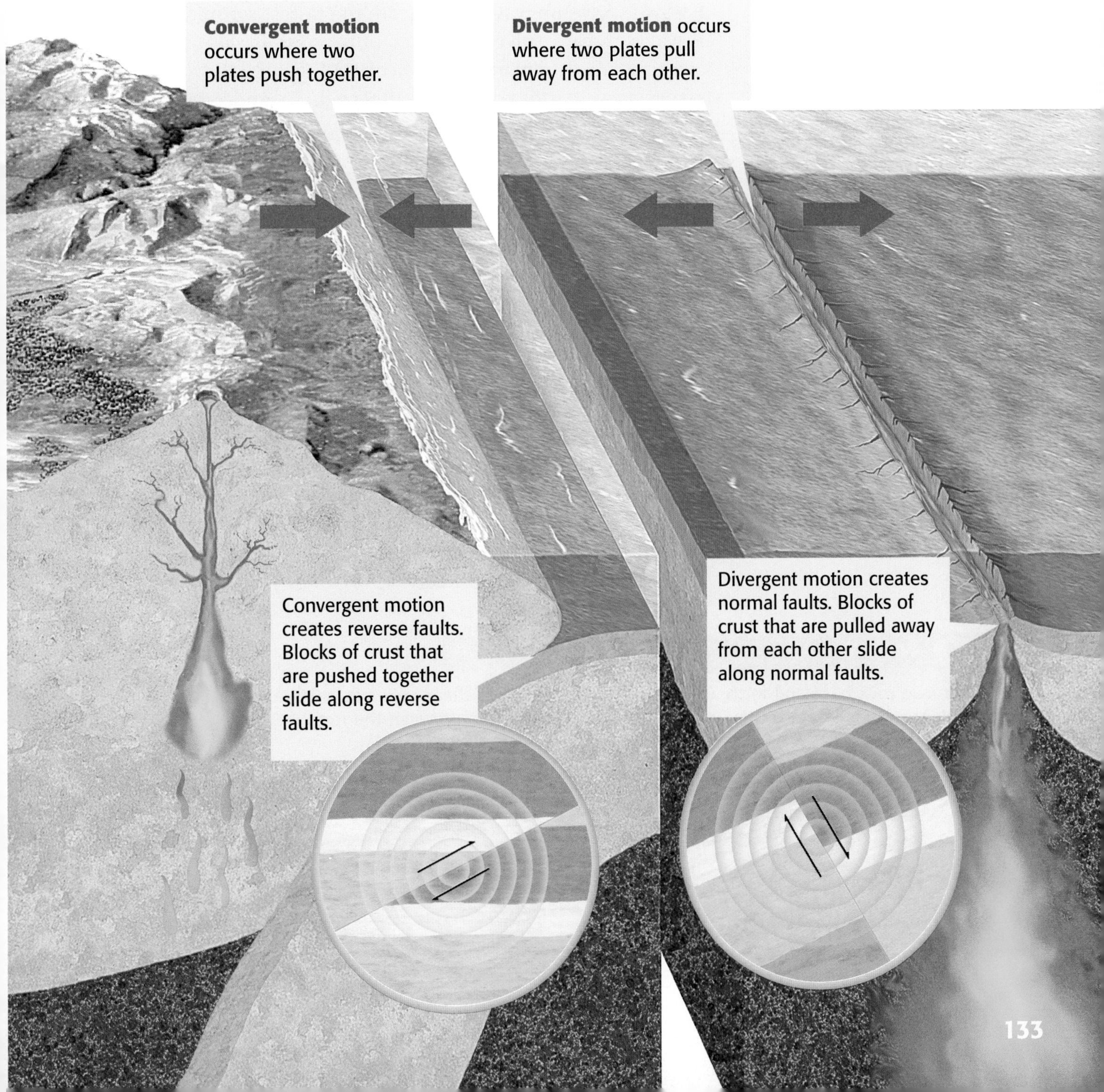

Convergent motion occurs where two plates push together.

Divergent motion occurs where two plates pull away from each other.

Convergent motion creates reverse faults. Blocks of crust that are pushed together slide along reverse faults.

Divergent motion creates normal faults. Blocks of crust that are pulled away from each other slide along normal faults.

seismic wave a wave of energy that travels through the Earth, away from an earthquake in all directions

P wave a seismic wave that causes particles of rock to move in a back-and-forth direction

S wave a seismic wave that causes particles of rock to move in a side-to-side direction

How Do Earthquake Waves Travel?

Waves of energy that travel through the Earth are called **seismic waves.** Seismic waves that travel through the Earth's interior are called *body waves*. There are two types of body waves: P waves and S waves. Seismic waves that travel along the Earth's surface are called *surface waves*. Each type of seismic wave travels through Earth's layers in a different way and at a different speed. Also, the speed of a seismic wave depends on the kind of material the wave travels through.

P Waves

Waves that travel through solids, liquids, and gases are called **P waves** (pressure waves). They are the fastest seismic waves, so P waves always travel ahead of other seismic waves. P waves are also called *primary waves,* because they are always the first waves of an earthquake to be detected. To understand how P waves affect rock, imagine a cube of gelatin sitting on a plate. Like most solids, gelatin is an elastic material. It wiggles if you tap it. Tapping the cube of gelatin changes the pressure inside the cube, which momentarily deforms the cube. The gelatin then reacts by springing back to its original shape. This process is how P waves affect rock, as shown in **Figure 4.**

S Waves

Rock can also be deformed from side to side. After being deformed from side to side, the rock springs back to its original position and S waves are created. **S waves,** or shear waves, are the second-fastest seismic waves. S waves shear rock side to side, as shown in **Figure 4,** which means they stretch the rock sideways. Unlike P waves, S waves cannot travel through parts of the Earth that are completely liquid. Also, S waves are slower than P waves and always arrive later. Thus, another name for S waves is *secondary waves.*

Figure 4 Body Waves

P **waves** move rock back and forth, which squeezes and stretches the rock, as they travel through the rock.

Direction of wave travel

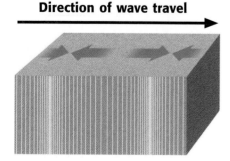

S **waves** shear rock side to side as they travel through the rock.

Direction of wave travel

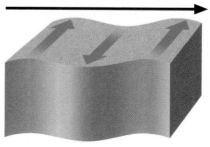

Surface Waves

Surface waves move along the Earth's surface and produce motion mostly in the upper few kilometers of Earth's crust. There are two types of surface waves. One type of surface wave produces motion up, down, and around, as shown in **Figure 5.** The other type produces back-and-forth motion like the motion produced by S waves. Surface waves are different from body waves in that surface waves travel more slowly and are more destructive.

✓ **Reading Check** Explain the differences between surface waves and body waves.

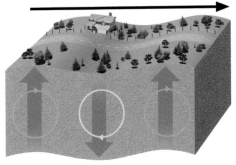

Figure 5 **Surface Waves**

Surface waves move the ground much like ocean waves move water particles.

Direction of wave travel

SECTION
Review

Summary

- Earthquakes occur mainly near the edges of tectonic plates.
- Elastic rebound is the direct cause of earthquakes.
- Three major types of faults occur at tectonic plate boundaries: normal faults, reverse faults, and strike-slip faults.
- Earthquake energy travels as body waves through the Earth's interior or as surface waves along the surface of the Earth.

Using Key Terms

Complete each of the following sentences by choosing the correct term from the word bank.

Deformation	P waves
Elastic rebound	S waves

1. _____ is the change in shape of rock due to stress.

2. _____ always travel ahead of other waves.

Understanding Key Ideas

3. Seismic waves that shear rock side to side are called
   a. surface waves.
   b. S waves.
   c. P waves.
   d. Both (b) and (c)

4. Where do earthquakes occur?

5. What is the direct cause of earthquakes?

6. Describe the three types of plate motion and the faults that are characteristic of each type of motion.

7. What is an earthquake zone?

Math Skills

8. A seismic wave is traveling through the Earth at an average rate of speed of 8 km/s. How long will it take the wave to travel 480 km?

Critical Thinking

9. **Applying Concepts** Given what you know about elastic rebound, why do you think some earthquakes are stronger than others?

10. **Identifying Relationships** Why are surface waves more destructive to buildings than P waves or S waves are?

11. **Identifying Relationships** Why do you think the majority of earthquake zones are located at tectonic plate boundaries?

SCI**LINKS**®

NSTA

Developed and maintained by the National Science Teachers Association

For a variety of links related to this chapter, go to www.scilinks.org

Topic: What Is an Earthquake?
SciLinks code: HSM1658

Earthquake Measurement

Imagine walls shaking, windows rattling, and glassware and dishes clinking and clanking. After only seconds, the vibrating stops and the sounds die away.

Within minutes, news reports give information about the strength, the time, and the location of the earthquake. You are amazed at how scientists could have learned this information so quickly.

Locating Earthquakes

How do seismologists know when and where earthquakes begin? They depend on earthquake-sensing instruments called seismographs. **Seismographs** are instruments located at or near the surface of the Earth that record seismic waves. When the waves reach a seismograph, the seismograph creates a seismogram. A **seismogram** is a tracing of earthquake motion and is created by a seismograph.

Determining Time and Location of Earthquakes

Seismologists use seismograms to calculate when an earthquake began. Seismologists find an earthquake's start time by comparing seismograms and noting the differences in arrival times of P waves and S waves. Seismologists also use seismograms to find an earthquake's epicenter. An **epicenter** is the point on the Earth's surface directly above an earthquake's starting point. A **focus** is the point inside the Earth where an earthquake begins. **Figure 1** shows the location of an earthquake's epicenter and its focus.

Reading Check How do seismologists determine an earthquake's start time? (*See the Appendix for answers to Reading Checks.*)

What You Will Learn

● Explain how earthquakes are detected.
● Describe how to locate an earthquake's epicenter.
● Explain how the strength of an earthquake is measured.
● Explain how the intensity of an earthquake is measured.

Vocabulary

seismograph   epicenter
seismogram   focus

READING STRATEGY

Reading Organizer As you read this section, create an outline of the section. Use the headings from the section in your outline.

seismograph an instrument that records vibrations in the ground and determines the location and strength of an earthquake

seismogram a tracing of earthquake motion that is created by a seismograph

epicenter the point on Earth's surface directly above an earthquake's starting point, or focus

focus the point along a fault at which the first motion of an earthquake occurs

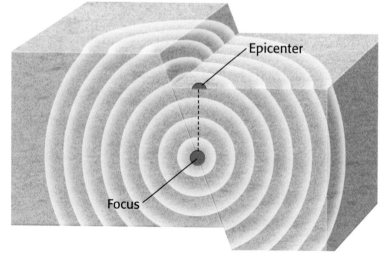

Figure 1 *An earthquake's epicenter is on the Earth's surface directly above the earthquake's focus.*

Epicenter

Focus

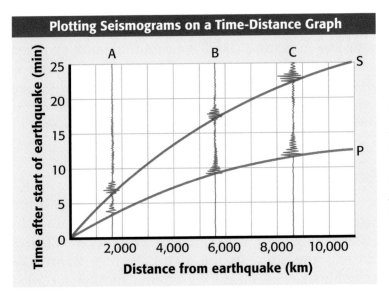

Plotting Seismograms on a Time-Distance Graph

Time after start of earthquake (min)

Distance from earthquake (km)

Figure 2 *After identifying P and S waves, seismologists can use the time difference to determine an earthquake's start time and the distance from the epicenter to each station. The vertical axis tells how much time passed between the start of the earthquake and the arrival of seismic waves at a station. The horizontal axis tells the distance between a station and the earthquake's epicenter.*

The S-P Time Method

Perhaps the simplest method by which seismologists find an earthquake's epicenter is the *S-P time method*. The first step in this method is to collect several seismograms of the same earthquake from different locations. Then, the seismograms are placed on a time-distance graph. The seismogram tracing of the first P wave is lined up with the P-wave time-distance curve, and the tracing of the first S wave is lined up with the S-wave curve, as shown in **Figure 2.** The distance of each station from the earthquake can be found by reading the horizontal axis. After finding out the distances, a seismologist can locate an earthquake's epicenter, as shown in **Figure 3.**

Figure 3 **Finding an Earthquake's Epicenter**

❶ A circle is drawn around a seismograph station. The radius of the circle equals the distance from the seismograph to the epicenter. (This distance is taken from the time-distance graph.)

❷ When a second circle is drawn around another seismograph station, the circle overlaps the first circle in two spots. One of these spots is the earthquake's epicenter.

❸ When a circle is drawn around a third seismograph station, all three circles intersect in one spot—the earthquake's epicenter. In this case, the epicenter was in San Francisco.

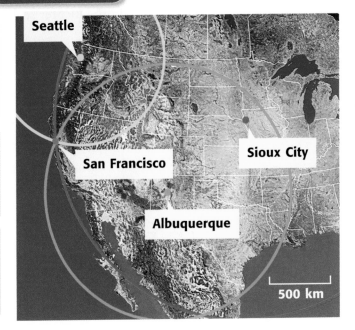

Seattle

Sioux City

San Francisco

Albuquerque

500 km

Measuring Earthquake Strength and Intensity

"How strong was the earthquake?" is a common question asked of seismologists. This question is not easy to answer. But it is an important question for anyone living near an earthquake zone. Fortunately, seismograms can be used not only to determine an earthquake's epicenter and its start time but also to find out an earthquake's strength.

The Richter Magnitude Scale

Throughout much of the 20th century, seismologists used the *Richter magnitude scale*, commonly called the Richter scale, to measure the strength of earthquakes. Seismologist Charles Richter created the scale in the 1930s. Richter wanted to compare earthquakes by measuring ground motion recorded by seismograms at seismograph stations.

Earthquake Ground Motion

A measure of the strength of an earthquake is called *magnitude*. The Richter scale measures the ground motion from an earthquake and adjusts for distance to find its strength. Each time the magnitude increases by one unit, the measured ground motion becomes 10 times larger. For example, an earthquake with a magnitude of 5.0 on the Richter scale will produce 10 times as much ground motion as an earthquake with a magnitude of 4.0. Furthermore, an earthquake with a magnitude of 6.0 will produce 100 times as much ground motion (10 × 10) as an earthquake with a magnitude of 4.0. **Table 1** shows the differences in the estimated effects of earthquakes with each increase of one unit of magnitude.

✓ **Reading Check** How are magnitude and ground motion related in the Richter scale?

Table 1 Effects of Different-Sized Earthquakes	
Magnitude	**Estimated effects**
2.0	can be detected only by seismograph
3.0	can be felt at epicenter
4.0	can be felt by most people in the area
5.0	causes damage at epicenter
6.0	can cause widespread damage
7.0	can cause great, widespread damage

Modified Mercalli Intensity Scale

A measure of the degree to which an earthquake is felt by people and the amount of damage caused by the earthquake, if any, is called *intensity*. Currently, seismologists in the United States use the Modified Mercalli Intensity Scale to measure earthquake intensity. This scale is a numerical scale that uses Roman numerals from I to XII to describe increasing earthquake intensity levels. An intensity level of I describes an earthquake that is not felt by most people. An intensity level of XII indicates total damage of an area. **Figure 4** shows the type of damage caused by an earthquake that has a Modified Mercalli intensity level of XI.

Because the effects of an earthquake vary from place to place, any earthquake will have more than one intensity value. Intensity values are usually higher near an earthquake's epicenter.

Figure 4 *Intensity values for the 1906 San Francisco earthquake varied from place to place. The maximum intensity level was XI.*

SECTION Review

Summary

- Seismologists detect seismic waves and record them as seismograms.
- The S-P time method is the simplest method to use to find an earthquake's epicenter.
- Seismologists use the Richter scale to measure an earthquake's strength.
- Seismologists use the Modified Mercalli Intensity Scale to measure an earthquake's intensity.

Using Key Terms

1. In your own words, write a definition for each of the following terms: *epicenter* and *focus*.

Understanding Key Ideas

2. What is the difference between a seismograph and a seismogram?

3. Explain how earthquakes are detected.

4. Briefly explain the steps of the S-P time method for locating an earthquake's epicenter.

5. Why might an earthquake have more than one intensity value?

Math Skills

6. How much more ground motion is produced by an earthquake of magnitude 7.0 than by an earthquake of magnitude 4.0?

Critical Thinking

7. **Making Inferences** Why is a 6.0 magnitude earthquake so much more destructive than a 5.0 magnitude earthquake?

8. **Identifying Bias** Which do you think is the more important measure of earthquakes, strength or intensity? Explain.

9. **Making Inferences** Do you think an earthquake of moderate magnitude can produce high Modified Mercalli intensity values?

SCILINKS®

NSTA
Developed and maintained by the
National Science Teachers Association

For a variety of links related to this chapter, go to www.scilinks.org

Topic: Earthquake Measurement
SciLinks code: HSM0452

Earthquakes and Society

Imagine that you are in class and the ground begins to shake beneath your feet. What do you do?

Seismologists are not able to predict the exact time when and place where an earthquake will occur. They can, at best, make forecasts based on the frequency with which earthquakes take place. Therefore, seismologists are always looking for better ways to forecast when and where earthquakes will happen. In the meantime, it is important for people in earthquake zones to be prepared before an earthquake strikes.

Earthquake Hazard

Earthquake hazard is a measurement of how likely an area is to have damaging earthquakes in the future. An area's earthquake-hazard level is determined by past and present seismic activity. The map in **Figure 1** shows that some areas of the United States have a higher earthquake-hazard level than others do. This variation is caused by differences in seismic activity. The greater the seismic activity, the higher the earthquake-hazard level. The West Coast, for example, has a very high earthquake-hazard level because it has a lot of seismic activity.

Look at the map. What earthquake-hazard level or levels are shown in the area in which you live? How do the hazard levels of nearby areas compare with your area's hazard level?

What You Will Learn

● Explain how earthquake-hazard level is determined.
● Compare methods of earthquake forecasting.
● Describe five ways to safeguard buildings against earthquakes.
● Outline earthquake safety procedures.

Vocabulary

gap hypothesis
seismic gap

READING STRATEGY

Discussion Read this section silently. Write down questions that you have about this section. Discuss your questions in a small group.

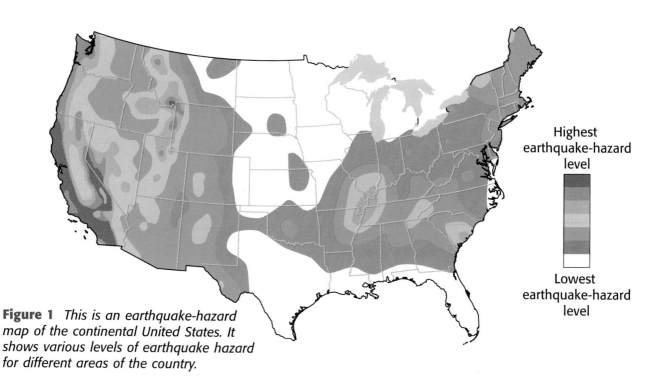

Highest earthquake-hazard level

Lowest earthquake-hazard level

Figure 1 *This is an earthquake-hazard map of the continental United States. It shows various levels of earthquake hazard for different areas of the country.*

Table 1 Worldwide Earthquake Frequency (Based on Observations Since 1900)

Descriptor	Magnitude	Average number annually
Great	8.0 and higher	1
Major	7.0–7.9	18
Strong	6.0–6.9	120
Moderate	5.0–5.9	800
Light	4.0–4.9	about 6,200
Minor	3.0–3.9	about 49,000
Very minor	2.0–2.9	about 365,000

Earthquake Forecasting

Forecasting when and where earthquakes will occur and their strength is difficult. By looking carefully at areas of seismic activity, seismologists have discovered some patterns in earthquakes that allow them to make some general predictions.

Strength and Frequency

Earthquakes vary in strength. And you can probably guess that earthquakes don't occur on a set schedule. But what you may not know is that the strength of earthquakes is related to how often they occur. **Table 1** provides more detail about this relationship worldwide.

The relationship between earthquake strength and frequency is also at work on a local scale. For example, each year approximately 1.6 earthquakes with a magnitude of 4.0 on the Richter scale occur in the Puget Sound area of Washington State. Over this same time period, approximately 10 times as many earthquakes with a magnitude of 3.0 occur in this area. Scientists use these statistics to make forecasts about the strength, location, and frequency of future earthquakes.

✓ Reading Check What is the relationship between the strength of earthquakes and earthquake frequency? (*See the Appendix for answers to Reading Checks.*)

The Gap Hypothesis

Another method of forecasting an earthquake's strength, location, and frequency is based on the gap hypothesis. The **gap hypothesis** is a hypothesis that states that sections of active faults that have had relatively few earthquakes are likely to be the sites of strong earthquakes in the future. The areas along a fault where relatively few earthquakes have occurred are called **seismic gaps.**

gap hypothesis a hypothesis that is based on the idea that a major earthquake is more likely to occur along the part of an active fault where no earthquakes have occurred for a certain period of time

seismic gap an area along a fault where relatively few earthquakes have occurred recently but where strong earthquakes have occurred in the past

Figure 2 A Seismic Gap on the San Andreas Fault

This diagram shows a cross section of the San Andreas Fault. Note how the seismic gap was filled by the 1989 Loma Prieta earthquake and its aftershocks. *Aftershocks* are weaker earthquakes that follow a stronger earthquake.

● Earthquakes prior to 1989 earthquake

● 1989 earthquake and aftershocks

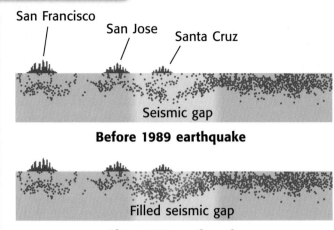

Before 1989 earthquake

After 1989 earthquake

Using the Gap Hypothesis

Not all seismologists believe the gap hypothesis is an accurate method of forecasting earthquakes. But some seismologists think the gap hypothesis helped forecast the approximate location and strength of the 1989 Loma Prieta earthquake in the San Francisco Bay area. The seismic gap that they identified is illustrated in **Figure 2.** In 1988, these seismologists predicted that over the next 30 years there was a 30% chance that an earthquake with a magnitude of at least 6.5 would fill this seismic gap. Were they correct? The Loma Prieta earthquake, which filled in the seismic gap in 1989, measured 6.9 on the Richter scale. Their prediction was very close, considering how complicated the forecasting of earthquakes is.

Figure 3 *During the January 17, 1995, earthquake, the fronts of entire buildings collapsed into the streets of Kobe, Japan.*

Earthquakes and Buildings

Figure 3 shows what can happen to buildings during an earthquake. These buildings were not designed or constructed to withstand the forces of an earthquake.

Today, older structures in seismically active places, such as California, are being made more earthquake resistant. The process of making older structures more earthquake resistant is called *retrofitting.* A common way to retrofit an older home is to securely fasten it to its foundation. Steel can be used to strengthen structures made of brick.

✓ Reading Check Explain the meaning of the term *retrofitting.*

Earthquake-Resistant Buildings

A lot has been learned from building failure during earthquakes. Armed with this knowledge, architects and engineers use the newest technology to design and construct buildings and bridges to better withstand earthquakes. Carefully study **Figure 4** to learn more about this modern technology.

Figure 4 Earthquake-Resistant Building Technology

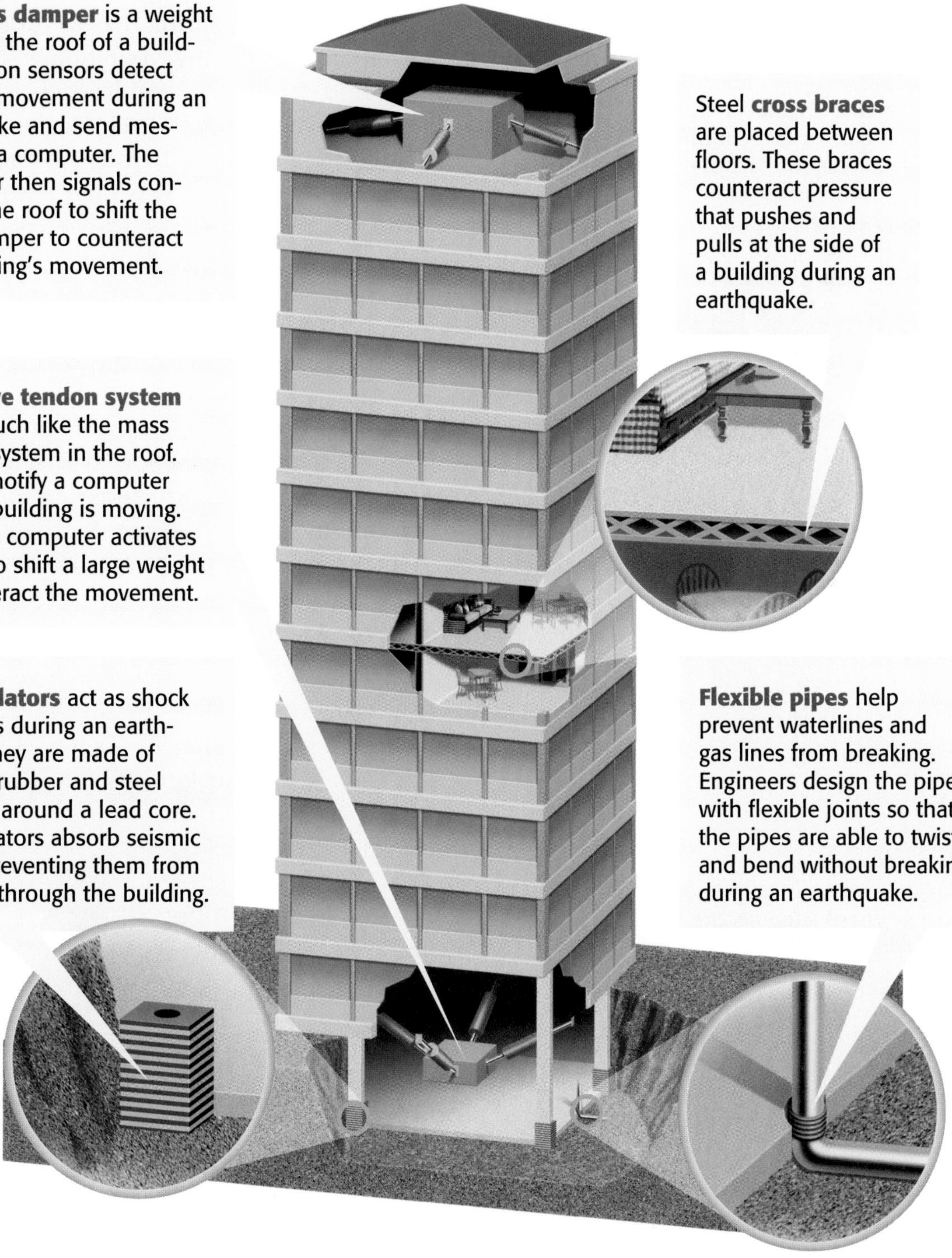

The **mass damper** is a weight placed in the roof of a building. Motion sensors detect building movement during an earthquake and send messages to a computer. The computer then signals controls in the roof to shift the mass damper to counteract the building's movement.

Steel **cross braces** are placed between floors. These braces counteract pressure that pushes and pulls at the side of a building during an earthquake.

The **active tendon system** works much like the mass damper system in the roof. Sensors notify a computer that the building is moving. Then, the computer activates devices to shift a large weight to counteract the movement.

Base isolators act as shock absorbers during an earthquake. They are made of layers of rubber and steel wrapped around a lead core. Base isolators absorb seismic waves, preventing them from traveling through the building.

Flexible pipes help prevent waterlines and gas lines from breaking. Engineers design the pipes with flexible joints so that the pipes are able to twist and bend without breaking during an earthquake.

CONNECTION TO
Physics

WRITING SKILL **Earthquake Proof Buildings** During earthquakes, buildings often sway from side to side when the ground beneath them moves. This swaying can cause structural damage to buildings. Scientists and engineers are developing computer-controlled systems that counteract the swaying of buildings during earthquakes. Research a computer-controlled system that uses mass dampers or active tendons to reduce damage to buildings. Summarize your research in a short essay.

Are You Prepared for an Earthquake?

If you live in an area where earthquakes are common, there are many things you can do to protect yourself and your property from earthquakes. Plan ahead so that you will know what to do before, during, and after an earthquake. Stick to your plan as closely as possible.

Before the Shaking Starts

The first thing you should do is safeguard your home against earthquakes. You can do so by putting heavier objects on lower shelves so that they do not fall during the earthquake. You can also talk to a parent about having your home strengthened. Next, you should find safe places within each room of your home and outside of your home. Then, make a plan with others (your family, neighbors, or friends) to meet in a safe place after the earthquake is over. This plan ensures that you will all know who is safe. During the earthquake, waterlines, power lines, and roadways may be damaged. So, you should store water, nonperishable food, a fire extinguisher, a flashlight with batteries, a portable radio, medicines, and a first-aid kit in a place you can access after the earthquake.

When the Shaking Starts

The best thing to do if you are indoors when an earthquake begins is to crouch or lie face down under a table or desk in the center of a room, as shown in **Figure 5.** If you are outside, lie face down away from buildings, power lines, and trees and cover your head with your hands. If you are in a car on an open road, you should stop the car and remain inside.

Reading Check Explain what you would do if you were in class and an earthquake began to shake the ground.

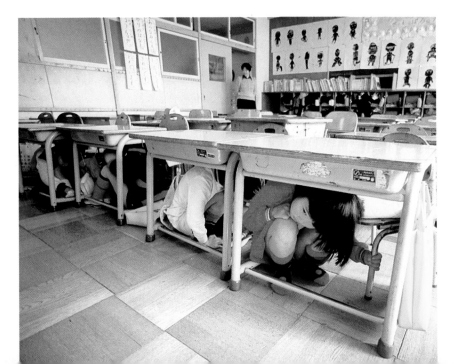

Figure 5 *These students are participating in an earthquake drill.*

After the Shaking Stops

Being in an earthquake is a startling and often frightening experience for most people. After being in an earthquake, you should not be surprised to find yourself and others puzzled about what took place. You should try to calm down and get your bearings as quickly as possible. Then, remove yourself from immediate danger, such as downed power lines, broken glass, and fire hazards. Always stay out of damaged buildings, and return home only when you are told that it is safe to do so by someone in authority. Be aware that there may be aftershocks, which may cause more damage to structures. Recall your earthquake plan, and follow it.

SCHOOL to HOME

Disaster Planning

With an adult, create a plan that will protect your family in the event of a natural disaster, such as an earthquake. The plan should include steps to take before, during, and after a disaster. Present your disaster plan in the form of an oral report to your class.

ACTIVITY

SECTION Review

Summary

- Earthquake hazard is a measure of how likely an area is to have earthquakes in the future.
- Seismologists use their knowledge of the relationship between earthquake strength and frequency and of the gap hypothesis to forecast earthquakes.
- Homes and buildings and bridges can be strengthened to decrease earthquake damage.
- People who live in earthquake zones should safeguard their home against earthquakes.

Using Key Terms

1. In your own words, write a definition for each of the following terms: *gap hypothesis* and *seismic gap*.

Understanding Key Ideas

2. A weight that is placed on a building to make the building earthquake resistant is called a(n)
   a. active tendon system.
   b. cross brace.
   c. mass damper.
   d. base isolator.

3. How is an area's earthquake-hazard level determined?

4. Compare the strength and frequency method with the gap hypothesis method for predicting earthquakes.

5. What is a common way of making homes more earthquake resistant?

6. Describe four pieces of technology that are designed to make buildings earthquake resistant.

7. Name five items that you should store in case of an earthquake.

Math Skills

8. Of the approximately 420,000 earthquakes recorded each year, about 140 have a magnitude greater than 6.0. What percentage of total earthquakes have a magnitude greater than 6.0?

Critical Thinking

9. **Evaluating Hypotheses** Seismologists predict that there is a 20% chance that an earthquake of magnitude 7.0 or greater will fill a seismic gap during the next 50 years. Is the hypothesis incorrect if the earthquake does not happen? Explain your answer.

10. **Applying Concepts** Why is a large earthquake often followed by numerous aftershocks?

SCILINKS.

NSTA
Developed and maintained by the
National Science Teachers Association

For a variety of links related to this chapter, go to www.scilinks.org

Topic: Earthquakes and Society
SciLinks code: HSM0455

145

Inquiry Lab

OBJECTIVES

Build a model of a structure that can withstand a simulated earthquake.

Evaluate ways in which you can strengthen your model.

MATERIALS

- gelatin, square, approximately 8 × 8 cm
- marshmallows (10)
- paper plate
- toothpicks (10)

SAFETY

Quake Challenge

In many parts of the world, people must have earthquakes in mind when they construct buildings. Each building must be designed so that the structure is protected during an earthquake. Architects have greatly improved the design of buildings since 1906, when an earthquake and the fires it caused destroyed much of San Francisco. In this activity, you will use marshmallows and toothpicks to build a structure that can withstand a simulated earthquake. In the process, you will discover some of the ways a building can be built to withstand an earthquake.

Ask a Question

1. What features help a building withstand an earthquake? How can I use this information to build my structure?

Form a Hypothesis

2. Brainstorm with a classmate to design a structure that will resist the simulated earthquake. Write two or three sentences to describe your design. Explain why you think your design will be able to withstand a simulated earthquake.

Test the Hypothesis

3. Follow your design to build a structure using the toothpicks and marshmallows.

4. Set your structure on a square of gelatin, and place the gelatin on a paper plate.

5. Shake the square of gelatin to test whether your building will remain standing during a quake. Do not pick up the gelatin.

6. If your first design does not work well, change it until you find a design that does. Try to determine why your building is falling so that you can improve your design each time.

7. Sketch your final design.

8. After you have tested your final design, place your structure on the gelatin square on your teacher's desk.

9. When every group has added a structure to the teacher's gelatin, your teacher will simulate an earthquake by shaking the gelatin. Watch to see which buildings withstand the most severe quake.

Analyze the Results

1. **Explaining Events** Which buildings were still standing after the final earthquake? What features made them more stable?

2. **Analyzing Results** How would you change your design in order to make your structure more stable?

Draw Conclusions

3. **Evaluating Models** This was a simple model of a real-life problem for architects. Based on this activity, what advice would you give to architects who design buildings in earthquake zones?

4. **Evaluating Models** What are some limitations of your earthquake model?

5. **Making Predictions** How could your research have an impact on society?

USING KEY TERMS

1 Use each of the following terms in a separate sentence: *seismic wave*, *P wave*, and *S wave*.

For each pair of terms, explain how the meanings of the terms differ.

2 *seismograph* and *seismogram*

3 *epicenter* and *focus*

4 *gap hypothesis* and *seismic gap*

UNDERSTANDING KEY IDEAS

Multiple Choice

5 When rock is ___, energy builds up in it. Seismic waves occur as this energy is ___.

   a. plastically deformed, increased

   b. elastically deformed, released

   c. plastically deformed, released

   d. elastically deformed, increased

6 Reverse faults are created

   a. by divergent plate motion.

   b. by convergent plate motion.

   c. by transform plate motion.

   d. All of the above

7 The last seismic waves to arrive are

   a. P waves.

   b. body waves.

   c. S waves.

   d. surface waves.

8 If an earthquake begins while you are in a building, the safest thing for you to do is

   a. to run out into an open space.

   b. to get under the strongest table, chair, or other piece of furniture.

   c. to call home.

   d. to crouch near a wall.

9 How many major earthquakes (magnitude 7.0 to 7.9) happen on average in the world each year?

   a. 1

   b. 18

   c. 120

   d. 800

10 ___ counteract pressure that pushes and pulls at the side of a building during an earthquake.

   a. Base isolators

   b. Mass dampers

   c. Active tendon systems

   d. Cross braces

Short Answer

11 Can the S-P time method be used with one seismograph station to locate the epicenter of an earthquake? Explain your answer.

12 Explain how the Richter scale and the Modified Mercalli Intensity Scale are different.

13 What is the relationship between the strength of earthquakes and earthquake frequency?

14 Explain the way that different seismic waves affect rock as they travel through it.

15 Describe some steps you can take to protect yourself and your property from earthquakes.

16 **Concept Mapping** Use the following terms to create a concept map: *focus, epicenter, earthquake start time, seismic waves, P waves,* and *S waves.*

17 **Identifying Relationships** Would a strong or light earthquake be more likely to happen along a major fault where there have not been many recent earthquakes? Explain. (Hint: Think about the average number of earthquakes of different magnitudes that occur annually.)

18 **Applying Concepts** Japan is located near a point where three tectonic plates converge. What would you imagine the earthquake-hazard level in Japan to be? Explain why.

19 **Applying Concepts** You learned that if you are in a car during an earthquake and are out in the open, it is best to stay in the car. Can you think of any situation in which you might want to leave a car during an earthquake?

20 **Identifying Relationships** You use gelatin to simulate rock in an experiment in which you are investigating the way different seismic waves affect rock. In what ways is your gelatin model limited?

The graph below illustrates the relationship between earthquake magnitude and the height of tracings on a seismogram. Charles Richter initially formed his magnitude scale by comparing the heights of seismogram readings for different earthquakes. Use the graph below to answer the questions that follow.

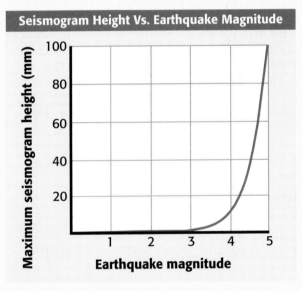

Seismogram Height Vs. Earthquake Magnitude

21 According to the graph, what would the magnitude of an earthquake be if its maximum seismogram height is 10 mm?

22 According to the graph, what is the difference in maximum seismogram height (in mm) between an earthquake of magnitude 4.0 and an earthquake of magnitude 5.0?

23 Look at the shape of the curve on the graph. What does this tell you about the relationship between seismogram heights and earthquake magnitudes? Explain.

Standardized Test Preparation

Read each of the passages below. Then, answer the questions that follow each passage.

Passage 1 At 5:04 P.M. on October 14, 1989, life in California's San Francisco Bay area seemed normal. While 62,000 fans filled Candlestick Park to watch the third game of the World Series, other people were rushing home from a day's work. By 5:05 P.M., the area had changed <u>drastically</u>. The area was rocked by the 6.9 magnitude Loma Prieta earthquake, which lasted 20 s and caused 68 deaths, 3,757 injuries, and the destruction of more than 1,000 homes. Considering that the earthquake was of such a high magnitude and that the earthquake happened during rush hour, it is amazing that more people did not die.

1. In the passage, what does the word *drastically* mean?

  A continuously

  B severely

  C gradually

  D not at all

2. Which of the following statements about the Loma Prieta earthquake is false?

  F The earthquake happened during rush hour.

  G The earthquake destroyed more than 1,000 homes.

  H The earthquake lasted for 1 min.

  I The earthquake had a magnitude of 6.9.

3. Which of the following statements is a fact in the passage?

  A Thousands of people were killed in the Loma Prieta earthquake.

  B The Loma Prieta earthquake happened during the morning rush hour.

  C The Loma Prieta earthquake was a light to moderate earthquake.

  D The Loma Prieta earthquake occurred during the 1989 World Series.

Passage 2 In the United States, seismologists use the Modified Mercalli Intensity Scale to measure the intensity of earthquakes. Japanese seismologists, however, use the Shindo scale to measure earthquake intensity. Earthquakes are <u>assigned</u> a number between 1 and 7 on the scale. Shindo 1 indicates a slight earthquake. Such an earthquake is felt by few people, usually people who are sitting. Shindo 7 indicates a severe earthquake. An earthquake that causes great destruction, such as the earthquake that struck Kobe, Japan, in January 1995, would be classified as Shindo 7.

1. In the passage, what does the word *assigned* mean?

  A named

  B voted

  C given

  D chosen

2. Which of the following statements about the Shindo scale is true?

  F The Shindo scale is used to measure earthquake strength.

  G The Shindo scale, which ranges from 1 to 7, is used to rank earthquake intensity.

  H The Shindo scale is the same as the Modified Mercalli Intensity Scale.

  I Seismologists all over the world use the Shindo scale.

3. Which of the following is a fact in the passage?

  A American seismologists use the Richter scale instead of the Shindo scale.

  B Japanese seismologists measure the intensity of large earthquakes only.

  C The Kobe earthquake was too destructive to be given a Shindo number.

  D Shindo 1 indicates a slight earthquake.

INTERPRETING GRAPHICS

Use the graph below to answer the questions that follow.

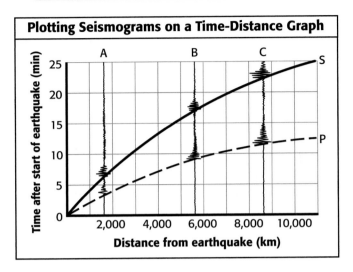

Plotting Seismograms on a Time-Distance Graph

1. According to the seismogram, which waves travel the **fastest**?

   A P waves travel the fastest.

   B S waves travel the fastest.

   C P waves and S waves travel at the same speed.

   D The graph does not show how fast P waves and S waves travel.

2. What is the approximate difference in minutes between the time the first P waves arrived at station B and the time the first S waves arrived at station B?

   F 22 1/2 min

   G 10 1/2 min

   H 8 min

   I 3 min

3. Station A is approximately how much closer to the epicenter than station B is?

   A 1,800 km

   B 4,000 km

   C 5,800 km

   D 8,600 km

MATH

Read each question below, and choose the best answer.

1. If a seismic wave travels at a rate of 12 km/s, how far will it travel away from the earthquake in 1 min?

   A 7,200 km

   B 720 km

   C 72 km

   D 7.2 km

2. If a P wave travels a distance of 70 km in 10 s, what is its speed?

   F 700 km/s

   G 70 km/s

   H 7 km/s

   I 0.7 km/s

3. Each time the magnitude of an earthquake increases by 1 unit, the amount of energy released is 31.7 times greater. How much greater is the energy for a magnitude 7.0 earthquake than a magnitude 5.0 earthquake?

   A 31,855 times as strong

   B 63.4 times as strong

   C 634 times as strong

   D 1,005 times as strong

4. An approximate relationship between earthquake magnitude and frequency is that when magnitude increases by 1.0, 10 times fewer earthquakes occur. Thus, if 150 earthquakes of magnitude 2.0 happen in your area this year, about how many 4.0 magnitude earthquakes will happen in your area this year?

   F 50

   G 10

   H 2

   I 0

5. If an average of 421,140 earthquakes occur annually, what percentage of these earthquakes are minor earthquakes if 49,000 minor earthquakes occur annually?

   A approximately .01%

   B approximately .12%

   C approximately 12%

   D approximately 86%

Standardized Test Preparation

Science in Action

Source: Martyn Unsworth

Weird Science

Can Animals Predict Earthquakes?

Is it possible that animals close to the epicenter of an earthquake are able to sense changes in their environment? And should we be paying attention to such animal behavior? As long ago as the 1700s, unusual animal activity prior to earthquakes has been recorded. Examples include domestic cattle seeking higher ground and zoo animals refusing to enter their shelters at night. Other animals, such as lizards, snakes, and small mammals, evacuate their underground burrows, and wild birds leave their usual habitats. These events occur days, hours, or even minutes before an earthquake.

Science, Technology, and Society

San Andreas Fault Observatory at Depth (SAFOD)

Seismologists are creating an underground observatory in Parkfield, California, to study earthquakes along the San Andreas Fault. The observatory will be named the San Andreas Fault Observatory at Depth (SAFOD). A deep hole will be drilled directly into the fault zone near a point where earthquakes of magnitude 6.0 have been recorded. Instruments will be placed at the bottom of the hole, 3 to 4 km beneath Earth's surface. These instruments will make seismological measurements of earthquakes and measure the deformation of rock.

Language Arts ACTIVITY

WRITING SKILL Create an illustrated field guide of animal activity to show how animal activity can predict earthquakes. Each illustration must have a paragraph that describes the activity of a specific animal.

Social Studies ACTIVITY

Research the great San Francisco earthquake of 1906. Find images of the earthquake on the Internet and download them, or cut them out of old magazines. Create a photo collage of the earthquake that shows San Francisco before and after the earthquake.

Hiroo Kanamori

Seismologist Hiroo Kanamori is a seismologist at the California Institute of Technology in Pasadena, California. Dr. Kanamori studies how earthquakes occur and tries to reduce their impact on our society. He also analyzes what the effects of earthquakes on oceans are and how earthquakes create giant ocean waves called *tsunamis* (tsoo NAH meez). Tsunamis are very destructive to life and property when they reach land. Kanamori has discovered that even some weak earthquakes can cause powerful tsunamis. He calls these events *tsunami earthquakes,* and he has learned to predict when tsunamis will form. In short, when tectonic plates grind together slowly, special waves called *long-period seismic waves* are created. When Kanamori sees a long-period wave recorded on a seismogram, he knows a tsunami will form. Because long-period waves travel faster than tsunamis, they arrive at recording stations earlier. When an earthquake station records an earthquake, information about that earthquake is provided to a tsunami warning center. The center determines if the earthquake may cause a tsunami and, if so, issues a tsunami warning to areas that may be affected.

Math ACTiViTY

An undersea earthquake causes a tsunami to form. The tsunami travels across the open ocean at 800 km/h. How long will the tsunami take to travel from the point where it formed to a coastline 3,600 km away?

To learn more about these Science in Action topics, visit go.hrw.com and type in the keyword HZ5EQKF.

Current Science

Check out Current Science® articles related to this chapter by visiting go.hrw.com. Just type in the keyword HZ5CS08.

Volcanoes

The Big Idea

Volcanoes are locations where molten rock reaches Earth's surface, and volcanoes can affect landforms and societies.

About the  PHOTO

When you think of a volcanic eruption, you probably think of a cone-shaped mountain exploding and sending huge clouds of ash into the air. Some volcanic eruptions do just that! Most volcanic eruptions, such as the one shown here, which is flowing over a road in Hawaii, are slow and quiet. Volcanic eruptions happen throughout the world, and they play a major role in shaping the Earth's surface.

PRE-READING ACTIVITY

FOLDNOTES **Layered Book** Before you read the chapter, create the FoldNote entitled "Layered Book" described in the **Study Skills** section of the Appendix. Label the tabs of the layered book with "Volcanic eruptions," "Effects of eruptions," and "Causes of eruptions." As you read the chapter, write information you learn about each category under the appropriate tab.

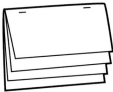

START-UP ACTIVITY

Anticipation

In this activity, you will build a simple model of a volcano and you will try to predict an eruption.

Procedure

1. Place **10 mL of baking soda** on a **sheet of tissue.** Fold the corners of the tissue over the baking soda, and place the tissue packet in a **large pan.**

2. Put **modeling clay** around the top edge of a **funnel.** Press that end of the funnel over the tissue packet to make a tight seal.

3. After you put on **safety goggles,** add **50 mL of vinegar** and **several drops of liquid dish soap** to a **200 mL beaker** and stir.

4. Predict how long it will take the volcano to erupt after the liquid is poured into the funnel. Then, carefully pour the liquid into the funnel, and use a **stopwatch** to measure how long the volcano takes to begin erupting.

Analysis

1. Based on your observations, explain what happened to cause the eruption.

2. How accurate was your prediction? By how many seconds did the class predictions vary?

3. How do the size of the funnel opening and the amount of baking soda and vinegar affect the amount of time that the volcano takes to erupt?

Volcanoes **155**

Volcanic Eruptions

Think about the force released when the first atomic bomb exploded during World War II. Now imagine an explosion 10,000 times stronger, and you will get an idea of how powerful a volcanic eruption can be.

The explosive pressure of a volcanic eruption can turn an entire mountain into a billowing cloud of ash and rock in a matter of seconds. But eruptions are also creative forces—they help form fertile farmland. They also create some of the largest mountains on Earth. During an eruption, molten rock, or *magma,* is forced to the Earth's surface. Magma that flows onto the Earth's surface is called *lava.* **Volcanoes** are areas of Earth's surface through which magma and volcanic gases pass.

Nonexplosive Eruptions

At this moment, volcanic eruptions are occurring around the world—on the ocean floor and on land. Nonexplosive eruptions are the most common type of eruption. These eruptions produce relatively calm flows of lava, such as those shown in **Figure 1.** Nonexplosive eruptions can release huge amounts of lava. Vast areas of the Earth's surface, including much of the sea floor and the Northwest region of the United States, are covered with lava from nonexplosive eruptions.

What You Will Learn

- Distinguish between nonexplosive and explosive volcanic eruptions.
- Identify the features of a volcano.
- Explain how the composition of magma affects the type of volcanic eruption that will occur.
- Describe four types of lava and four types of pyroclastic material.

Vocabulary

volcano   vent
magma chamber

READING STRATEGY

Reading Organizer As you read this section, make a table comparing types of lava and pyroclastic material.

volcano a vent or fissure in the Earth's surface through which magma and gases are expelled

Figure 1   **Examples of Nonexplosive Eruptions**

Sometimes, nonexplosive eruptions can spray lava into the air. Lava fountains, such as this one, pulse with the pressure of escaping gases.

The speed of a lava flow can range from a slow creep to as fast as 60 km/h.

Explosive Eruptions

Explosive eruptions, such as the one shown in **Figure 2,** are much rarer than nonexplosive eruptions. However, the effects of explosive eruptions can be incredibly destructive. During an explosive eruption, clouds of hot debris, ash, and gas rapidly shoot out from a volcano. Instead of producing lava flows, explosive eruptions cause molten rock to be blown into tiny particles that harden in the air. The dust-sized particles, called *ash,* can reach the upper atmosphere and can circle the Earth for years. Larger pieces of debris fall closer to the volcano. An explosive eruption can also blast millions of tons of lava and rock from a volcano. In a matter of seconds, an explosive eruption can demolish an entire mountainside, as shown in **Figure 3.**

✓ Reading Check List two differences between explosive and nonexplosive eruptions. (*See the Appendix for answers to Reading Checks.*)

Figure 2 *In what resembles a nuclear explosion, volcanic ash rockets skyward during the 1990 eruption of Mount Redoubt in Alaska.*

Figure 3 *Within seconds, the 1980 eruption of Mount St. Helens in Washington State caused the side of the mountain to collapse. The blast scorched and flattened 600 km² of forest.*

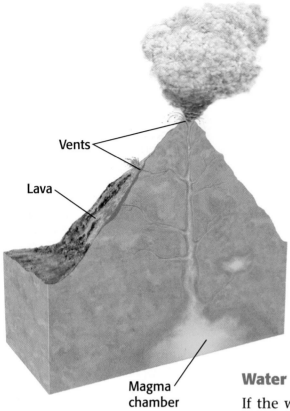

Vents

Lava

Magma
chamber

Figure 4 *Volcanoes form when lava is released from vents.*

magma chamber the body of molten rock that feeds a volcano

vent an opening at the surface of the Earth through which volcanic material passes

What Is Inside a Volcano?

If you could look inside an erupting volcano, you would see the features shown in **Figure 4.** A **magma chamber** is a body of molten rock deep underground that feeds a volcano. Magma rises from the magma chamber through cracks in the Earth's crust to openings called **vents.** Magma is released from the vents during an eruption.

What Makes Up Magma?

By comparing the composition of magma from different eruptions, scientists have made an important discovery. The composition of the magma affects how explosive a volcanic eruption is. The key to whether an eruption will be explosive lies in the silica, water, and gas content of the magma.

Water and Magma Are an Explosive Combination

If the water content of magma is high, an explosive eruption is more likely. Because magma is underground, it is under intense pressure and water stays dissolved in the magma. If the magma quickly moves to the surface, the pressure suddenly decreases and the water and other compounds, such as carbon dioxide, become gases. As the gases expand rapidly, an explosion can result. This process is similar to what happens when you shake a can of soda and open it. When a can of soda is shaken, the CO_2 dissolved in the soda is released and pressure builds up. When the can is opened, the soda shoots out, just as lava shoots out of a volcano during an explosive eruption. In fact, some lava is so frothy with gas when it reaches the surface that its solid form, called *pumice,* can float in water!

Silica-Rich Magma Traps Explosive Gases

Magma that has a high silica content also tends to cause explosive eruptions. Silica-rich magma has a stiff consistency. It flows slowly and tends to harden in a volcano's vents. As a result, it plugs the vent. As more magma pushes up from below, pressure increases. If enough pressure builds up, an explosive eruption takes place. Stiff magma also prevents water vapor and other gases from easily escaping. Gas bubbles trapped in magma can expand until they explode. When they explode, the magma shatters and ash and pumice are blasted from the vent. Magma that contains less silica has a more fluid, runnier consistency. Because gases escape this type of magma more easily, explosive eruptions are less likely to occur.

Reading Check How do silica levels affect an eruption?

What Erupts from a Volcano?

Magma erupts as either lava or pyroclastic (PIE roh KLAS tik) material. *Lava* is liquid magma that flows from a volcanic vent. *Pyroclastic material* forms when magma is blasted into the air and hardens. Nonexplosive eruptions produce mostly lava. Explosive eruptions produce mostly pyroclastic material. Over many years—or even during the same eruption—a volcano's eruptions may alternate between lava and pyroclastic eruptions.

Types of Lava

The viscosity of lava, or how lava flows, varies greatly. To understand viscosity, remember that a milkshake has high viscosity and a glass of milk has low viscosity. Lava that has high viscosity is stiff. Lava that has low viscosity is more fluid. The viscosity of lava affects the surface of a lava flow in different ways, as shown in **Figure 5.** *Blocky lava* and *pahoehoe* (puh HOY HOY) have a high viscosity and flow slowly. Other types of lava flows, such as *aa* (AH AH) and *pillow lava,* have lower viscosities and flow more quickly.

CONNECTION TO Social Studies

Fertile Farmlands Volcanic ash helps create some of the most fertile farmland in the world. Use a world map and reference materials to find the location of volcanoes that have helped create farmland in Italy, Africa, South America, and the United States. Make an illustrated map on a piece of poster board to share your findings.

ACTIVITY

Figure 5   Four Types of Lava

Aa lava pours out quickly and forms a brittle crust. The crust is torn into jagged pieces as molten lava continues to flow underneath.

Pahoehoe lava flows slowly, like wax dripping from a candle. Its glassy surface has rounded wrinkles.

Pillow lava forms when lava erupts underwater. As you can see here, this lava forms rounded lumps that are the shape of pillows.

Blocky lava is cool, stiff lava that does not travel far from the erupting vent. Blocky lava usually oozes from a volcano and forms jumbled heaps of sharp-edged chunks.

Figure 6 Four Types of Pyroclastic Material

Volcanic bombs are large blobs of magma that harden in the air. The shape of this bomb was caused by the magma spinning through the air as it cooled.

Lapilli, which means "little stones" in Italian, are pebblelike bits of magma that hardened before they hit the ground.

Volcanic ash forms when the gases in stiff magma expand rapidly and the walls of the gas bubbles explode into tiny, glasslike slivers. Ash makes up most of the pyroclastic material in an eruption.

Volcanic blocks, the largest pieces of pyroclastic material, are pieces of solid rock erupted from a volcano.

Types of Pyroclastic Material

Pyroclastic material forms when magma explodes from a volcano and solidifies in the air. This material also forms when powerful eruptions shatter existing rock. The size of pyroclastic material ranges from boulders that are the size of houses to tiny particles that can remain suspended in the atmosphere for years. **Figure 6** shows four types of pyroclastic material: volcanic bombs, volcanic blocks, lapilli (lah PIL ɪᴇ), and volcanic ash.

Reading Check Describe four types of pyroclastic material.

Modeling an Explosive Eruption

1. Inflate a **large balloon,** and place it in a **cardboard box.**

2. Spread a **sheet** on the floor. Place the box in the middle of the sheet. Mound a thin layer of **sand** over the balloon to make a volcano that is taller than the edges of the box.

3. Lightly mist the volcano with **water.** Sprinkle **tempera paint** on the volcano until the volcano is completely covered.

4. Place **small objects** such as **raisins** randomly on the volcano. Draw a sketch of the volcano.

5. Put on your **safety goggles.** Pop the balloon with a **pin.**

6. Use a **metric ruler** to calculate the average distance that 10 grains of sand and 10 raisins traveled.

7. How did the relative weight of each type of material affect the average distance that the material traveled?

8. Draw a sketch of the exploded volcano.

Pyroclastic Flows

One particularly dangerous type of volcanic flow is called a *pyroclastic flow*. Pyroclastic flows are produced when enormous amounts of hot ash, dust, and gases are ejected from a volcano. This glowing cloud of pyroclastic material can race downhill at speeds of more than 200 km/h—faster than most hurricane-force winds! The temperature at the center of a pyroclastic flow can exceed 700°C. A pyroclastic flow from the eruption of Mount Pinatubo is shown in **Figure 7.** Fortunately, scientists were able to predict the eruption and a quarter of a million people were evacuated before the eruption.

Figure 7 *The 1991 eruption of Mount Pinatubo in the Philippines released terrifying pyroclastic flows.*

SECTION Review

Summary

- Volcanoes erupt both explosively and nonexplosively.

- Magma that has a high level of water, CO_2, or silica tends to erupt explosively.

- Lava can be classified by its viscosity and by the surface texture of lava flows.

- Pyroclastic material, such as ash and volcanic bombs, forms when magma solidifies as it travels through the air.

Using Key Terms

1. In your own words, write a definition for each of the following terms: *volcano, magma chamber,* and *vent.*

Understanding Key Ideas

2. Which of the following factors influences whether a volcano erupts explosively?
   a. the concentration of volcanic bombs in the magma
   b. the concentration of phosphorus in the magma
   c. the concentration of aa in the magma
   d. the concentration of water in the magma

3. How are lava and pyroclastic material classified? Describe four types of lava.

4. Which produces more pyroclastic material: an explosive eruption or a nonexplosive eruption?

5. Explain how the presence of silica and water in magma increases the chances of an explosive eruption.

6. What is a pyroclastic flow?

Math Skills

7. A sample of magma is 64% silica. Express this percentage as a simplified fraction.

Critical Thinking

8. **Analyzing Ideas** How is an explosive eruption similar to opening a can of soda that has been shaken? Be sure to describe the role of carbon dioxide.

9. **Making Inferences** Predict the silica content of aa, pillow lava, and blocky lava.

10. **Making Inferences** Explain why the names of many types of lava are Hawaiian but the names of many types of pyroclastic material are Italian and Indonesian.

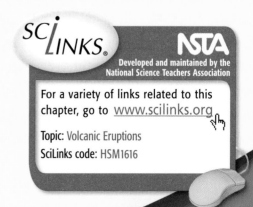

SCI*LINKS*.

NSTA
Developed and maintained by the
National Science Teachers Association

For a variety of links related to this chapter, go to www.scilinks.org

Topic: Volcanic Eruptions
SciLinks code: HSM1616

Effects of Volcanic Eruptions

In 1816, Chauncey Jerome, a resident of Connecticut, wrote that the clothes his wife had laid out to dry the day before had frozen during the night. This event would not have been unusual except that the date was June 10!

At that time, residents of New England did not know that the explosion of a volcanic island on the other side of the world had severely changed the global climate and was causing "The Year Without a Summer."

What You Will Learn

● Explain how volcanic eruptions can affect climate.
● Compare the three types of volcanoes.
● Compare craters, calderas, and lava plateaus.

Vocabulary

crater
caldera
lava plateau

READING STRATEGY

Paired Summarizing Read this section silently. In pairs, take turns summarizing the material. Stop to discuss ideas that seem confusing.

Volcanic Eruptions and Climate Change

The explosion of Mount Tambora in 1815 blanketed most of Indonesia in darkness for three days. It is estimated that 12,000 people died directly from the explosion and 80,000 people died from the resulting hunger and disease. The global effects of the eruption were not felt until the next year, however. During large-scale eruptions, enormous amounts of volcanic ash and gases are ejected into the upper atmosphere.

As volcanic ash and gases spread throughout the atmosphere, they can block enough sunlight to cause global temperatures to drop. The Tambora eruption affected the global climate enough to cause food shortages in North America and Europe. More recently, the eruption of Mount Pinatubo, shown in **Figure 1,** caused average global temperatures to drop by as much as 0.5°C. Although this may seem insignificant, such a shift can disrupt climates all over the world.

✓ Reading Check How does a volcanic eruption affect climate? *(See the Appendix for answers to Reading Checks.)*

Figure 1 *Ash from the eruption of Mount Pinatubo blocked out the sun in the Philippines for several days. The eruption also affected global climate.*

Different Types of Volcanoes

Volcanic eruptions can cause profound changes in climate. But the changes to Earth's surface caused by eruptions are probably more familiar. Perhaps the best known of all volcanic landforms are the volcanoes themselves. The three basic types of volcanoes are illustrated in **Figure 2.**

Shield Volcanoes

Shield volcanoes are built of layers of lava released from repeated nonexplosive eruptions. Because the lava is very runny, it spreads out over a wide area. Over time, the layers of lava create a volcano that has gently sloping sides. Although their sides are not very steep, shield volcanoes can be enormous. Hawaii's Mauna Kea, the shield volcano shown here, is the tallest mountain on Earth. Measured from its base on the sea floor, Mauna Kea is taller than Mount Everest.

Cinder Cone Volcanoes

Cinder cone volcanoes are made of pyroclastic material usually produced from moderately explosive eruptions. The pyroclastic material forms steep slopes, as shown in this photo of the Mexican volcano Paricutín. Cinder cones are small and usually erupt for only a short time. Paricutín appeared in a cornfield in 1943 and erupted for only nine years before stopping at a height of 400 m. Cinder cones often occur in clusters, commonly on the sides of other volcanoes. They usually erode quickly because the pyroclastic material is not cemented together.

Composite Volcanoes

Composite volcanoes, sometimes called *stratovolcanoes*, are one of the most common types of volcanoes. They form from explosive eruptions of pyroclastic material followed by quieter flows of lava. The combination of both types of eruptions forms alternating layers of pyroclastic material and lava. Composite volcanoes, such as Japan's Mount Fuji (shown here), have broad bases and sides that get steeper toward the top. Composite volcanoes in the western region of the United States include Mount Hood, Mount Rainier, Mount Shasta, and Mount St. Helens.

Figure 2 Three Types of Volcanoes

Shield volcano

Cinder cone volcano

Composite volcano

Other Types of Volcanic Landforms

In addition to volcanoes, other landforms are produced by volcanic activity. These landforms include craters, calderas, and lava plateaus. Read on to learn more about these landforms.

Craters

Around the central vent at the top of many volcanoes is a funnel-shaped pit called a **crater.** An example of a crater is shown in **Figure 3.** During less explosive eruptions, lava flows and pyroclastic material can pile up around the vent creating a cone with a central crater. As the eruption stops, the lava that is left in the crater often drains back underground. The vent may then collapse to form a larger crater. If the lava hardens in the crater, the next eruption may blast it away. In this way, a crater becomes larger and deeper.

Figure 3 *A crater, such as this one in Kamchatka, Russia, forms around the central vent of a volcano.*

crater a funnel-shaped pit near the top of the central vent of a volcano

caldera a large, semicircular depression that forms when the magma chamber below a volcano partially empties and causes the ground above to sink

Calderas

Calderas can appear similar to craters, but they are many times larger. A **caldera** is a large, semicircular depression that forms when the chamber that supplies magma to a volcano partially empties and the chamber's roof collapses. As a result, the ground above the magma chamber sinks, as shown in **Figure 4.** Much of Yellowstone Park is made up of three large calderas that formed when volcanoes collapsed between 1.9 million and 0.6 million years ago. Today, hot springs, such as Old Faithful, are heated by the thermal energy left over from those events.

Reading Check How do calderas form?

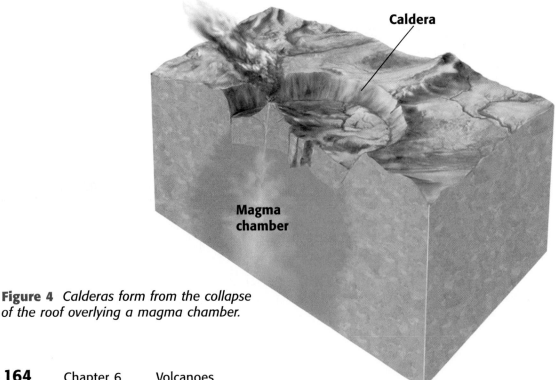

Caldera

Magma chamber

Figure 4 *Calderas form from the collapse of the roof overlying a magma chamber.*

Lava Plateaus

The most massive outpourings of lava do not come from individual volcanoes. Most of the lava on Earth's surface erupted from long cracks, or *rifts,* in the crust. In this type of eruption, runny lava can pour out for millions of years and spread over huge areas. A landform that results from repeated eruptions of lava spread over a large area is called a **lava plateau.** The Columbia River Plateau, part of which is shown in **Figure 5,** is a lava plateau that formed between 17 million and 14 million years ago in the northwestern region of the United States. In some places, the Columbia River Plateau is 3 km thick.

Figure 5 *The Columbia River Plateau formed from a massive outpouring of lava that began 17 million years ago.*

lava plateau a wide, flat landform that results from repeated nonexplosive eruptions of lava that spread over a large area

SECTION Review

Summary

- The large volumes of gas and ash released from volcanic eruptions can affect climate.

- Shield volcanoes result from many eruptions of relatively runny lava.

- Cinder cone volcanoes result from mildly explosive eruptions of pyroclastic material.

- Composite volcanoes result from alternating explosive and nonexplosive eruptions.

- Craters, calderas, and lava plateaus are volcanic landforms.

Using Key Terms

Complete each of the following sentences by choosing the correct term from the word bank.

    caldera   crater

1. A ___ is a funnel-shaped hole around the central vent.

2. A ___ results when a magma chamber partially empties.

Understanding Key Ideas

3. Which type of volcano results from alternating explosive and nonexplosive eruptions?
    a. composite volcano
    b. cinder cone volcano
    c. rift-zone volcano
    d. shield volcano

4. Why do cinder cone volcanoes have narrower bases and steeper sides than shield volcanoes do?

5. Why does a volcano's crater tend to get larger over time?

Math Skills

6. The fastest lava flow recorded was 60 km/h. A horse can gallop as fast as 48 mi/h. Could a galloping horse outrun the fastest lava flow? (Hint: 1 km = 0.621 mi)

Critical Thinking

7. **Making Inferences** Why did it take a year for the effects of the Tambora eruption to be experienced in New England?

SCi LINKS.

Developed and maintained by the National Science Teachers Association

For a variety of links related to this chapter, go to www.scilinks.org

Topic: Volcanic Effects
SciLinks code: HSM1615

165

Causes of Volcanic Eruptions

More than 2,000 years ago, Pompeii was a busy Roman city near the sleeping volcano Mount Vesuvius. People did not see Vesuvius as much of a threat. Everything changed when Vesuvius suddenly erupted and buried the city in a deadly blanket of ash that was almost 20 ft thick!

Today, even more people are living on and near active volcanoes. Scientists closely monitor volcanoes to avoid this type of disaster. They study the gases coming from active volcanoes and look for slight changes in the volcano's shape that could indicate that an eruption is near. Scientists know much more about the causes of eruptions than the ancient Pompeiians did, but there is much more to be discovered.

What You Will Learn

- Describe the formation and movement of magma.
- Explain the relationship between volcanoes and plate tectonics.
- Summarize the methods scientists use to predict volcanic eruptions.

Vocabulary

rift zone
hot spot

READING STRATEGY

Reading Organizer As you read this section, make a flowchart of the steps of magma formation in different tectonic environments.

The Formation of Magma

Understanding how magma forms helps explain why volcanoes erupt. Magma forms in the deeper regions of the Earth's crust and in the uppermost layers of the mantle where the temperature and pressure are very high. Changes in pressure and temperature cause magma to form.

Pressure and Temperature

Part of the upper mantle is made of very hot, puttylike rock that flows slowly. The rock of the mantle is hot enough to melt at Earth's surface, but it remains a puttylike solid because of pressure. This pressure is caused by the weight of the rock above the mantle. In other words, the rock above the mantle presses the atoms of the mantle so close together that the rock cannot melt. As **Figure 1** shows, rock melts when its temperature increases or when the pressure on the rock decreases.

Figure 1 *The curved line indicates the melting point of a rock. As pressure decreases and temperature increases, the rock begins to melt.*

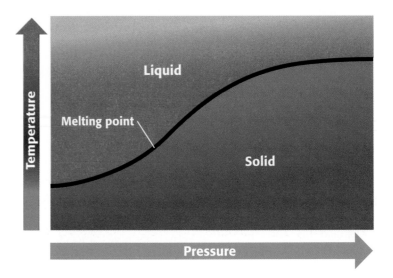

Magma Formation in the Mantle

Because the temperature of the mantle is fairly constant, a decrease in pressure is the most common cause of magma formation. Magma often forms at the boundary between separating tectonic plates, where pressure is decreased. Once formed, the magma is less dense than the surrounding rock, so the magma slowly rises toward the surface like an air bubble in a jar of honey.

Where Volcanoes Form

The locations of volcanoes give clues about how volcanoes form. The map in **Figure 2** shows the location of some of the world's major active volcanoes. The map also shows the boundaries between tectonic plates. A large number of volcanoes lie directly on tectonic plate boundaries. In fact, the plate boundaries surrounding the Pacific Ocean have so many volcanoes that the area is called the *Ring of Fire*.

Tectonic plate boundaries are areas where tectonic plates either collide, separate, or slide past one another. At these boundaries, it is possible for magma to form and travel to the surface. About 80% of active volcanoes on land form where plates collide, and about 15% form where plates separate. The remaining few occur far from tectonic plate boundaries.

Reading Check Why are most volcanoes on plate boundaries? *(See the Appendix for answers to Reading Checks.)*

Reaction to Stress

1. Make a pliable "rock" by pouring **60 mL of water** into a **plastic cup** and adding **150 mL of cornstarch,** 15 mL at a time. Stir well each time.

2. Pour half of the cornstarch mixture into a **clear bowl.** Carefully observe how the "rock" flows. Be patient—this process is slow!

3. Scrape the rest of the "rock" out of the cup with a **spoon.** Observe the behavior of the "rock" as you scrape.

4. What happened to the "rock" when you let it flow by itself? What happened when you put stress on the "rock"?

5. How is this pliable "rock" similar to the rock of the upper part of the mantle?

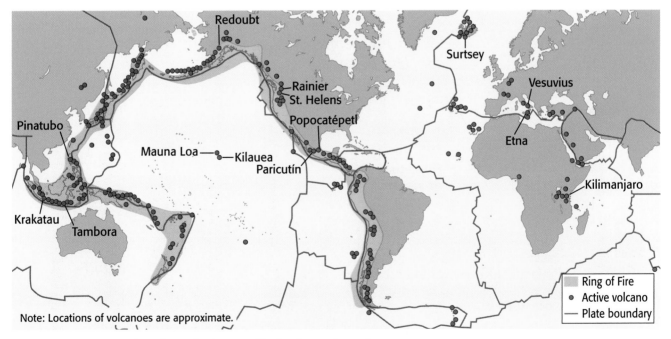

Note: Locations of volcanoes are approximate.

Ring of Fire
• Active volcano
— Plate boundary

Figure 2 *Tectonic plate boundaries are likely places for volcanoes to form. The Ring of Fire contains nearly 75% of the world's active volcanoes on land.*

rift zone an area of deep cracks that forms between two tectonic plates that are pulling away from each other

When Tectonic Plates Separate

At a *divergent boundary,* tectonic plates move away from each other. As tectonic plates separate, a set of deep cracks called a **rift zone** forms between the plates. Mantle rock then rises to fill in the gap. When mantle rock gets closer to the surface, the pressure decreases. The pressure decrease causes the mantle rock to melt and form magma. Because magma is less dense than the surrounding rock, it rises through the rifts. When the magma reaches the surface, it spills out and hardens, creating new crust, as shown in **Figure 3.**

Mid-Ocean Ridges Form at Divergent Boundaries

Lava that flows from undersea rift zones produces volcanoes and mountain chains called *mid-ocean ridges.* Just as a baseball has stitches, the Earth is circled with mid-ocean ridges. At these ridges, lava flows out and creates new crust. Most volcanic activity on Earth occurs at mid-ocean ridges. While most mid-ocean ridges are underwater, Iceland, with its volcanoes and hot springs, was created by lava from the Mid-Atlantic Ridge. In 1963, enough lava poured out of the Mid-Atlantic Ridge near Iceland to form a new island called *Surtsey.* Scientists watched this new island being born!

Figure 3 **How Magma Forms at a Divergent Boundary**

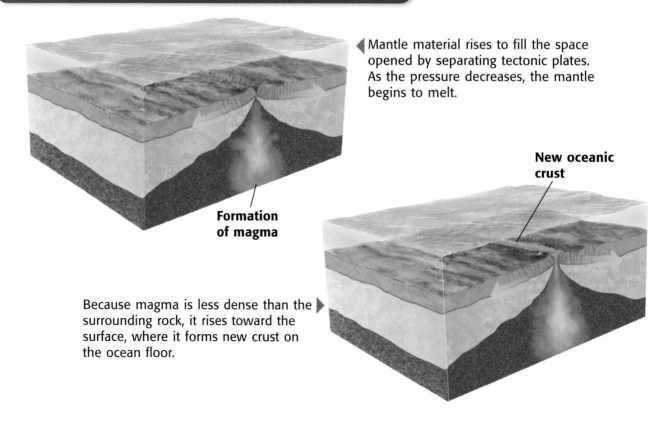

Mantle material rises to fill the space opened by separating tectonic plates. As the pressure decreases, the mantle begins to melt.

New oceanic crust

Formation of magma

Because magma is less dense than the surrounding rock, it rises toward the surface, where it forms new crust on the ocean floor.

Figure 4 How Magma Forms at a Convergent Boundary

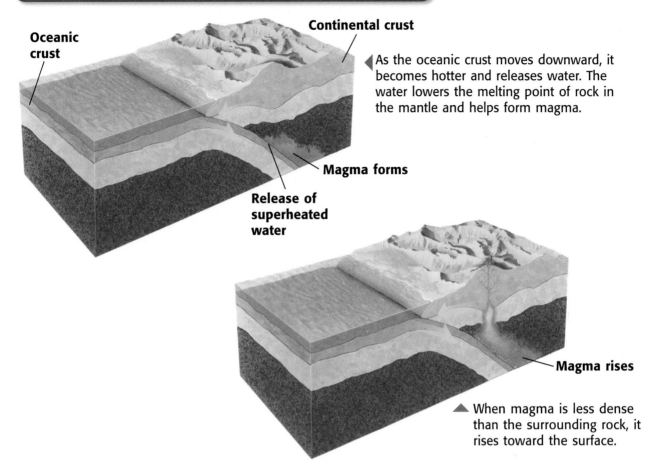

Oceanic crust

Continental crust

◀ As the oceanic crust moves downward, it becomes hotter and releases water. The water lowers the melting point of rock in the mantle and helps form magma.

Magma forms

Release of superheated water

Magma rises

▲ When magma is less dense than the surrounding rock, it rises toward the surface.

When Tectonic Plates Collide

If you slide two pieces of notebook paper into one another on a flat desktop, the papers will either buckle upward or one piece of paper will move under the other. This is similar to what happens at a convergent boundary. A *convergent boundary* is a place where tectonic plates collide. When an oceanic plate collides with a continental plate, the oceanic plate usually slides underneath the continental plate. The process of *subduction,* the movement of one tectonic plate underneath another, is shown in **Figure 4.** Oceanic crust is subducted because it is denser and thinner than continental crust.

Subduction Produces Magma

As the descending oceanic crust scrapes past the continental crust, the temperature and pressure increase. The combination of increased heat and pressure causes the water contained in the oceanic crust to be released. The water then mixes with the mantle rock, which lowers the rock's melting point, causing it to melt. This body of magma can rise to form a volcano.

✔ *Reading Check* How does subduction produce magma?

SCHOOL to HOME

Tectonic Models

Create models of convergent and divergent boundaries by using materials of your choice. Have your teacher approve your list before you start building your model at home with an adult. In class, use your model to explain how each type of boundary leads to the formation of magma.

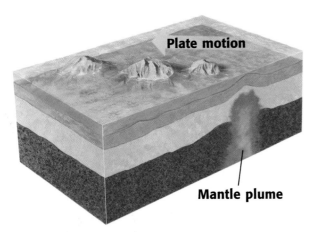

Plate motion

Mantle plume

Figure 5 According to one theory, a string of volcanic islands forms as a tectonic plate passes over a mantle plume.

hot spot a volcanically active area of Earth's surface far from a tectonic plate boundary

Figure 6 As if being this close to an active volcano is not dangerous enough, the gases being collected are extremely poisonous.

Hot Spots

Not all magma develops along tectonic plate boundaries. For example, the Hawaiian Islands, some of the most well-known volcanoes on Earth, are nowhere near a plate boundary. The volcanoes of Hawaii and several other places on Earth are known as *hot spots*. **Hot spots** are volcanically active places on the Earth's surface that are far from plate boundaries. Some scientists think that hot spots are directly above columns of rising magma, called *mantle plumes*. Other scientists think that hot spots are the result of cracks in the Earth's crust.

A hot spot often produces a long chain of volcanoes. One theory is that the mantle plume stays in the same spot while the tectonic plate moves over it, as shown in **Figure 5.** Another theory argues that hot-spot volcanoes occur in long chains because they form along the cracks in the Earth's crust. Both theories may be correct.

Reading Check Describe two theories that explain the existence of hot spots.

Predicting Volcanic Eruptions

You now understand some of the processes that produce volcanoes, but how do scientists predict when a volcano is going to erupt? Volcanoes are classified in three categories. *Extinct volcanoes* have not erupted in recorded history and probably never will erupt again. *Dormant volcanoes* are currently not erupting, but the record of past eruptions suggests that they may erupt again. *Active volcanoes* are currently erupting or show signs of erupting in the near future. Scientists study active and dormant volcanoes for signs of a future eruption.

Measuring Small Quakes and Volcanic Gases

Most active volcanoes produce small earthquakes as the magma within them moves upward and causes the surrounding rock to shift. Just before an eruption, the number and intensity of the earthquakes increase and the occurrence of quakes may be continuous. Monitoring these quakes is one of the best ways to predict an eruption.

As **Figure 6** shows, scientists also study the volume and composition of volcanic gases. The ratio of certain gases, especially that of sulfur dioxide, SO_2, to carbon dioxide, CO_2, may be important in predicting eruptions. Changes in this ratio may indicate changes in the magma chamber below.

Measuring Slope and Temperature

As magma moves upward prior to an eruption, it can cause the Earth's surface to swell. The side of a volcano may even bulge as the magma moves upward. An instrument called a *tiltmeter* helps scientists detect small changes in the angle of a volcano's slope. Scientists also use satellite technology such as the Global Positioning System (GPS) to detect the changes in a volcano's slope that may signal an eruption.

One of the newest methods for predicting volcanic eruptions includes using satellite images. Infrared satellite images record changes in the surface temperature and gas emissions of a volcano over time. If the site is getting hotter, the magma below is probably rising!

INTERNET ACTIVITY

For another activity related to this chapter, go to **go.hrw.com** and type in the keyword **HZ5VOLW**.

SECTION Review

Summary

- Temperature and pressure influence magma formation.
- Most volcanoes form at tectonic boundaries.
- As tectonic plates separate, magma rises to fill the cracks, or rifts, that develop.
- As oceanic and continental plates collide, the oceanic plate tends to subduct and cause the formation of magma.
- To predict eruptions, scientists study the frequency and type of earthquakes associated with the volcano as well as changes in slope, changes in the gases released, and changes in the volcano's surface temperature.

Using Key Terms

1. Use each of the following terms in a separate sentence: *hot spot* and *rift zone*.

Understanding Key Ideas

2. If the temperature of a rock remains constant but the pressure on the rock decreases, what tends to happen?
   a. The temperature increases.
   b. The rock becomes liquid.
   c. The rock becomes solid.
   d. The rock subducts.

3. Which of the following words is a synonym for *dormant*?
   a. predictable
   b. active
   c. dead
   d. sleeping

4. What is the Ring of Fire?

5. Explain how convergent and divergent plate boundaries cause magma formation.

6. Describe four methods that scientists use to predict volcanic eruptions.

7. Why does a oceanic plate tend to subduct when it collides with a continental plate?

Math Skills

8. If a tectonic plate moves at a rate of 2 km every 1 million years, how long would it take a hot spot to form a chain of volcanoes 100 km long?

Critical Thinking

9. **Making Inferences** New crust is constantly being created at mid-ocean ridges. So, why is the oldest oceanic crust only about 150 million years old?

10. **Identifying Relationships** If you are studying a volcanic deposit, would the youngest layers be more likely to be found on the top or on the bottom? Explain your answer.

SCILINKS

Developed and maintained by the National Science Teachers Association

For a variety of links related to this chapter, go to www.scilinks.org

Topic: What Causes Volcanoes?
SciLinks code: HSM1654

Skills Practice Lab

Volcano Verdict

You will need to pair up with a partner for this exploration. You and your partner will act as geologists who work in a city located near a volcano. City officials are counting on you to predict when the volcano will erupt next. You and your partner have decided to use limewater as a gas-emissions tester. You will use this tester to measure the levels of carbon dioxide emitted from a simulated volcano. The more active the volcano is, the more carbon dioxide it releases.

OBJECTIVES

Build a working apparatus to test carbon dioxide levels.

Test the levels of carbon dioxide emitted from a model volcano.

MATERIALS

- baking soda, 15 mL
- bottle, drinking, 16 oz
- box or stand for plastic cup
- clay, modeling
- coin
- cup, clear plastic, 9 oz
- graduated cylinder
- limewater, 1 L
- straw, drinking, flexible
- tissue, bathroom (2 sheets)
- vinegar, white, 140 mL
- water, 100 mL

SAFETY

Procedure

1. Put on your safety goggles, and carefully pour limewater into the plastic cup until the cup is three-fourths full. You have just made your gas-emissions tester.

2. Now, build a model volcano. Begin by pouring 50 mL of water and 70 mL of vinegar into the drink bottle.

3. Form a plug of clay around the short end of the straw, as shown at left. The clay plug must be large enough to cover the opening of the bottle. Be careful not to get the clay wet.

4. Sprinkle 5 mL of baking soda along the center of a single section of bathroom tissue. Then, roll the tissue, and twist the ends so that the baking soda can't fall out.

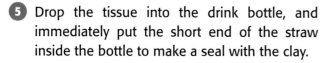

5 Drop the tissue into the drink bottle, and immediately put the short end of the straw inside the bottle to make a seal with the clay.

6 Put the other end of the straw into the lime-water, as shown at right.

7 You have just taken your first measurement of gas levels from the volcano. Record your observations.

8 Imagine that it is several days later and you need to test the volcano again to collect more data. Before you continue, toss a coin. If it lands heads up, go to step 9. If it lands tails up, go to step 10. Write down the step that you follow.

9 Repeat steps 1–7. This time, add 2 mL of baking soda to the vinegar and water. (Note: You must use fresh water, vinegar, and limewater.) Write down your observations. Go to step 11.

10 Repeat steps 1–7. This time, add 8 mL of baking soda to the vinegar and water. (Note: You must use fresh water, vinegar, and limewater.) Write down your observations. Go to step 11.

11 Return to step 8 once. Then, answer the questions below.

Analyze the Results

1 **Explaining Events** How do you explain the difference in the appearance of the limewater from one trial to the next?

2 **Recognizing Patterns** What does the data that you collected indicate about the activity in the volcano?

Draw Conclusions

3 **Evaluating Results** Based on your results, do you think it would be necessary to evacuate the city?

4 **Applying Conclusions** How would a geologist use a gas-emissions tester to predict volcanic eruptions?

Chapter Review

USING KEY TERMS

For each pair of terms, explain how the meanings of the terms differ.

1 *caldera* and *crater*

2 *lava* and *magma*

3 *lava* and *pyroclastic material*

4 *vent* and *rift*

5 *cinder cone volcano* and *shield volcano*

UNDERSTANDING KEY IDEAS

Multiple Choice

6 The type of magma that tends to cause explosive eruptions has a

  a. high silica content and high viscosity.

  b. high silica content and low viscosity.

  c. low silica content and low viscosity.

  d. low silica content and high viscosity.

7 Lava that flows slowly to form a glassy surface with rounded wrinkles is called

  a. aa lava.

  b. pahoehoe lava.

  c. pillow lava.

  d. blocky lava.

8 Magma forms within the mantle most often as a result of

  a. high temperature and high pressure.

  b. high temperature and low pressure.

  c. low temperature and high pressure.

  d. low temperature and low pressure.

9 What causes an increase in the number and intensity of small earthquakes before an eruption?

  a. the movement of magma

  b. the formation of pyroclastic material

  c. the hardening of magma

  d. the movement of tectonic plates

10 If volcanic dust and ash remain in the atmosphere for months or years, what do you predict will happen?

  a. Solar reflection will decrease, and temperatures will increase.

  b. Solar reflection will increase, and temperatures will increase.

  c. Solar reflection will decrease, and temperatures will decrease.

  d. Solar reflection will increase, and temperatures will decrease.

11 At divergent plate boundaries,

  a. heat from Earth's core causes mantle plumes.

  b. oceanic plates sink, which causes magma to form.

  c. tectonic plates move apart.

  d. hot spots cause volcanoes.

12 A theory that helps explain the causes of both earthquakes and volcanoes is the theory of

  a. pyroclastics.

  b. plate tectonics.

  c. climatic fluctuation.

  d. mantle plumes.

Short Answer

13 How does the presence of water in magma affect a volcanic eruption?

14 Describe four clues that scientists use to predict eruptions.

15 Identify the characteristics of the three types of volcanoes.

16 Describe the positive effects of volcanic eruptions.

CRITICAL THINKING

17 **Concept Mapping** Use the following terms to create a concept map: *volcanic bombs, aa, pyroclastic material, pahoehoe, lapilli, lava,* and *volcano.*

18 **Identifying Relationships** You are exploring a volcano that has been dormant for some time. You begin to keep notes on the types of volcanic debris that you see as you walk. Your first notes describe volcanic ash. Later, your notes describe lapilli. In what direction are you most likely traveling—toward the crater or away from the crater? Explain your answer.

19 **Making Inferences** Loihi is a submarine Hawaiian volcano that might grow to form a new island. The Hawaiian Islands are located on the Pacific plate, which is moving northwest. Considering how this island chain may have formed, where do you think the new volcanic island will be located? Explain your answer.

20 **Evaluating Hypotheses** What evidence could confirm the existence of mantle plumes?

INTERPRETING GRAPHICS

The graph below illustrates the average change in temperature above or below normal for a community over several years. Use the graph below to answer the questions that follow.

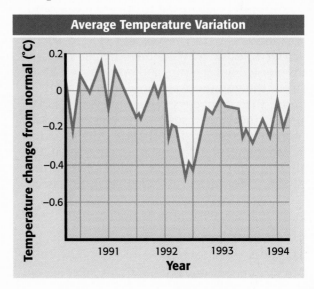

21 If the variation in temperature over the years was influenced by a major volcanic eruption, when did the eruption most likely take place? Explain.

22 If the temperature were measured only once each year (at the beginning of the year), how would your interpretation be different?

Standardized Test Preparation

Read each of the passages below. Then, answer the questions that follow each passage.

Passage 1 When the volcanic island of Krakatau in Indonesia exploded in 1883, a shock wave sped around the world seven times. The explosion was probably the loudest sound in recorded human history. What caused this enormous explosion? Most likely, the walls of the volcano ruptured, and ocean water flowed into the magma chamber of the volcano. The water instantly turned into steam, and the volcano exploded with the force of 100 million tons of TNT. The volcano ejected about 18 km³ of volcanic material into the air. The ash clouds blocked out the sun, and everything within 80 km of the volcano was plunged into darkness for more than two days. The explosion caused a <u>tsunami</u> that was nearly 40 m high. Detected as far away as the English Channel, the tsunami destroyed almost 300 coastal towns. In 1928, another volcano rose from the caldera left by the explosion. This volcano is called <u>Anak</u> Krakatau.

1. In the passage, what does *tsunami* mean?
   A a large earthquake
   B a shock wave
   C a giant ocean wave
   D a cloud of gas and dust

2. According to the passage, what was the size of the Krakatau explosion probably the result of?
   F pyroclastic material rapidly mixing with air
   G 100 million tons of TNT
   H an ancient caldera
   I the flow of water into the magma chamber

3. What does the Indonesian word *anak* probably mean?
   A father
   B child
   C mother
   D grandmother

Passage 2 Yellowstone National Park in Montana and Wyoming contains three overlapping calderas and evidence of the <u>cataclysmic</u> ash flows that erupted from them. The oldest eruption occurred 1.9 million years ago, the second eruption happened 1.3 million years ago, and the most recent eruption occurred 0.6 million years ago. Seismographs regularly detect the movement of magma beneath the caldera, and the hot springs and geysers of the park indicate that a large body of magma lies beneath the park. The geology of the area shows that major eruptions occurred about once every 0.6 or 0.7 million years. Thus, a devastating eruption is long overdue. People living near the park should be evacuated immediately.

1. In the passage, what does *cataclysmic* mean?
   A nonexplosive
   B ancient
   C destructive
   D characterized by ash flows

2. Which of the following clues are evidence of an active magma body beneath the park?
   F cataclysmic ash flows
   G the discovery of seismoclasts
   H minor eruptions
   I seismograph readings

3. Which of the following contradicts the author's conclusion that an eruption is "long overdue"?
   A Magma has been detected beneath the park.
   B With a variation of 0.1 million years, an eruption may occur in the next 100,000 years.
   C The composition of gases emitted indicates that an eruption is near.
   D Seismographs have detected the movement of magma.

The map below shows some of the Earth's major volcanoes and the tectonic plate boundaries. Use the map below to answer the questions that follow.

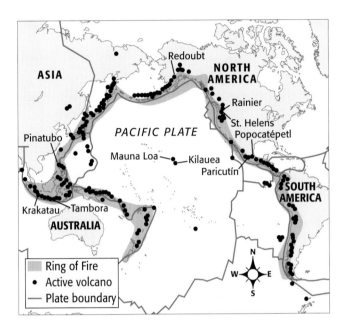

1. If ash from Popocatépetl landed on the west coast of the United States, what direction did the ash travel?

   A northeast

   B northwest

   C southeast

   D southwest

2. Why aren't there any active volcanoes in Australia?

   F Australia is not located on a plate boundary.

   G Australia is close to Krakatau and Tambora.

   H Australia is near a plate boundary.

   I Australia is near a rift zone.

3. If a scientist traveled along the Ring of Fire from Mt. Redoubt to Krakatau, which of the following most accurately describes the directions in which she traveled?

   A west, southeast, east

   B west, southeast, west

   C west, southwest, east

   D west, southwest, west

Read each question below, and choose the best answer.

1. Midway Island is 1,935 km northwest of Hawaii. If the Pacific plate is moving to the northwest at a rate of 9 cm per year, how long ago was Midway Island over the hot spot that formed the island?

   A 215,000 years

   B 2,150,000 years

   C 21,500,000 years

   D 215,000,000 years

2. In the first year that the Mexican volcano Paricutín appeared in a cornfield, it grew 360 m. The volcano stopped growing at about 400 m. What percentage of the volcano's total growth occurred in the first year?

   F 67%

   G 82%

   H 90%

   I 92%

3. A pyroclastic flow is moving down a hill at 120 km/h. If you lived in a town 5 km away, how much time would you have before the flow reached your town?

   A 2 min and 30 s

   B 1 min and 21 s

   C 3 min and 12 s

   D 8 min and 3 s

4. The Columbia River plateau is a lava plateau that contains 350,000 km³ of solidified lava. The plateau took 3 million years to form. What was the average rate of lava deposition each century?

   F 0.116 km^3

   G 11.6 km^3

   H 116 km^3

   I 11,600 km^3

Standardized Test Preparation

Science in Action

Weird Science

Pele's Hair

It is hard to believe that the fragile specimen shown below is a volcanic rock. This strange type of lava, called *Pele's hair,* forms when volcanic gases spray molten rock high into the air. When conditions are right, the lava can harden into strands of volcanic glass as thin as a human hair. This type of lava is named after Pele, the Hawaiian goddess of volcanoes. Several other types of lava are named in Pele's honor. Pele's tears are tear-shaped globs of volcanic glass often found at the end of strands of Pele's hair. Pele's diamonds are green, gemlike stones found in hardened lava flows.

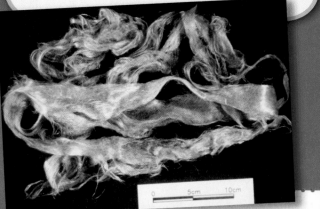

Science, Technology, and Society

Fighting Lava with Fire Hoses

What would you do if a 60 ft wall of lava was advancing toward your home? Most people would head for safety. But when an eruption threatened to engulf the Icelandic fishing village of Heimaey in 1973, some villagers held their ground and fought back. Working 14-hour days in conditions so hot that their boots would catch on fire, villagers used fire-hoses to spray sea water on the lava flow. For several weeks, the lava advanced toward the town, and it seemed as if there was no hope. But the water eventually cooled the lava fast enough to divert the flow and save the village. It took 5 months and about 1.5 billion gallons of water to fight the lava flow. When the eruption stopped, villagers found that the island had grown by 20%!

Language Arts ACTiViTY

Volcanic terms come from many languages. Research some volcanic terms on the Internet, and create an illustrated volcanic glossary to share with your class.

Social Studies ACTiViTY

WRITING SKILL To try to protect the city of Hilo, Hawaii, from an eruption in 1935, planes dropped bombs on the lava. Find out if this mission was successful, and write a report about other attempts to stop lava flows.

Tina Neal

Volcanologist Would you like to study volcanoes for a living? Tina Neal is a volcanologist at the Alaska Volcano Observatory in Anchorage, Alaska. Her job is to monitor and study some of Alaska's 41 active volcanoes. Much of her work focuses on studying volcanoes in order to protect the public. According to Neal, being near a volcano when it is erupting is a wonderful adventure for the senses. "Sometimes you can get so close to an erupting volcano that you can feel the heat, hear the activity, and smell the lava. It's amazing! In Alaska, erupting volcanoes are too dangerous to get very close to, but they create a stunning visual display even from a distance."

Neal also enjoys the science of volcanoes. "It's fascinating to be near an active volcano and become aware of all the chemical and physical processes taking place. When I'm watching a volcano, I think about everything we understand and don't understand about what is happening. It's mind-boggling!" Neal says that if you are interested in becoming a volcanologist, it is important to be well rounded as a scientist. So, you would have to study math, geology, chemistry, and physics. Having a good understanding of computer tools is also important because volcanologists use computers to manage a lot of data and to create models. Neal also suggests learning a second language, such as Spanish. In her spare time, Neal is learning Russian so that she can better communicate with research partners in Kamchatka, Siberia.

Math ACTIVITY

The 1912 eruption of Mt. Katmai in Alaska could be heard 5,620 km away in Atlanta, Georgia. If the average speed of sound in the atmosphere is 342 m/s, how many hours after the eruption did the citizens of Atlanta hear the explosion?

To learn more about these Science in Action topics, visit go.hrw.com and type in the keyword **HZ5VOLF.**

Check out Current Science® articles related to this chapter by visiting go.hrw.com. Just type in the keyword HZ5CS09.

Skills Practice Lab

Mysterious Minerals

Imagine sitting on a rocky hilltop, gazing at the ground below you. You can see dozens of different types of rocks. How can scientists possibly identify the countless variations? It's a mystery!

In this activity, you'll use your powers of observation and a few simple tests to determine the identities of rocks and minerals. Take a look at the Mineral Identification Key on the next page. That key will help you use clues to discover the identity of several minerals.

MATERIALS

- gloves, protective
- iron filings
- minerals, samples
- slides, microscope, glass
- streak plate

SAFETY

Procedure

1. On a separate sheet of paper, create a data chart like the one below.

2. Choose one mineral sample, and locate its column in your data chart.

3. Follow the Mineral Identification Key to find the identity of your sample. When you are finished, record the mineral's name and primary characteristics in the appropriate column in your data chart. **Caution:** Put on your safety goggles and gloves when scratching the glass slide.

4. Select another mineral sample, and repeat steps 2 and 3 until your data table is complete.

Analyze the Results

1. Were some minerals easier to identify than others? Explain.

2. A streak test is a better indicator of a mineral's true color than visual observation is. Why isn't a streak test used to help identify every mineral?

3. On a separate sheet of paper, summarize what you learned about the various characteristics of each mineral sample you identified.

Mineral Summary Chart						
Characteristics	1	2	3	4	5	6
Mineral name						
Luster						
Color						
Streak			*DO NOT WRITE IN BOOK*			
Hardness						
Cleavage						
Special properties						

Mineral Identification Key

1. **a.** If your mineral has a metallic luster, **GO TO STEP 2.**
    b. If your mineral has a nonmetallic luster, **GO TO STEP 3.**

2. **a.** If your mineral is black, **GO TO STEP 4.**
    b. If your mineral is yellow, it is **PYRITE.**
    c. If your mineral is silver, it is **GALENA.**

3. **a.** If your mineral is light in color, **GO TO STEP 5.**
    b. If your mineral is dark in color, **GO TO STEP 6.**

4. **a.** If your mineral leaves a red-brown line on the streak plate, it is **HEMATITE.**
    b. If your mineral leaves a black line on the streak plate, it is **MAGNETITE.** Test your sample for its magnetic properties by holding it near some iron filings.

5. **a.** If your mineral scratches the glass microscope slide, **GO TO STEP 7.**
    b. If your mineral does not scratch the glass microscope slide, **GO TO STEP 8.**

6. **a.** If your mineral scratches the glass slide, **GO TO STEP 9.**
    b. If your mineral does not scratch the glass slide, **GO TO STEP 10.**

7. **a.** If your mineral shows signs of cleavage, it is **ORTHOCLASE FELDSPAR.**
    b. If your mineral does not show signs of cleavage, it is **QUARTZ.**

8. **a.** If your mineral shows signs of cleavage, it is **MUSCOVITE.** Examine this sample for twin sheets.
    b. If your mineral does not show signs of cleavage, it is **GYPSUM.**

9. **a.** If your mineral shows signs of cleavage, it is **HORNBLENDE.**
    b. If your mineral does not show signs of cleavage, it is **GARNET.**

10. **a.** If your mineral shows signs of cleavage, it is **BIOTITE.** Examine your sample for twin sheets.
    b. If your mineral does not show signs of cleavage, it is **GRAPHITE.**

Applying Your Data

Using your textbook and other reference books, research other methods of identifying different types of minerals. Based on your findings, create a new identification key. Give the key and a few sample minerals to a friend, and see if your friend can unravel the mystery!

Skills Practice Lab

Crystal Growth

Magma forms deep below the Earth's surface at depths of 25 km to 160 km and at extremely high temperatures. Some magma reaches the surface and cools quickly. Other magma gets trapped in cracks or magma chambers beneath the surface and cools very slowly. When magma cools slowly, large, well-developed crystals form. But when magma erupts onto the surface, it cools more quickly. There is not enough time for large crystals to grow. The size of the crystals found in igneous rocks gives geologists clues about where and how the rocks formed.

In this experiment, you will demonstrate how the rate of cooling affects the size of crystals in igneous rocks by cooling crystals of magnesium sulfate at two different rates.

Ask a Question

1 How does temperature affect the formation of crystals?

Form a Hypothesis

2 Suppose you have two solutions that are identical in every way except for temperature. How will the temperature of a solution affect the size of the crystals and the rate at which they form?

Test the Hypothesis

3 Put on your gloves, apron, and goggles.

4 Fill the beaker halfway with tap water. Place the beaker on the hot plate, and let it begin to warm. The temperature of the water should be between 40°C and 50°C. **Caution:** Make sure the hot plate is away from the edge of the lab table.

5 Examine two or three crystals of the magnesium sulfate with your magnifying lens. On a separate sheet of paper, describe the color, shape, luster, and other interesting features of the crystals.

6 On a separate sheet of paper, draw a sketch of the magnesium sulfate crystals.

MATERIALS

- aluminum foil
- basalt
- beaker, 400 mL
- gloves, heat-resistant
- granite
- hot plate
- laboratory scoop, pointed
- magnesium sulfate ($MgSO_4$) (Epsom salts)
- magnifying lens
- marker, dark
- pumice
- tape, masking
- test tube, medium-sized
- thermometer, Celsius
- tongs, test-tube
- watch (or clock)
- water, distilled
- water, tap, 200 mL

SAFETY

7 Use the pointed laboratory scoop to fill the test tube about halfway with the magnesium sulfate. Add an equal amount of distilled water.

8 Hold the test tube in one hand, and use one finger from your other hand to tap the test tube gently. Observe the solution mixing as you continue to tap the test tube.

9 Place the test tube in the beaker of hot water, and heat it for approximately 3 min. **Caution:** Be sure to direct the opening of the test tube away from you and other students.

10 While the test tube is heating, shape your aluminum foil into two small boatlike containers by doubling the foil and turning up each edge.

11 If all the magnesium sulfate is not dissolved after 3 min, tap the test tube again, and heat it for 3 min longer. **Caution:** Use the test-tube tongs to handle the hot test tube.

12 With a marker and a piece of masking tape, label one of your aluminum boats "Sample 1," and place it on the hot plate. Turn the hot plate off.

13 Label the other aluminum boat "Sample 2," and place it on the lab table.

14 Using the test-tube tongs, remove the test tube from the beaker of water, and evenly distribute the contents to each of your foil boats. Carefully pour the hot water in the beaker down the drain. Do not move or disturb either of your foil boats.

15 Copy the table below onto a separate sheet of paper. Using the magnifying lens, carefully observe the foil boats. Record the time it takes for the first crystals to appear.

Crystal-Formation Table			
Crystal formation	Time	Size and appearance of crystals	Sketch of crystals
Sample 1			
Sample 2			

DO NOT WRITE IN BOOK

16 If crystals have not formed in the boats before class is over, carefully place the boats in a safe place. You may then record the time in days instead of in minutes.

17 When crystals have formed in both boats, use your magnifying lens to examine the crystals carefully.

Analyze the Results

1 Was your prediction correct? Explain.

2 Compare the size and shape of the crystals in Samples 1 and 2 with the size and shape of the crystals you examined in step 5. How long do you think the formation of the original crystals must have taken?

Draw Conclusions

3 Granite, basalt, and pumice are all igneous rocks. The most distinctive feature of each is the size of its crystals. Different igneous rocks form when magma cools at different rates. Examine a sample of each with your magnifying lens.

4 Copy the table below onto a separate sheet of paper, and sketch each rock sample.

5 Use what you have learned in this activity to explain how each rock sample formed and how long it took for the crystals to form. Record your answers in your table.

Igneous Rock Observations			
	Granite	**Basalt**	**Pumice**
Sketch			
How did the rock sample form?		DO NOT WRITE IN BOOK	
Rate of cooling			

Communicating Your Data

Describe the size and shape of the crystals you would expect to find when a volcano erupts and sends material into the air and when magma oozes down the volcano's slope.

Model-Making Lab

Metamorphic Mash

Metamorphism is a complex process that takes place deep within the Earth, where the temperature and pressure would turn a human into a crispy pancake. The effects of this extreme temperature and pressure are obvious in some metamorphic rocks. One of these effects is the reorganization of mineral grains within the rock. In this activity, you will investigate the process of metamorphism without being charred, flattened, or buried.

MATERIALS

- cardboard (or plywood), very stiff, small pieces
- clay, modeling
- knife, plastic
- sequins (or other small flat objects)

SAFETY

Procedure

1. Flatten the clay into a layer about 1 cm thick. Sprinkle the surface with sequins.

2. Roll the corners of the clay toward the middle to form a neat ball.

3. Carefully use the plastic knife to cut the ball in half. On a separate sheet of paper, describe the position and location of the sequins inside the ball.

4. Put the ball back together, and use the sheets of cardboard or plywood to flatten the ball until it is about 2 cm thick.

5. Using the plastic knife, slice open the slab of clay in several places. Describe the position and location of the sequins in the slab.

Analyze the Results

1. What physical process does flattening the ball represent?

2. Describe any changes in the position and location of the sequins that occurred as the clay ball was flattened into a slab.

Draw Conclusions

3. How are the sequins oriented in relation to the force you put on the ball to flatten it?

4. Do you think the orientation of the mineral grains in a foliated metamorphic rock tells you anything about the rock? Defend your answer.

Applying Your Data

Suppose you find a foliated metamorphic rock that has grains running in two distinct directions. Use what you have learned in this activity to offer a possible explanation for this observation.

Model-Making Lab

Oh, the Pressure!

When scientists want to understand natural processes, such as mountain formation, they often make models to help them. Models are useful in studying how rocks react to the forces of plate tectonics. A model can demonstrate in a short amount of time geological processes that take millions of years. Do the following activity to find out how folding and faulting occur in the Earth's crust.

MATERIALS

- can, soup (or rolling pin)
- clay, modeling, 4 colors
- knife, plastic
- newspaper
- pencils, colored
- poster board, 5 cm × 5 cm squares (2)
- poster board, 5 cm × 15 cm strip

SAFETY

Ask a Question

1 How do synclines, anticlines, and faults form?

Form a Hypothesis

2 On a separate piece of paper, write a hypothesis that is a possible answer to the question above. Explain your reasoning.

Test the Hypothesis

3 Use modeling clay of one color to form a long cylinder, and place the cylinder in the center of the glossy side of the poster-board strip.

4 Mold the clay to the strip. Try to make the clay layer the same thickness all along the strip; you can use the soup can or rolling pin to even it out. Pinch the sides of the clay so that the clay is the same width and length as the strip. Your strip should be at least 15 cm long and 5 cm wide.

5 Flip the strip over on the newspaper your teacher has placed across your desk. Carefully peel the strip from the modeling clay.

6 Repeat steps 3–5 with the other colors of modeling clay. Each person should have a turn molding the clay. Each time you flip the strip over, stack the new clay layer on top of the previous one. When you are finished, you should have a block of clay made of four layers.

7 Lift the block of clay, and hold it parallel to and just above the tabletop. Push gently on the block from opposite sides, as shown below.

8 Use the colored pencils to draw the results of step 6. Use the terms *syncline* and *anticline* to label your diagram. Draw arrows to show the direction that each edge of the clay was pushed.

9 Repeat steps 3–6 to form a second block of clay.

10 Cut the second block of clay in two at a 45° angle as seen from the side of the block.

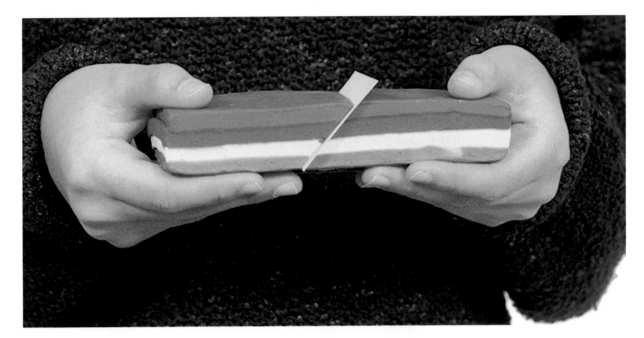

11. Press one poster-board square on the angled end of each of the block's two pieces. The poster board represents a fault. The two angled ends represent a hanging wall and a footwall. The model should resemble the one in the photograph above.

12. Keeping the angled edges together, lift the blocks, and hold them parallel to and just above the tabletop. Push gently on the two blocks until they move. Record your observations.

13. Now, hold the two pieces of the clay block in their original position, and slowly pull them apart, allowing the hanging wall to move downward. Record your observations.

Analyze the Results

1. What happened to the first block of clay in step 7? What kind of force did you apply to the block of clay?

2. What happened to the pieces of the second block of clay in step 12? What kind of force did you apply to them?

3. What happened to the pieces of the second block of clay in step 13? Describe the forces that acted on the block and the way the pieces of the block reacted.

Draw Conclusions

4. Summarize how the forces you applied to the blocks of clay relate to the way tectonic forces affect rock layers. Be sure to use the terms *fold, fault, anticline, syncline, hanging wall, footwall, tension,* and *compression* in your summary.

Skills Practice Lab

Earthquake Waves

The energy from an earthquake travels as seismic waves in all directions through the Earth. Seismologists can use the properties of certain types of seismic waves to find the epicenter of an earthquake.

P waves travel more quickly than S waves and are always detected first. The average speed of P waves in the Earth's crust is 6.1 km/s. The average speed of S waves in the Earth's crust is 4.1 km/s. The difference in arrival time between P waves and S waves is called *lag time.*

In this activity, you will use the S-P-time method to determine the location of an earthquake's epicenter.

MATERIALS

- calculator (optional)
- compass
- ruler, metric

SAFETY

Procedure

1. The illustration below shows seismographic records made in three cities following an earthquake. These traces begin at the left and show the arrival of P waves at time zero. The second set of waves on each record represents the arrival of S waves.

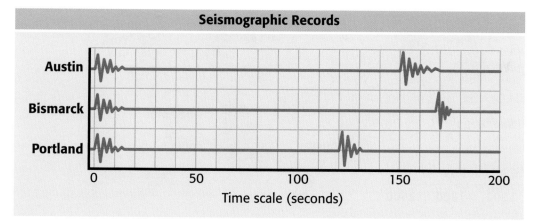

Seismographic Records

Austin

Bismarck

Portland

0   50   100   150   200

Time scale (seconds)

2. Copy the data table on the next page.

3. Use the time scale provided with the seismographic records to find the lag time between the P waves and the S waves for each city. Remember that the lag time is the time between the moment when the first P wave arrives and the moment when the first S wave arrives. Record this data in your table.

4. Use the following equation to calculate how long it takes each wave type to travel 100 km:

100 km ÷ *average speed of the wave = time*

⑤ To find lag time for earthquake waves at 100 km, subtract the time it takes P waves to travel 100 km from the time it takes S waves to travel 100 km. Record the lag time.

⑥ Use the following formula to find the distance from each city to the epicenter:

$$distance = \frac{measured\ lag\ time\ (s) \times 100\ km}{lag\ time\ for\ 100\ km\ (s)}$$

In your data table, record the distance from each city to the epicenter.

⑦ Trace the map below onto a separate sheet of paper.

⑧ Use the scale to adjust your compass so that the radius of a circle with Austin at the center is equal to the distance between Austin and the epicenter of the earthquake.

Epicenter Data Table		
City	Lag time (seconds)	Distance to the epicenter (km)
Austin, TX		
Bismarck, ND	DO NOT WRITE IN BOOK	
Portland, OR		

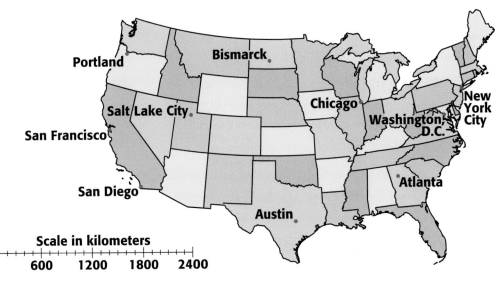

Scale in kilometers

0   600   1200   1800   2400

⑨ Put the point of your compass at Austin on your copy of the map, and draw a circle.

⑩ Repeat steps 8 and 9 for Bismarck and Portland. The epicenter of the earthquake is located near the point where the three circles meet.

Anayze the Results

① Which city is closest to the epicenter?

Draw Conclusions

② Why do seismologists need measurements from three different locations to find the epicenter of an earthquake?

Skills Practice Lab

Some Go "Pop," Some Do Not

Volcanic eruptions range from mild to violent. When volcanoes erupt, the materials left behind provide information to scientists studying the Earth's crust. Mild, or nonexplosive, eruptions produce thin, runny lava that is low in silica. During nonexplosive eruptions, lava simply flows down the side of the volcano. Explosive eruptions, on the other hand, do not produce much lava. Instead, the explosions hurl ash and debris into the air. The materials left behind are light in color and high in silica. These materials help geologists determine the composition of the crust underneath the volcanoes.

MATERIALS

- paper, graph (1 sheet)
- pencils (or markers), red, yellow, and orange
- ruler, metric

Procedure

1. Copy the map below onto graph paper. Take care to line the grid up properly.

2. Locate each volcano from the list on the next page by drawing a circle with a diameter of about 2 mm in the proper location on your copy of the map. Use the latitude and longitude grids to help you.

3. Review all the eruptions for each volcano. For each explosive eruption, color the circle red. For each quiet volcano, color the circle yellow. For volcanoes that have erupted in both ways, color the circle orange.

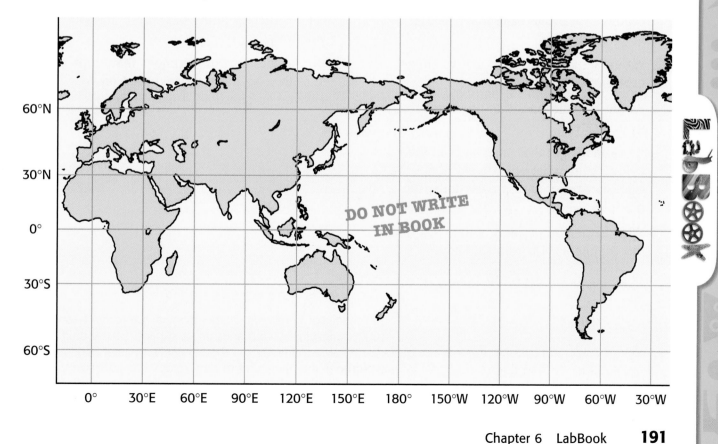

DO NOT WRITE IN BOOK

Volcanic Activity Chart

Volcano name	Location	Description
Mount St. Helens	46°N 122°W	An explosive eruption blew the top off the mountain. Light-colored ash covered thousands of square kilometers. Another eruption sent a lava flow down the southeast side of the mountain.
Kilauea	19°N 155°W	One small eruption sent a lava flow along 12 km of highway.
Rabaul caldera	4°S 152°E	Explosive eruptions have caused tsunamis and have left 1–2 m of ash on nearby buildings.
Popocatépetl	19°N 98°W	During one explosion, Mexico City closed the airport for 14 hours because huge columns of ash made it too difficult for pilots to see. Eruptions from this volcano have also caused damaging avalanches.
Soufriere Hills	16°N 62°W	Small eruptions have sent lava flows down the hills. Other explosive eruptions have sent large columns of ash into the air.
Long Valley caldera	37°N 119°W	Explosive eruptions have sent ash into the air.
Okmok	53°N 168°W	Recently, there have been slow lava flows from this volcano. Twenty-five hundred years ago, ash and debris exploded from the top of this volcano.
Pavlof	55°N 161°W	Eruption clouds have been sent 200 m above the summit. Eruptions have sent ash columns 10 km into the air. Occasionally, small eruptions have caused lava flows.
Fernandina	42°N 12°E	Eruptions have ejected large blocks of rock from this volcano.
Mount Pinatubo	15°N 120°E	Ash and debris from an explosive eruption destroyed homes, crops, and roads within 52,000 km^2 around the volcano.

Analyze the Results

1. According to your map, where are volcanoes that always have nonexplosive eruptions located?

2. Where are volcanoes that always erupt explosively located?

3. Where are volcanoes that erupt in both ways located?

4. If volcanoes get their magma from the crust below them, what can you say about the silica content of Earth's crust under the oceans?

5. What is the composition of the crust under the continents? How do we know?

Draw Conclusions

6. What is the source of materials for volcanoes that erupt in both ways? How do you know?

7. Do the locations of volcanoes that erupt in both ways make sense, based on your answers to questions 4 and 5? Explain.

Applying Your Data

Volcanoes are present on other planets. If a planet had only nonexplosive volcanoes on its surface, what would we be able to infer about the planet? If a planet had volcanoes that ranged from nonexplosive to explosive, what might that tell us about the planet?

Contents

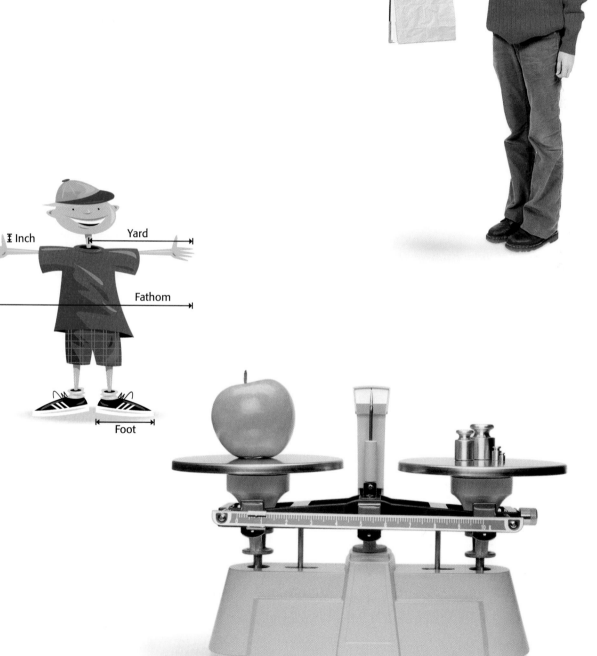

Appendix

✓ *Reading Check* Answers

Chapter 1   Minerals of the Earth's Crust

Section 1

Page 5: An element is a pure substance that cannot be broken down into simpler substances by ordinary chemical means. A compound is a substance made of two or more elements that have been chemically bonded.

Page 6: Answers may vary. Silicate minerals contain a combination of silicon and oxygen; nonsilicate minerals do not contain a combination of silicon and oxygen.

Section 2

Page 9: A mineral's streak is not affected by air or water, but a mineral's color may be affected by air or water.

Page 10: Scratch the mineral with a series of 10 reference minerals. If the reference mineral scratches the unidentified mineral, the reference mineral is harder than the unidentified mineral.

Section 3

Page 15: Surface mining is used to remove mineral deposits that are at or near the Earth's surface. Subsurface mining is used to remove mineral deposits that are too deep to be removed by surface mining.

Page 17: Sample answer: Gemstones are nonmetallic minerals that are valued for their beauty and rarity rather than for their usefulness.

Chapter 2   Rocks: Mineral Mixtures

Section 1

Page 28: Types of rocks that have been used by humans to construct buildings include granite, limestone, marble, sandstone, and slate.

Page 32: Rock within the Earth is affected by temperature and pressure.

Page 33: The minerals that a rock contains determine a rock's composition.

Page 34: Fine-grained rocks are made of small grains, such as silt or clay particles. Medium-grained rocks are made of medium-sized grains, such as sand. Coarse-grained rocks are made of large grains, such as pebbles.

Section 2

Page 37: Felsic rocks are light-colored igneous rocks rich in aluminum, potassium, silicon, and sodium. Mafic rocks are dark-colored igneous rocks rich in calcium, iron, and magnesium.

Page 39: New sea floor forms when lava that flows from fissures on the ocean floor cools and hardens.

Section 3

Page 41: Halite forms when sodium and chlorine ions in shallow bodies of water become so concentrated that halite crystallizes from solution.

Page 43: Ripple marks are the marks left by wind and water waves on lakes, seas, rivers, and sand dunes.

Page 45: Regional metamorphism occurs when pressure builds up in rock that is buried deep below other rock formations or when large pieces of the Earth's crust collide. The increased pressure can cause thousands of square miles of rock to become deformed and chemically changed.

Page 46: An index mineral is a metamorphic mineral that forms only at certain temperatures and pressures and therefore can be used by scientists to estimate the temperature, pressure, and depth at which a rock undergoes metamorphosis.

Page 49: Deformation causes metamorphic structures, such as folds.

Chapter 3   The Rock and Fossil Record

Section 1

Page 61: Catastrophists believed that all geologic change occurs rapidly.

Page 62: A global catastrophe can cause the extinction of species.

Section 2

Page 65: Geologists use the geologic column to interpret rock sequences and to identify layers in puzzling rock sequences.

Page 67: An unconformity is a surface that represents a missing part of the geologic column.

Page 68: A disconformity is found where part of a sequence of parallel rock layers is missing. A nonconformity is found where horizontal sedimentary rock layers lie on top of an eroded surface of igneous or metamorphic rock. Angular unconformities are found between horizontal sedimentary rock layers and rock layers that have been tilted or folded.

Section 3

Page 71: A half-life is the time it takes one-half of a radioactive sample to decay.

Page 72: strontium-87

Section 4

Page 74: An organism is caught in soft, sticky tree sap, which hardens and preserves the organism.

Page 76: A mold is a cavity in rock where a plant or an animal was buried. A cast is an object created when sediment fills a mold and becomes rock.

Page 78: To fill in missing information about changes in organisms in the fossil record, paleontologists look for similarities between fossilized organisms or between fossilized organisms and their closest living relatives.

Page 79: *Phacops* can be used to establish the age of rock layers because *Phacops* lived during a relatively short, well-defined time span and is found in rock layers throughout the world.

Section 5

Page 81: approximately 2 billion years

Page 82: The geologic time scale is a scale that divides Earth's 4.6 billion–year history into distinct intervals of time.

Page 84: The Mesozoic era is known as the *Age of Reptiles* because reptiles, including the dinosaurs, were the dominant organisms on land.

Chapter 4   Plate Tectonics

Section 1

Page 97: The crust is the thin, outermost layer of the Earth. It is 5 km to 100 km thick and is mainly made up of the elements oxygen, silicon, and aluminum. The mantle is the layer between the crust and core. It is 2,900 km thick, is denser than the crust, and contains most of the Earth's mass. The core is the Earth's innermost layer. The core has a radius of 3,430 km and is made mostly of iron.

Page 98: The five physical layers of the Earth are the lithosphere, asthenosphere, mesosphere, outer core, and inner core.

Page 101: Although continental lithosphere is less dense than oceanic lithosphere is, continental lithosphere has a greater weight and will displace more asthenosphere than oceanic lithosphere.

Page 102: Answers may vary. A seismic wave traveling through a solid will go faster than a seismic wave traveling through a liquid.

Section 2

Page 104: Similar fossils were found on landmasses that are very far apart. The best explanation for this phenomenon is that the landmasses were once joined.

Page 107: The molten rock at mid-ocean ridges contains tiny grains of magnetic minerals. The minerals align with the Earth's magnetic field before the rock cools and hardens. When the Earth's magnetic field reverses, the orientation of the mineral grains in the rocks will also change.

Section 3

Page 109: A transform boundary forms when two tectonic plates slide past each other horizontally.

Page 110: The circulation of thermal energy causes changes in density in the asthenosphere. As rock is heated, it expands, becomes less dense, and rises. As rock cools, it contracts, becomes denser, and sinks.

Section 4

Page 112: Compression can cause rocks to be pushed into mountain ranges as tectonic plates collide at convergent boundaries. Tension can pull rocks apart as tectonic plates separate at divergent boundaries.

Page 114: In a normal fault, the hanging wall moves down. In a reverse fault, the hanging wall moves up.

Page 116: Folded mountains form when rock layers are squeezed together and pushed upward.

Chapter 5   Earthquakes

Section 1

Page 131: During elastic rebound, rock releases energy. Some of this energy travels as seismic waves that cause earthquakes.

Page 133: Earthquake zones are usually located along tectonic plate boundaries.

Page 135: Surface waves travel more slowly than body waves but are more destructive.

Section 2

Page 137: Seismologists determine an earthquake's start time by comparing seismograms and noting differences in arrival times of P and S waves.

Page 138: Each time the magnitude increases by 1 unit, the amount of ground motion increases by 10 times.

Section 3

Page 141: With a decrease of one unit in earthquake magnitude, the number of earthquakes occurring annually increases by about 10 times.

Page 142: Retrofitting is the process of making older structures more earthquake resistant.

Page 144: You should crouch or lie face down under a table or desk.

Chapter 6   Volcanoes

Section 1

Page 157: Nonexplosive eruptions are common, and they feature relatively calm flows of lava. Explosive eruptions are less common and produce large, explosive clouds of ash and gases.

Page 158: Because silica-rich magma has a high viscosity, it tends to trap gases and plug volcanic vents. This causes pressure to build up and can result in an explosive eruption.

Page 160: Volcanic bombs are large blobs of magma that harden in the air. Lapilli are small pieces of magma that harden in the air. Volcanic blocks are pieces of solid rock erupted from a volcano. Ash forms when gases in stiff magma expand rapidly and the walls of the gas bubbles shatter into tiny glasslike slivers.

Section 2

Page 162: Eruptions release large quantities of ash and gases, which can block sunlight and cause global temperatures to drop.

Page 164: Calderas form when a magma chamber partially empties and the roof overlying the chamber collapses.

Section 3

Page 167: Volcanic activity is common at tectonic plate boundaries because magma tends to form at plate boundaries.

Page 169: When a tectonic plate subducts, it becomes hotter and releases water vapor. The water lowers the melting point of the rock above the plate, causing magma to form.

Page 170: According to one theory, a rising body of magma, called a mantle plume, causes a chain of volcanoes to form on a moving tectonic plate. According to another theory, a chain of volcanoes forms along cracks in the Earth's crust.

Study Skills

FoldNote Instructions

FOLDNOTES

Have you ever tried to study for a test or quiz but didn't know where to start? Or have you read a chapter and found that you can remember only a few ideas? Well, FoldNotes are a fun and exciting way to help you learn and remember the ideas you encounter as you learn science!

FoldNotes are tools that you can use to organize concepts. By focusing on a few main concepts, FoldNotes help you learn and remember how the concepts fit together. They can help you see the "big picture." Below you will find instructions for building 10 different FoldNotes.

Pyramid

1. Place a sheet of paper in front of you. Fold the lower left-hand corner of the paper diagonally to the opposite edge of the paper.

2. Cut off the tab of paper created by the fold (at the top).

3. Open the paper so that it is a square. Fold the lower right-hand corner of the paper diagonally to the opposite corner to form a triangle.

4. Open the paper. The creases of the two folds will have created an X.

5. Using scissors, cut along one of the creases. Start from any corner, and stop at the center point to create two flaps. Use tape or glue to attach one of the flaps on top of the other flap.

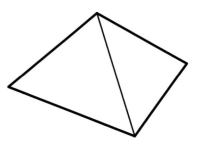

Double Door

1. Fold a sheet of paper in half from the top to the bottom. Then, unfold the paper.

2. Fold the top and bottom edges of the paper to the crease.

Appendix

Booklet

1. Fold a sheet of paper in half from left to right. Then, unfold the paper.

2. Fold the sheet of paper in half again from the top to the bottom. Then, unfold the paper.

3. Refold the sheet of paper in half from left to right.

4. Fold the top and bottom edges to the center crease.

5. Completely unfold the paper.

6. Refold the paper from top to bottom.

7. Using scissors, cut a slit along the center crease of the sheet from the folded edge to the creases made in step 4. Do not cut the entire sheet in half.

8. Fold the sheet of paper in half from left to right. While holding the bottom and top edges of the paper, push the bottom and top edges together so that the center collapses at the center slit. Fold the four flaps to form a four-page book.

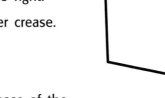

Layered Book

1. Lay one sheet of paper on top of another sheet. Slide the top sheet up so that 2 cm of the bottom sheet is showing.

2. Hold the two sheets together, fold down the top of the two sheets so that you see four 2 cm tabs along the bottom.

3. Using a stapler, staple the top of the FoldNote.

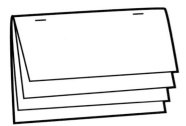

Key-Term Fold

1. Fold a sheet of lined notebook paper in half from left to right.

2. Using scissors, cut along every third line from the right edge of the paper to the center fold to make tabs.

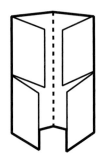

Four-Corner Fold

1. Fold a sheet of paper in half from left to right. Then, unfold the paper.

2. Fold each side of the paper to the crease in the center of the paper.

3. Fold the paper in half from the top to the bottom. Then, unfold the paper.

4. Using scissors, cut the top flap creases made in step 3 to form four flaps.

Three-Panel Flip Chart

1. Fold a piece of paper in half from the top to the bottom.

2. Fold the paper in thirds from side to side. Then, unfold the paper so that you can see the three sections.

3. From the top of the paper, cut along each of the vertical fold lines to the fold in the middle of the paper. You will now have three flaps.

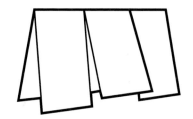

Table Fold

1. Fold a piece of paper in half from the top to the bottom. Then, fold the paper in half again.

2. Fold the paper in thirds from side to side.

3. Unfold the paper completely. Carefully trace the fold lines by using a pen or pencil.

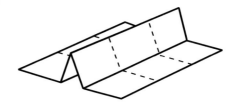

Two-Panel Flip Chart

1. Fold a piece of paper in half from the top to the bottom.

2. Fold the paper in half from side to side. Then, unfold the paper so that you can see the two sections.

3. From the top of the paper, cut along the vertical fold line to the fold in the middle of the paper. You will now have two flaps.

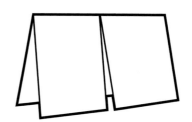

Tri-Fold

1. Fold a piece a paper in thirds from the top to the bottom.

2. Unfold the paper so that you can see the three sections. Then, turn the paper sideways so that the three sections form vertical columns.

3. Trace the fold lines by using a pen or pencil. Label the columns "Know," "Want," and "Learn."

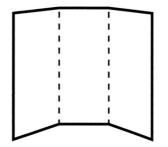

Graphic Organizer Instructions

 Have you ever wished that you could "draw out" the many concepts you learn in your science class? Sometimes, being able to *see* how concepts are related really helps you remember what you've learned. Graphic Organizers do just that! They give you a way to draw or map out concepts.

All you need to make a Graphic Organizer is a piece of paper and a pencil. Below you will find instructions for four different Graphic Organizers designed to help you organize the concepts you'll learn in this book.

Spider Map

1. Draw a diagram like the one shown. In the circle, write the main topic.

2. From the circle, draw legs to represent different categories of the main topic. You can have as many categories as you want.

3. From the category legs, draw horizontal lines. As you read the chapter, write details about each category on the horizontal lines.

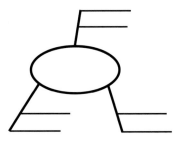

Comparison Table

1. Draw a chart like the one shown. Your chart can have as many columns and rows as you want.

2. In the top row, write the topics that you want to compare.

3. In the left column, write characteristics of the topics that you want to compare. As you read the chapter, fill in the characteristics for each topic in the appropriate boxes.

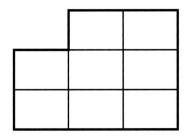

Appendix

200 Appendix

Chain-of-Events-Chart

1. Draw a box. In the box, write the first step of a process or the first event of a timeline.

2. Under the box, draw another box, and use an arrow to connect the two boxes. In the second box, write the next step of the process or the next event in the timeline.

3. Continue adding boxes until the process or timeline is finished.

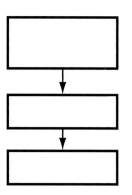

Concept Map

1. Draw a circle in the center of a piece of paper. Write the main idea of the chapter in the center of the circle.

2. From the circle, draw other circles. In those circles, write characteristics of the main idea. Draw arrows from the center circle to the circles that contain the characteristics.

3. From each circle that contains a characteristic, draw other circles. In those circles, write specific details about the characteristic. Draw arrows from each circle that contains a characteristic to the circles that contain specific details. You may draw as many circles as you want.

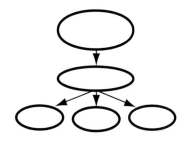

SI Measurement

The International System of Units, or SI, is the standard system of measurement used by many scientists. Using the same standards of measurement makes it easier for scientists to communicate with one another.

SI works by combining prefixes and base units. Each base unit can be used with different prefixes to define smaller and larger quantities. The table below lists common SI prefixes.

SI Prefixes

Prefix	Symbol	Factor	Example
kilo-	k	1,000	kilogram, 1 kg = 1,000 g
hecto-	h	100	hectoliter, 1 hL = 100 L
deka-	da	10	dekameter, 1 dam = 10 m
		1	meter, liter, gram
deci-	d	0.1	decigram, 1 dg = 0.1 g
centi-	c	0.01	centimeter, 1 cm = 0.01 m
milli-	m	0.001	milliliter, 1 mL = 0.001 L
micro-	μ	0.000 001	micrometer, 1 μm = 0.000 001 m

SI Conversion Table

SI units	From SI to English	From English to SI
Length		
kilometer (km) = 1,000 m	1 km = 0.621 mi	1 mi = 1.609 km
meter (m) = 100 cm	1 m = 3.281 ft	1 ft = 0.305 m
centimeter (cm) = 0.01 m	1 cm = 0.394 in.	1 in. = 2.540 cm
millimeter (mm) = 0.001 m	1 mm = 0.039 in.	
micrometer (μm) = 0.000 001 m		
nanometer (nm) = 0.000 000 001 m		
Area		
square kilometer (km^2) = 100 hectares	1 km^2 = 0.386 mi^2	1 mi^2 = 2.590 km^2
hectare (ha) = 10,000 m^2	1 ha = 2.471 acres	1 acre = 0.405 ha
square meter (m^2) = 10,000 cm^2	1 m^2 = 10.764 ft^2	1 ft^2 = 0.093 m^2
square centimeter (cm^2) = 100 mm^2	1 cm^2 = 0.155 in.^{2}	1 in.^{2} = 6.452 cm^2
Volume		
liter (L) = 1,000 mL = 1 dm^3	1 L = 1.057 fl qt	1 fl qt = 0.946 L
milliliter (mL) = 0.001 L = 1 cm^3	1 mL = 0.034 fl oz	1 fl oz = 29.574 mL
microliter (μL) = 0.000 001 L		
Mass		*Equivalent weight at Earth's surface
kilogram (kg) = 1,000 g	1 kg = 2.205 lb*	1 lb* = 0.454 kg
gram (g) = 1,000 mg	1 g = 0.035 oz*	1 oz* = 28.350 g
milligram (mg) = 0.001 g		
microgram (μg) = 0.000 001 g		

Measuring Skills

Using a Graduated Cylinder

When using a graduated cylinder to measure volume, keep the following procedures in mind:

1 Place the cylinder on a flat, level surface before measuring liquid.

2 Move your head so that your eye is level with the surface of the liquid.

3 Read the mark closest to the liquid level. On glass graduated cylinders, read the mark closest to the center of the curve in the liquid's surface.

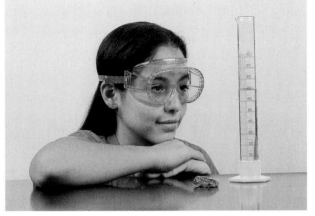

Using a Meterstick or Metric Ruler

When using a meterstick or metric ruler to measure length, keep the following procedures in mind:

1 Place the ruler firmly against the object that you are measuring.

2 Align one edge of the object exactly with the 0 end of the ruler.

3 Look at the other edge of the object to see which of the marks on the ruler is closest to that edge. (Note: Each small slash between the centimeters represents a millimeter, which is one-tenth of a centimeter.)

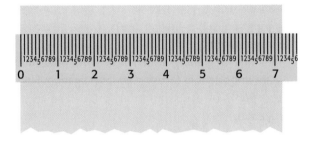

Using a Triple-Beam Balance

When using a triple-beam balance to measure mass, keep the following procedures in mind:

1 Make sure the balance is on a level surface.

2 Place all of the countermasses at 0. Adjust the balancing knob until the pointer rests at 0.

3 Place the object you wish to measure on the pan. **Caution:** Do not place hot objects or chemicals directly on the balance pan.

4 Move the largest countermass along the beam to the right until it is at the last notch that does not tip the balance. Follow the same procedure with the next-largest countermass. Then, move the smallest countermass until the pointer rests at 0.

5 Add the readings from the three beams together to determine the mass of the object.

6 When determining the mass of crystals or powders, first find the mass of a piece of filter paper. Then, add the crystals or powder to the paper, and remeasure. The actual mass of the crystals or powder is the total mass minus the mass of the paper. When finding the mass of liquids, first find the mass of the empty container. Then, find the combined mass of the liquid and container. The mass of the liquid is the total mass minus the mass of the container.

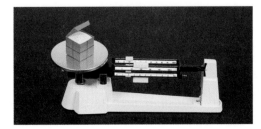

Scientific Methods

The ways in which scientists answer questions and solve problems are called **scientific methods.** The same steps are often used by scientists as they look for answers. However, there is more than one way to use these steps. Scientists may use all of the steps or just some of the steps during an investigation. They may even repeat some of the steps. The goal of using scientific methods is to come up with reliable answers and solutions.

Six Steps of Scientific Methods

1 Ask a Question

Good questions come from careful **observations.** You make observations by using your senses to gather information. Sometimes, you may use instruments, such as microscopes and telescopes, to extend the range of your senses. As you observe the natural world, you will discover that you have many more questions than answers. These questions drive investigations.

Questions beginning with *what, why, how,* and *when* are important in focusing an investigation. Here is an example of a question that could lead to an investigation.

Question: How does acid rain affect plant growth?

2 Form a Hypothesis

After you ask a question, you need to form a **hypothesis.** A hypothesis is a clear statement of what you expect the answer to your question to be. Your hypothesis will represent your best "educated guess" based on what you have observed and what you already know. A good hypothesis is testable. Otherwise, the investigation can go no further. Here is a hypothesis based on the question, "How does acid rain affect plant growth?"

Hypothesis: Acid rain slows plant growth.

The hypothesis can lead to predictions. A prediction is what you think the outcome of your experiment or data collection will be. Predictions are usually stated in an if-then format. Here is a sample prediction for the hypothesis that acid rain slows plant growth.

Prediction: If a plant is watered with only acid rain (which has a pH of 4), then the plant will grow at half its normal rate.

3 Test the Hypothesis

After you have formed a hypothesis and made a prediction, your hypothesis should be tested. One way to test a hypothesis is with a controlled experiment. A **controlled experiment** tests only one factor at a time. In an experiment to test the effect of acid rain on plant growth, the **control group** would be watered with normal rain water. The **experimental group** would be watered with acid rain. All of the plants should receive the same amount of sunlight and water each day. The air temperature should be the same for all groups. However, the acidity of the water will be a variable. In fact, any factor that is different from one group to another is a **variable.** If your hypothesis is correct, then the acidity of the water and plant growth are *dependant variables.* The amount a plant grows is dependent on the acidity of the water. However, the amount of water each plant receives and the amount of sunlight each plant receives are *independent variables.* Either of these factors could change without affecting the other factor.

Sometimes, the nature of an investigation makes a controlled experiment impossible. For example, the Earth's core is surrounded by thousands of meters of rock. Under such circumstances, a hypothesis may be tested by making detailed observations.

4 Analyze the Results

After you have completed your experiments, made your observations, and collected your data, you must analyze all the information you have gathered. Tables and graphs are often used in this step to organize the data.

5 Draw Conclusions

After analyzing your data, you can determine if your results support your hypothesis. If your hypothesis is supported, you (or others) might want to repeat the observations or experiments to verify your results. If your hypothesis is not supported by the data, you may have to check your procedure for errors. You may even have to reject your hypothesis and make a new one. If you cannot draw a conclusion from your results, you may have to try the investigation again or carry out further observations or experiments.

6 Communicate Results

After any scientific investigation, you should report your results. By preparing a written or oral report, you let others know what you have learned. They may repeat your investigation to see if they get the same results. Your report may even lead to another question and then to another investigation.

Scientific Methods in Action

Scientific methods contain loops in which several steps may be repeated over and over again. In some cases, certain steps are unnecessary. Thus, there is not a "straight line" of steps. For example, sometimes scientists find that testing one hypothesis raises new questions and new hypotheses to be tested. And sometimes, testing the hypothesis leads directly to a conclusion. Furthermore, the steps in scientific methods are not always used in the same order. Follow the steps in the diagram, and see how many different directions scientific methods can take you.

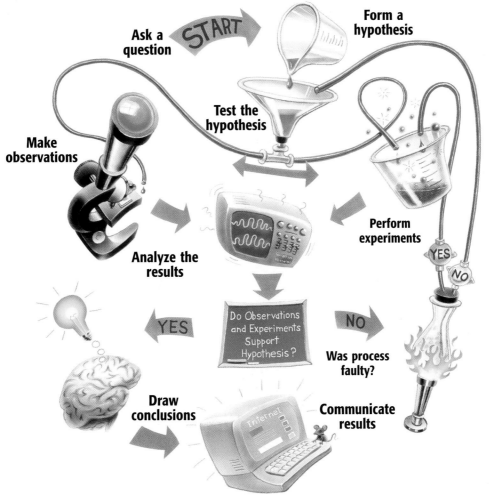

Math Refresher

Science requires an understanding of many math concepts. The following pages will help you review some important math skills.

Averages

An **average,** or **mean,** simplifies a set of numbers into a single number that *approximates* the value of the set.

> **Example:** Find the average of the following set of numbers: 5, 4, 7, and 8.

Step 1: Find the sum.

$$5 + 4 + 7 + 8 = 24$$

Step 2: Divide the sum by the number of numbers in your set. Because there are four numbers in this example, divide the sum by 4.

$$\frac{24}{4} = 6$$

The average, or mean, is **6.**

Ratios

A **ratio** is a comparison between numbers, and it is usually written as a fraction.

> **Example:** Find the ratio of thermometers to students if you have 36 thermometers and 48 students in your class.

Step 1: Make the ratio.

$$\frac{36 \text{ thermometers}}{48 \text{ students}}$$

Step 2: Reduce the fraction to its simplest form.

$$\frac{36}{48} = \frac{36 \div 12}{48 \div 12} = \frac{3}{4}$$

The ratio of thermometers to students is **3 to 4,** or $\frac{3}{4}$. The ratio may also be written in the form 3:4.

Proportions

A **proportion** is an equation that states that two ratios are equal.

$$\frac{3}{1} = \frac{12}{4}$$

To solve a proportion, first multiply across the equal sign. This is called *cross-multiplication.* If you know three of the quantities in a proportion, you can use cross-multiplication to find the fourth.

> **Example:** Imagine that you are making a scale model of the solar system for your science project. The diameter of Jupiter is 11.2 times the diameter of the Earth. If you are using a plastic-foam ball that has a diameter of 2 cm to represent the Earth, what must the diameter of the ball representing Jupiter be?

$$\frac{11.2}{1} = \frac{x}{2 \text{ cm}}$$

Step 1: Cross-multiply.

$$\frac{11.2}{1} \diagdown\!\!\!\!\diagup \frac{x}{2}$$

$$11.2 \times 2 = x \times 1$$

Step 2: Multiply.

$$22.4 = x \times 1$$

Step 3: Isolate the variable by dividing both sides by 1.

$$x = \frac{22.4}{1}$$
$$x = 22.4 \text{ cm}$$

You will need to use a ball that has a diameter of **22.4** cm to represent Jupiter.

Percentages

A **percentage** is a ratio of a given number to 100.

> **Example:** What is 85% of 40?

Step 1: Rewrite the percentage by moving the decimal point two places to the left.

0.85

Step 2: Multiply the decimal by the number that you are calculating the percentage of.

$0.85 \times 40 = 34$

85% of 40 is **34.**

Decimals

To **add** or **subtract decimals,** line up the digits vertically so that the decimal points line up. Then, add or subtract the columns from right to left. Carry or borrow numbers as necessary.

> **Example:** Add the following numbers: 3.1415 and 2.96.

Step 1: Line up the digits vertically so that the decimal points line up.

$$\begin{array}{r} 3.1415 \\ + 2.96 \\ \hline \end{array}$$

Step 2: Add the columns from right to left, and carry when necessary.

$$\begin{array}{r} {}^{1\ 1} \\ 3.1415 \\ + 2.96 \\ \hline 6.1015 \end{array}$$

The sum is **6.1015.**

Fractions

Numbers tell you how many; **fractions** tell you *how much of a whole.*

> **Example:** Your class has 24 plants. Your teacher instructs you to put 5 plants in a shady spot. What fraction of the plants in your class will you put in a shady spot?

Step 1: In the denominator, write the total number of parts in the whole.

$$\frac{?}{24}$$

Step 2: In the numerator, write the number of parts of the whole that are being considered.

$$\frac{5}{24}$$

So, $\frac{5}{24}$ of the plants will be in the shade.

Reducing Fractions

It is usually best to express a fraction in its simplest form. Expressing a fraction in its simplest form is called *reducing* a fraction.

> **Example:** Reduce the fraction $\frac{30}{45}$ to its simplest form.

Step 1: Find the largest whole number that will divide evenly into both the numerator and denominator. This number is called the *greatest common factor* (GCF).

Factors of the numerator 30:
1, 2, 3, 5, 6, 10, **15,** 30

Factors of the denominator 45:
1, 3, 5, 9, **15,** 45

Step 2: Divide both the numerator and the denominator by the GCF, which in this case is 15.

$$\frac{30}{45} = \frac{30 \div 15}{45 \div 15} = \frac{2}{3}$$

Thus, $\frac{30}{45}$ reduced to its simplest form is $\frac{2}{3}$.

Appendix

Adding and Subtracting Fractions

To **add** or **subtract fractions** that have the **same denominator,** simply add or subtract the numerators.

Examples:

$$\frac{3}{5} + \frac{1}{5} = ? \text{ and } \frac{3}{4} - \frac{1}{4} = ?$$

Step 1: Add or subtract the numerators.

$$\frac{3}{5} + \frac{1}{5} = \frac{4}{\quad} \text{ and } \frac{3}{4} - \frac{1}{4} = \frac{2}{\quad}$$

Step 2: Write the sum or difference over the denominator.

$$\frac{3}{5} + \frac{1}{5} = \frac{4}{5} \text{ and } \frac{3}{4} - \frac{1}{4} = \frac{2}{4}$$

Step 3: If necessary, reduce the fraction to its simplest form.

$\frac{4}{5}$ cannot be reduced, and $\frac{2}{4} = \frac{1}{2}$.

To **add** or **subtract fractions** that have **different denominators,** first find the least common denominator (LCD).

Examples:

$$\frac{1}{2} + \frac{1}{6} = ? \text{ and } \frac{3}{4} - \frac{2}{3} = ?$$

Step 1: Write the equivalent fractions that have a common denominator.

$$\frac{3}{6} + \frac{1}{6} = ? \text{ and } \frac{9}{12} - \frac{8}{12} = ?$$

Step 2: Add or subtract the fractions.

$$\frac{3}{6} + \frac{1}{6} = \frac{4}{6} \text{ and } \frac{9}{12} - \frac{8}{12} = \frac{1}{12}$$

Step 3: If necessary, reduce the fraction to its simplest form.

The fraction $\frac{4}{6} = \frac{2}{3}$, and $\frac{1}{12}$ cannot be reduced.

Multiplying Fractions

To **multiply fractions,** multiply the numerators and the denominators together, and then reduce the fraction to its simplest form.

Example:

$$\frac{5}{9} \times \frac{7}{10} = ?$$

Step 1: Multiply the numerators and denominators.

$$\frac{5}{9} \times \frac{7}{10} = \frac{5 \times 7}{9 \times 10} = \frac{35}{90}$$

Step 2: Reduce the fraction.

$$\frac{35}{90} = \frac{35 \div 5}{90 \div 5} = \frac{7}{18}$$

Dividing Fractions

To **divide fractions,** first rewrite the divisor (the number you divide by) upside down. This number is called the *reciprocal* of the divisor. Then multiply and reduce if necessary.

Example:

$$\frac{5}{8} \div \frac{3}{2} = ?$$

Step 1: Rewrite the divisor as its reciprocal.

$$\frac{3}{2} \rightarrow \frac{2}{3}$$

Step 2: Multiply the fractions.

$$\frac{5}{8} \times \frac{2}{3} = \frac{5 \times 2}{8 \times 3} = \frac{10}{24}$$

Step 3: Reduce the fraction.

$$\frac{10}{24} = \frac{10 \div 2}{24 \div 2} = \frac{5}{12}$$

Scientific Notation

Scientific notation is a short way of representing very large and very small numbers without writing all of the place-holding zeros.

Example: Write 653,000,000 in scientific notation.

Step 1: Write the number without the place-holding zeros.

653

Step 2: Place the decimal point after the first digit.

6.53

Step 3: Find the exponent by counting the number of places that you moved the decimal point.

6.53000000

The decimal point was moved eight places to the left. Therefore, the exponent of 10 is positive 8. If you had moved the decimal point to the right, the exponent would be negative.

Step 4: Write the number in scientific notation.

$$6.53 \times 10^8$$

Area

Area is the number of square units needed to cover the surface of an object.

Formulas:

$area\ of\ a\ square = side \times side$

$area\ of\ a\ rectangle = length \times width$

$area\ of\ a\ triangle = \frac{1}{2} \times base \times height$

Examples: Find the areas.

Triangle

4 cm

3 cm

$area = \frac{1}{2} \times base \times height$

$area = \frac{1}{2} \times 3\ cm \times 4\ cm$

$area = \textbf{6 cm}^2$

Rectangle

3 cm

6 cm

$area = length \times width$

$area = 6\ cm \times 3\ cm$

$area = \textbf{18 cm}^2$

Square

3 cm

3 cm

$area = side \times side$

$area = 3\ cm \times 3\ cm$

$area = \textbf{9 cm}^2$

Volume

Volume is the amount of space that something occupies.

Formulas:

$volume\ of\ a\ cube = side \times side \times side$

$volume\ of\ a\ prism = area\ of\ base \times height$

Examples:

Find the volume of the solids.

Cube

$volume = side \times side \times side$

$volume = 4\ cm \times 4\ cm \times 4\ cm$

$volume = \textbf{64 cm}^3$

4 cm

4 cm

4 cm

Prism

4 cm

3 cm

5 cm

$volume = area\ of\ base \times height$

$volume = (area\ of\ triangle) \times height$

$volume = (\frac{1}{2} \times 3\ cm \times 4\ cm) \times 5\ cm$

$volume = 6\ cm^2 \times 5\ cm$

$volume = \textbf{30 cm}^3$

Properties of Common Minerals

Mineral	Color	Luster	Streak	Hardness
Beryl	deep green, pink, white, bluish green, or yellow	vitreous	white	7.5–8
Chlorite	green	vitreous to pearly	pale green	2–2.5
Garnet	green, red, brown, black	vitreous	white	6.5–7.5
Hornblende	dark green, brown, or black	vitreous	none	5–6
Muscovite	colorless, silvery white, or brown	vitreous or pearly	white	2–2.5
Olivine	olive green, yellow	vitreous	white or none	6.5–7
Orthoclase	colorless, white, pink, or other colors	vitreous	white or none	6
Plagioclase	colorless, white, yellow, pink, green	vitreous	white	6
Quartz	colorless or white; any color when not pure	vitreous or waxy	white or none	7

Native Elements				
Copper	copper-red	metallic	copper-red	2.5–3
Diamond	pale yellow or colorless	adamantine	none	10
Graphite	black to gray	submetallic	black	1–2
Carbonates				
Aragonite	colorless, white, or pale yellow	vitreous	white	3.5–4
Calcite	colorless or white to tan	vitreous	white	3
Halides				
Fluorite	light green, yellow, purple, bluish green, or other colors	vitreous	none	4
Halite	white	vitreous	white	2.0–2.5
Oxides				
Hematite	reddish brown to black	metallic to earthy	dark red to red-brown	5.6–6.5
Magnetite	iron-black	metallic	black	5.5–6.5
Sulfates				
Anhydrite	colorless, bluish, or violet	vitreous to pearly	white	3–3.5
Gypsum	white, pink, gray, or colorless	vitreous, pearly, or silky	white	2.0
Sulfides				
Galena	lead-gray	metallic	lead-gray to black	2.5–2.8
Pyrite	brassy yellow	metallic	greenish, brownish, or black	6–6.5

Density (g/cm³)	Cleavage, Fracture, Special Properties	Common Uses
2.6–2.8	1 cleavage direction; irregular fracture; some varieties fluoresce in ultraviolet light	gemstones, ore of the metal beryllium
2.6–3.3	1 cleavage direction; irregular fracture	
4.2	no cleavage; conchoidal to splintery fracture	gemstones, abrasives
3.0–3.4	2 cleavage directions; hackly to splintery fracture	
2.7–3	1 cleavage direction; irregular fracture	electrical insulation, wallpaper, fireproofing material, lubricant
3.2–3.3	no cleavage; conchoidal fracture	gemstones, casting
2.6	2 cleavage directions; irregular fracture	porcelain
2.6–2.7	2 cleavage directions; irregular fracture	ceramics
2.6	no cleavage; conchoidal fracture	gemstones, concrete, glass, porcelain, sandpaper, lenses
8.9	no cleavage; hackly fracture	wiring, brass, bronze, coins
3.5	4 cleavage directions; irregular to conchoidal fracture	gemstones, drilling
2.3	1 cleavage direction; irregular fracture	pencils, paints, lubricants, batteries
2.95	2 cleavage directions; irregular fracture; reacts with hydrochloric acid	no important industrial uses
2.7	3 cleavage directions; irregular fracture; reacts with weak acid; double refraction	cements, soil conditioner, whitewash, construction materials
3.0–3.3	4 cleavage directions; irregular fracture; some varieties fluoresce	hydrofluoric acid, steel, glass, fiberglass, pottery, enamel
2.1–2.2	3 cleavage directions; splintery to conchoidal fracture; salty taste	tanning hides, salting icy roads, food preservation
5.2–5.3	no cleavage; splintery fracture; magnetic when heated	iron ore for steel, pigments
5.2	no cleavage; splintery fracture; magnetic	iron ore
3.0	3 cleavage directions; conchoidal to splintery fracture	soil conditioner, sulfuric acid
2.3	3 cleavage directions; conchoidal to splintery fracture	plaster of Paris, wallboard, soil conditioner
7.4–7.6	3 cleavage directions; irregular fracture	batteries, paints
5	no cleavage; conchoidal to splintery fracture	sulfuric acid

Glossary

A

absolute dating any method of measuring the age of an event or object in years (70)

asthenosphere the soft layer of the mantle on which the tectonic plates move (98)

C

caldera a large, semicircular depression that forms when the magma chamber below a volcano partially empties and causes the ground above to sink (164)

cast a type of fossil that forms when sediments fill in the cavity left by a decomposed organism (76)

catastrophism a principle that states that geologic change occurs suddenly (61)

cleavage the splitting of a mineral along smooth, flat surfaces (9)

composition the chemical makeup of a rock; describes either the minerals or other materials in the rock (33)

compound a substance made up of atoms of two or more different elements joined by chemical bonds (5)

compression stress that occurs when forces act to squeeze an object (112)

continental drift the hypothesis that states that the continents once formed a single landmass, broke up, and drifted to their present locations (104)

convergent boundary the boundary formed by the collision of two lithospheric plates (109)

core the central part of the Earth below the mantle (97)

crater a funnel-shaped pit near the top of the central vent of a volcano (164)

crust the thin and solid outermost layer of the Earth above the mantle (96)

crystal a solid whose atoms, ions, or molecules are arranged in a definite pattern (5)

D

deformation the bending, tilting, and breaking of the Earth's crust; the change in the shape of rock in response to stress (131)

density the ratio of the mass of a substance to the volume of the substance (10)

deposition the process in which material is laid down (29)

divergent boundary the boundary between two tectonic plates that are moving away from each other (109)

E

elastic rebound the sudden return of elastically deformed rock to its undeformed shape (131)

element a substance that cannot be separated or broken down into simpler substances by chemical means (4)

eon (EE AHN) the largest division of geologic time (83)

epicenter the point on Earth's surface directly above an earthquake's starting point, or focus (136)

epoch (EP uhk) a subdivision of a geologic period (83)

era a unit of geologic time that includes two or more periods (83)

erosion the process by which wind, water, ice, or gravity transports soil and sediment from one location to another (29)

extinction the death of every member of a species (83)

extrusive igneous rock rock that forms as a result of volcanic activity at or near the Earth's surface (39)

F

fault a break in a body of rock along which one block slides relative to another (114)

focus the point along a fault at which the first motion of an earthquake occurs (136)

folding the bending of rock layers due to stress (113)

foliated describes the texture of metamorphic rock in which the mineral grains are arranged in planes or bands (47)

fossil the trace or remains of an organism that lived long ago, most commonly preserved in sedimentary rock (74)

fracture the manner in which a mineral breaks along either curved or irregular surfaces (9)

G

gap hypothesis a hypothesis that is based on the idea that a major earthquake is more likely to occur along the part of an active fault where no earthquakes have occurred for a certain period of time (141)

geologic column an arrangement of rock layers in which the oldest rocks are at the bottom (65)

geologic time scale the standard method used to divide the Earth's long natural history into manageable parts (82)

H

half-life the time needed for half of a sample of a radioactive substance to undergo radioactive decay (71)

hardness a measure of the ability of a mineral to resist scratching (10)

hot spot a volcanically active area of Earth's surface far from a tectonic plate boundary (170)

I

index fossil a fossil that is found in the rock layers of only one geologic age and that is used to establish the age of the rock layers (78)

intrusive igneous rock rock formed from the cooling and solidification of magma beneath the Earth's surface (38)

isotope an atom that has the same number of protons (or the same atomic number) as other atoms of the same element do but that has a different number of neutrons (and thus a different atomic mass) (70)

L

lava plateau a wide, flat landform that results from repeated nonexplosive eruptions of lava that spread over a large area (165)

lithosphere the solid, outer layer of the Earth that consists of the crust and the rigid upper part of the mantle (98)

luster the way in which a mineral reflects light (8)

M

magma chamber the body of molten rock that feeds a volcano (158)

mantle the layer of rock between the Earth's crust and core (97)

mesosphere the strong, lower part of the mantle between the asthenosphere and the outer core (99)

mineral a naturally formed, inorganic solid that has a definite chemical structure (4)

mold a mark or cavity made in a sedimentary surface by a shell or other body (76)

N

nonfoliated describes the texture of metamorphic rock in which the mineral grains are not arranged in planes or bands (48)

nonsilicate mineral a mineral that does not contain compounds of silicon and oxygen (6)

O

ore a natural material whose concentration of economically valuable minerals is high enough for the material to be mined profitably (14)

P

paleontology the scientific study of fossils (63)

period a unit of geologic time into which eras are divided (83)

plate tectonics the theory that explains how large pieces of the Earth's outermost layer, called *tectonic plates,* move and change shape (108)

P wave a seismic wave that causes particles of rock to move in a back-and-forth direction (134)

R

radioactive decay the process in which a radioactive isotope tends to break down into a stable isotope of the same element or another element (70)

radiometric dating a method of determining the age of an object by estimating the relative percentages of a radioactive (parent) isotope and a stable (daughter) isotope (71)

reclamation the process of returning land to its original condition after mining is completed (15)

relative dating any method of determining whether an event or object is older or younger than other events or objects (64)

rift zone an area of deep cracks that forms between two tectonic plates that are pulling away from each other (168)

rock a naturally occurring solid mixture of one or more minerals or organic matter (28)

rock cycle the series of processes in which a rock forms, changes from one type to another, is destroyed, and forms again by geological processes (28)

S

sea-floor spreading the process by which new oceanic lithosphere forms as magma rises toward the surface and solidifies (106)

seismic gap an area along a fault where relatively few earthquakes have occurred recently but where strong earthquakes have occurred in the past (141)

seismic wave a wave of energy that travels through the Earth and away from an earthquake in all directions (134)

seismogram a tracing of earthquake motion that is created by a seismograph (136)

seismograph an instrument that records vibrations in the ground and determines the location and strength of an earthquake (136)

seismology (siez MAHL uh jee) the study of earthquakes (130)

silicate mineral a mineral that contains a combination of silicon, oxygen, and one or more metals (6)

strata layers of rock (singular, *stratum*) (40)

stratification the process in which sedimentary rocks are arranged in layers (43)

streak the color of the powder of a mineral (9)

subsidence (suhb SIED'ns) the sinking of regions of the Earth's crust to lower elevations (118)

superposition a principle that states that younger rocks lie above older rocks if the layers have not been disturbed (64)

S wave a seismic wave that causes particles of rock to move in a side-to-side direction (134)

T

tectonic plate a block of lithosphere that consists of the crust and the rigid, outermost part of the mantle (100)

tension stress that occurs when forces act to stretch an object (112)

texture the quality of a rock that is based on the sizes, shapes, and positions of the rock's grains (34)

trace fossil a fossilized mark that is formed in soft sediment by the movement of an animal (76)

transform boundary the boundary between tectonic plates that are sliding past each other horizontally (109)

U

unconformity a break in the geologic record created when rock layers are eroded or when sediment is not deposited for a long period of time (67)

uniformitarianism a principle that states that geologic processes that occurred in the past can be explained by current geologic processes (60)

uplift the rising of regions of the Earth's crust to higher elevations (118)

V

vent an opening at the surface of the Earth through which volcanic material passes (158)

volcano a vent or fissure in the Earth's surface through which magma and gases are expelled (156)

Glossary

Spanish Glossary

A

absolute dating/datación absoluta cualquier método que sirve para determinar la edad de un suceso u objeto en años (70)

asthenosphere/astenosfera la capa blanda del manto sobre la que se mueven las placas tectónicas (98)

C

caldera/caldera una depresión grande y semicircular que se forma cuando se vacía parcialmente la cámara de magma que hay debajo de un volcán, lo cual hace que el suelo se hunda (164)

cast/molde un tipo de fósil que se forma cuando un organismo descompuesto deja una cavidad que es llenada por sedimentos (76)

catastrophism/catastrofismo un principio que establece que los cambios geológicos ocurren súbitamente (61)

cleavage/exfoliación el agrietamiento de un mineral en sus superficies lisas y planas (9)

composition/composición la constitución química de una roca; describe los minerales u otros materiales presentes en ella (33)

compound/compuesto una substancia formada por átomos de dos o más elementos diferentes unidos por enlaces químicos (5)

compression/compresión estrés que se produce cuando distintas fuerzas actúan para estrechar un objeto (112)

continental drift/deriva continental la hipótesis que establece que alguna vez los continentes formaron una sola masa de tierra, se dividieron y se fueron a la deriva hasta terminar en sus ubicaciones actuales (104)

convergent boundary/límite convergente el límite que se forma debido al choque de dos placas de la litosfera (109)

core/núcleo la parte central de la Tierra, debajo del manto (97)

crater/cráter una depresión con forma de embudo que se encuentra cerca de la parte superior de la chimenea central de un volcán (164)

crust/corteza la capa externa, delgada y sólida de la Tierra, que se encuentra sobre el manto (96)

crystal/cristal un sólido cuyos átomos, iones o moléculas están ordenados en un patrón definido (5)

D

deformation/deformación el proceso de doblar, inclinar y romper la corteza de la Tierra; el cambio en la forma de una roca en respuesta a la tensión (131)

density/densidad la relación entre la masa de una substancia y su volumen (10)

deposition/deposición el proceso por medio del cual un material se deposita (29)

divergent boundary/límite divergente el límite entre dos placas tectónicas que se están separando una de la otra (109)

E

elastic rebound/rebote elástico ocurre cuando una roca deformada elásticamente vuelve súbitamente a su forma no deformada (131)

element/elemento una substancia que no se puede separar o descomponer en substancias más simples por medio de métodos químicos (4)

eon/eón la mayor división del tiempo geológico (83)

epicenter/epicentro el punto de la superficie de la Tierra que queda justo arriba del punto de inicio, o foco, de un terremoto (136)

epoch/época una subdivisión de un período geológico (83)

era/era una unidad de tiempo geológico que incluye dos o más períodos (83)

erosion/erosión el proceso por medio del cual el viento, el agua, el hielo o la gravedad transporta tierra y sedimentos de un lugar a otro (29)

extinction/extinción la muerte de todos los miembros de una especie (83)

extrusive igneous rock/roca ígnea extrusiva una roca que se forma como resultado de la actividad volcánica en la superficie de la Tierra o cerca de ella (39)

F

fault/falla una grieta en un cuerpo rocoso a lo largo de la cual un bloque se desliza respecto a otro (114)

focus/foco el punto a lo largo de una falla donde ocurre el primer movimiento de un terremoto (136)

folding/plegamiento fenómeno que ocurre cuando las capas de roca se doblan debido a la compresión (113)

foliated/foliada término que describe la textura de una roca metamórfica en la que los granos de mineral están ordenados en planos o bandas (47)

fossil/fósil los indicios o los restos de un organismo que vivió hace mucho tiempo, comúnmente preservados en las rocas sedimentarias (74)

fracture/fractura la forma en la que se rompe un mineral a lo largo de superficies curvas o irregulares (9)

G

gap hypothesis/hipótesis del intervalo una hipótesis que se basa en la idea de que es más probable que ocurra un terremoto importante a lo largo de la parte de una falla activa donde no se han producido terremotos durante un determinado período de tiempo (141)

geologic column/columna geológica un arreglo de las capas de roca en el que las rocas más antiguas están al fondo (65)

geologic time scale/escala de tiempo geológico el método estándar que se usa para dividir la larga historia natural de la Tierra en partes razonables (82)

H

half-life/vida media el tiempo que tarda la mitad de la muestra de una substancia radiactiva en desintegrarse por desintegración radiactiva (71)

hardness/dureza una medida de la capacidad de un mineral de resistir ser rayado (10)

hot spot/mancha caliente un área volcánicamente activa de la superficie de la Tierra que se encuentra lejos de un límite entre placas tectónicas (170)

I

index fossil/fósil guía un fósil que se encuentra en las capas de roca de una sola era geológica y que se usa para establecer la edad de las capas de roca (78)

intrusive igneous rock/roca ígnea intrusiva una roca formada a partir del enfriamiento y solidificación del magma debajo de la superficie terrestre (38)

isotope/isótopo un átomo que tiene el mismo número de protones (o el mismo número atómico) que otros átomos del mismo elemento, pero que tiene un número diferente de neutrones (y, por lo tanto, otra masa atómica) (70)

L

lava plateau/meseta de lava un accidente geográfico amplio y plano que se forma debido a repetidas erupciones no explosivas de lava que se expanden por un área extensa (165)

lithosphere/litosfera la capa externa y sólida de la Tierra que está formada por la corteza y la parte superior y rígida del manto (98)

luster/brillo la forma en que un mineral refleja la luz (8)

M

magma chamber/cámara de magma la masa de roca fundida que alimenta un volcán (158)

mantle/manto la capa de roca que se encuentra entre la corteza terrestre y el núcleo (97)

mesosphere/mesosfera la parte fuerte e inferior del manto que se encuentra entre la astenosfera y el núcleo externo (99)

mineral/mineral un sólido natural e inorgánico que tiene una estructura química definida (4)

mold/molde una marca o cavidad hecha en una superficie sedimentaria por una concha u otro cuerpo (76)

N

nonfoliated/no foliada término que describe la textura de una roca metamórfica en la que los granos de mineral no están ordenados en planos ni bandas (48)

nonsilicate mineral/mineral no-silicato un mineral que no contiene compuestos de sílice y oxígeno (6)

O

ore/mena un material natural cuya concentración de minerales con valor económico es suficientemente alta como para que el material pueda ser explotado de manera rentable (14)

P

paleontology/paleontología el estudio científico de los fósiles (63)

period/período una unidad de tiempo geológico en la que se dividen las eras (83)

plate tectonics/tectónica de placas la teoría que explica cómo se mueven y cambian de forma las placas tectónicas, que son grandes porciones de la capa más externa de la Tierra (108)

P wave/onda P una onda sísmica que hace que las partículas de roca se muevan en una dirección de atrás hacia delante (134)

R

radioactive decay/desintegración radiactiva el proceso por medio del cual unlos isótopos radiactivos tienden a desintegrarse y formar un isótopos estables del mismo elemento o de otros elementos (70)

radiometric dating/datación radiométrica un método para determinar la edad de un objeto estimando los porcentajes relativos de un isótopo radiactivo (precursor) y un isótopo estable (hijo) (71)

reclamation/restauración el proceso de hacer que la tierra vuelva a su condición original después de que se terminan las actividades de explotación minera (15)

relative dating/datación relativa cualquier método que se utiliza para determinar si un acontecimiento u objeto es más viejo o más joven que otros acontecimientos u objetos (64)

rift zone/zona de rift un área de grietas profundas que se forma entre dos placas tectónicas que se están alejando una de la otra (168)

rock/roca una mezcla sólida de uno o más minerales o de materia orgánica que se produce de forma natural (28)

rock cycle/ciclo de las rocas la serie de procesos por medio de los cuales una roca se forma, cambia de un tipo a otro, se destruye y se forma nuevamente por procesos geológicos (28)

S

sea-floor spreading/expansión del suelo marino el proceso por medio del cual se forma nueva litosfera oceánica a medida que el magma se eleva hacia la superficie y se solidifica (106)

seismic gap/brecha sísmica un área a lo largo de una falla donde han ocurrido relativamente pocos terremotos recientemente, pero donde se han producido terremotos fuertes en el pasado (141)

seismic wave/onda sísmica una onda de energía que viaja a través de la Tierra y se aleja de un terremoto en todas direcciones (134)

seismogram/sismograma una gráfica del movimiento de un terremoto elaborada por un sismógrafo (136)

seismograph/sismógrafo un instrumento que registra las vibraciones en el suelo y determina la ubicación y la fuerza de un terremoto (136)

seismology/sismología el estudio de los terremotos (130)

silicate mineral/mineral silicato un mineral que contiene una combinación de sílice, oxígeno y uno o más metales (6)

strata/estratos capas de roca (40)

stratification/estratificación el proceso por medio del cual las rocas sedimentarias se acomodan en capas (43)

streak/veta el color del polvo de un mineral (9)

subsidence/hundimiento del terreno el hundimiento de regiones de la corteza terrestre a elevaciones más bajas (118)

superposition/superposición un principio que establece que las rocas más jóvenes se encontrarán sobre las rocas más viejas si las capas no han sido alteradas (64)

S wave/onda S una onda sísmica que hace que las partículas de roca se muevan en una dirección de lado a lado (134)

T

tectonic plate/placa tectónica un bloque de litosfera formado por la corteza y la parte rígida y más externa del manto (100)

tension/tensión estrés que se produce cuando distintas fuerzas actúan para estirar un objeto (112)

texture/textura la cualidad de una roca que se basa en el tamaño, la forma y la posición de los granos que la forman (34)

trace fossil/fósil traza una marca fosilizada que se forma en un sedimento blando debido al movimiento de un animal (76)

transform boundary/límite de transformación el límite entre placas tectónicas que se están deslizando horizontalmente una sobre otra (109)

U

unconformity/disconformidad una ruptura en el registro geológico, creada cuando las capas de roca se erosionan o cuando el sedimento no se deposita durante un largo período de tiempo (67)

uniformitarianism/uniformitarianismo un principio que establece que es posible explicar los procesos geológicos que ocurrieron en el pasado en función de los procesos geológicos actuales (60)

uplift/levantamiento la elevación de regiones de la corteza terrestre a elevaciones más altas (118)

V

vent/chimenea una abertura en la superficie de la Tierra a través de la cual pasa material volcánico (158)

volcano/volcán una chimenea o fisura en la superficie de la Tierra a través de la cual se expulsan magma y gases (156)

Index

Boldface page numbers refer to illustrative material, such as figures, tables, margin elements, photographs, and illustrations.

Index

Index

Index

Index

W

water
    density of, 10
    in volcanic eruptions, 158, 169,
      169
waxy luster, **8**
weathering, in the rock cycle, 29,
    29, 31
Wegener, Alfred, 104–105, 127
Wieliczka salt mine, 24
Williamson, Jack, 24
woolly mammoths, 75, **75,** 92

Y

Yellowstone National Park, 164
Yoho National Park, **77**

Credits

PHOTOGRAPHY

Front Cover Doug Scott/Age Fotostock

Skills Practice Lab Teens Sam Dudgeon/HRW

Connection to Astronomy Corbis Images; **Connection to Biology** David M. Phillips/Visuals Unlimited; **Connection to Chemistry** Digital Image copyright © 2005 PhotoDisc; **Connection to Environment** Digital Image copyright © 2005 PhotoDisc; **Connection to Geology** Letraset Phototone; **Connection to Language Arts** Digital Image copyright © 2005 PhotoDisc; **Connection to Meteorology** Digital Image copyright © 2005 PhotoDisc; **Connection to Oceanography** © ICONOTEC; **Connection to Physics** Digital Image copyright © 2005 PhotoDisc

Table of Contents iv (yellow), E. R. Degginger/Color–Pic, Inc.; iv (purple), Mark A. Schneider/Photo Researchers, Inc.; (green), Dr. E.R. Degginger/Bruce Coleman Inc.; iv (bl), The G.R. "Dick" Roberts Photo Library; v (b), ©National Geographic Image Collection/Robert W. Madden; x (bl), Sam Dudgeon/HRW; xi (tl), John Langford/HRW; xi (b), Sam Dudgeon/HRW; xii (tl), Victoria Smith/HRW; xii (bl), Stephanie Morris/HRW; xii (br), Sam Dudgeon/HRW; xiii (tl), Patti Murray/Animals, Animals; xiii (tr), Jana Birchum/HRW; xiii (b), Peter Van Steen/HRW

Chapter One 2–3, Terry Wilson; 4, Sam Dudgeon/HRW; 5 (br), © Wendell E. Wilson; 6 (tr), Victoria Smith/HRW; 6 (bc), Sam Dudgeon/HRW; 6 (tl), Sam Dudgeon/HRW; 7, (copper), E. R. Degginger/Color–Pic, Inc.; 7, (calcite), E. R. Degginger/Color–Pic, Inc.; 7, (fluorite), E. R. Degginger/Color–Pic, Inc.; 7, (corundum), E. R. Degginger/Color–Pic, Inc.; 7, (gypsum), SuperStock; 7, (galena), Visuals Unlimited/Ken Lucas; 8, (vitreous), Biophoto Associates/Photo Researchers, Inc.; 8, (waxy), Biophoto Associates/Photo Researchers, Inc.; 8, (silky), Dr. E.R. Degginger/Bruce Coleman Inc.; 8, (submetallic), John Cancalosi 1989/DRK Photo; 8 (bl), Kosmatsu Mining Systems; 8, (resinous), Charles D. Winters/Photo Researchers, Inc.; 8, (pearly), Victoria Smith/HRW; 8, (metallic), Victoria Smith/HRW; 8, (earthy), Sam Dudgeon/HRW; 9 (tr, c, bl), Sam Dudgeon/HRW; 9, Tom Pantages; 10, (1), Visuals Unlimited/Ken Lucas; 10, (3), Visuals Unlimited/Dane S. Johnson; 10, (7), Carlyn Iverson/Absolute Science Illustration and Photography; 10, (8), Mark A. Schneider/Visuals Unlimited; 10, (9), Charles D. Winters/Photo Researchers, Inc.; 10, (10), Bard Wrisley; 10, (5), Biophoto Associates/Photo Researchers, Inc.; 10, (6), Victoria Smith/HRW; 10, (4), Mark A. Schneider/Photo Researchers, Inc.; 10, (2), Sam Dudgeon/HRW; 11 (tc), Sam Dudgeon/HRW; 11 (tr), Sam Dudgeon/HRW, Courtesy Science Stuff, Austin, TX; 11 (br), Tom Pantages Photography; 11 (bc), Sam Dudgeon/HRW; 11 (tl), Mark A. Schneider/Photo Researchers, Inc.; 11 (bl), 12 (t), Sam Dudgeon/HRW; 12 (bl), Victoria Smith/HRW Courtesy Science Stuff, Austin, TX; 12 (c), Breck P. Kent; 13 (br), Sam Dudgeon/HRW; 13 (c), Breck P. Kent; 13 (bl), Visuals Unlimited/Ken Lucas; 14 (br), Wernher Krutein; 14 (bl), © Lester Lefkowitz/CORBIS; 15, Stewart Cohen/Index Stock Photography, Inc.; 16, Digital Image copyright © 2005 PhotoDisc; 17, © Superstock; 18 (c), Russell Dian/HRW; 18 (b), 19 (tr), Sam Dudgeon/HRW; 20, Digital Image copyright © 2005 PhotoDisc; 21 (b), E. R. Degginger/Color–Pic, Inc.; 24 (t), Esch Thierry/Paris Match/Gamma; 25 (t), Will & Dennie McIntyre/McIntyre Photography; 25 (b), Mark Schneider/Visuals Unlimited

Chapter Two 26–27, Tom Till; 28 (bl), Michael Melford/Getty Images/The Image Bank; 28 (br), Joseph Sohm; Visions of America/CORBIS; 29, CORBIS Images/HRW; 32 (t), Joyce Photographics/Photo Researchers, Inc.; 32 (l), Pat Lanza/Bruce Coleman Inc.; 32 (r), Sam Dudgeon/HRW ; 32 (b), James Watt/Animals Animals/Earth Scenes; 32 (l), Pat Lanza/Bruce Coleman Inc.; 33, (granite), Pat Lanza/Bruce Coleman Inc.; 33, (mica), E. R. Degginger/Color–Pic, Inc.; 33, (aragonite), Breck P. Kent; 33, (limestone), Breck P. Kent; 33, (calcite), Mark Schneider/Visuals Unlimited; 33, (feldspar), Mark Schneider/Visuals Unlimited; 33, (quartz), Digital Image copyright © 2005 PhotoDisc; 34 (tl), Sam Dudgeon/HRW; 34 (tc), Dorling Kindersley; 34 (tr, br), Breck P. Kent; 34 (bl), E. R. Degginger/Color–Pic, Inc.; 35, Joseph Sohm; Visions of America/CORBIS; 36 (l), E. R. Degginger/Color–Pic, Inc.; 37 (tr, tl, bl), Breck P. Kent; 37 (br), Victoria Smith/HRW; 39, J.D. Griggs/USGS; 40, CORBIS Images/HRW; 41, (conglomerate), Breck P. Kent; 41, (siltstone), Sam Dudgeon/HRW; 41, (sandstone), Joyce Photographics/Photo Researchers, Inc.; 41, (shale), Sam Dudgeon/HRW; 42 (tl), Stephen Frink/Corbis; 42 (br), Breck P. Kent; 42 (bc), David Muench/CORBIS; 43, Franklin P. OSF/Animals Animals/Earth Scenes; 44, George Wuerthner; 46, (calcite), Dane S. Johnson/Visuals Unlimited; 46, (quartz), Carlyn Iverson/Absolute Science Illustration and Photography; 46, (hematite), Breck P. Kent; 46, (garnet), Breck P. Kent/Animals Animals/Earth Scenes; 46, (chlorite), Sam Dudgeon/HRW; 46, (mica), Tom Pantages; 47, (shale), Ken Karp/HRW; 47, (slate), Sam Dudgeon/HRW; 47, (phyllite), Sam Dudgeon/HRW; 47, (gneiss), Breck P. Kent; 47, (schist), Sam Dudgeon/HRW; 48 (tl), E. R. Degginger/Color–Pic, Inc.; 48 (bl), Ray Simmons/Photo Researchers, Inc; 48 (tr), Andy Christiansen/HRW; 48 (br), Breck P. Kent; 49, Jim Wark/Airphoto; 51 (t), Sam Dudgeon/HRW; 51 (b), James Tallon; 56 (l), Wolfgang Kaehler/CORBIS; 56 (tr), Dr. David Kring/Science Photo Library/Photo Researchers, Inc.; 57 (r), James Miller/Courtesy Robert Folk, Department of Geological Sciences, University of Texas at Austin; 57 (l), Dr. Philppa Uwins, Whistler Research PTY/SPL/Photo Researchers, Inc.

Chapter Three 58, National Geographic Image Collection/Jonathan Blair, Courtesy Hessian Regional Museum, Darmstadt, Germany; 61 (t), Dr. Clifford E. Ford; 63, Museum of Northern Arizona; 64 (l), Sam Dudgeon/HRW; 64 (r), Andy Christiansen/HRW; 66 (tl), Fletcher & Baylis/Photo Researchers, Inc.; 66 (tr), Ken M. Johns/Photo Researchers, Inc.; 66 (bl), Glenn M. Oliver/Visuals Unlimited; 66 (br), Francois Gohier/Photo Researchers, Inc.; 71, Sam Dudgeon/HRW; 72, Tom Till/DRK Photo; 73, Courtesy Charles S. Tucek/University of Arizona at Tucson; 74, Howard Grey/Getty Images/Stone; 75, Francis Latreille/Nova Productions/AP/Wide World Photos; 76 (b), The G.R. "Dick" Roberts Photo Library; 76 (t), © Louie Psihoyos/psihoyos.com; 77 (l), Brian Exton; 77 (r), Chip Clark/Smithsonian; 78 (l), ; 79, Thomas R. Taylor/Photo Researchers, Inc.; 80, James L. Amos/CORBIS; 81 (tl), Tom Till Photography; 81 (fish), Tom Bean/CORBIS; 81 (leaf), James L. Amos/CORBIS; 81 (turtle), Layne Kennedy/CORBIS; 81 (fly), Ken Lucas/Visuals Unlimited; 83, Chip Clark/Smithsonian; 84 (t), Neg. no. 5793 Courtesy Dept. of Library Services., American Museum of Natural History; 84 (b), Neg. no. 5799 Courtesy Department of Library Services., American Museum of Natural History; 85, Neg. no. 5801 Courtesy Department of Library Services, American Museum of Natural History; 86, Jonathan Blair/CORBIS; 88 (b), The G.R. "Dick" Roberts Photo Library; 89 (fly), Ken Lucas/Visuals Unlimited; 92 (tl), Beth A. Keiser/AP/Wide World Photos; 92 (tr), Jonathan Blair/CORBIS; 93, Courtesy Kevin C. May

Chapter Four 94–95, James Balog/Getty Images/Stone; 97 (t), James Wall/Animals Animals/Earth Scenes; 100, Bruce C. Heezen and Marie Tharp; 111 (tc), ESA/CE/Eurocontrol/Science Photo Library/Photo Researchers, Inc.; 111 (tr), NASA; 112 (bl, br), Peter Van Steen/HRW; 113 (bc), Visuals Unlimited/SylvesterAllred; 113 (br), G.R. Roberts Photo Library; 115 (tl), Tom Bean; 115 (tr), Landform Slides; 116, Jay Dickman/CORBIS; 117 (b), Michele & Tom Grimm Photography; 118, Y. Arthus–B./Peter Arnold, Inc.; 119, Peter Van Steen/HRW; 121, Sam Dudgeon/HRW; 126 (bl), NASA/Science Photo Library/Photo Researchers, Inc.; 126 (c), Ron Miller/Fran Heyl Associates; 126 (tr), Photo by S. Thorarinsson/Solar–Filma/Sun Film–15/3/courtesy of Edward T. Baker, Pacific Marine Environmental Laboratory, NOAA; 127 (r), Bettman/CORBIS

Chapter Five 128–129, Robert Patrick/Sygma/CORBIS; 131, Roger Ressmeyer/CORBIS; 137, Earth Images/Getty Images/Stone; 139, Bettmann/CORBIS; 142, Michael S. Yamashita/CORBIS; 144, Paul Chesley/Getty Images/Stone; 146, NOAA/NGDC; 147, Sam Dudgeon/HRW; 149, Bettmann/CORBIS; 152, Sam Dudgeon/HRW; 152 (t), Courtesy Stephen H. Hickman, USGS; 153 (t), Todd Bigelow/HRW; 153 (b), Corbis Images

Chapter Six 154–155, Carl Shaneff/Pacific Stock; 156 (bl), National Geographic Image Collection/Robert W. Madden; 156 (br), Ken Sakamoto/Black Star; 157 (b), Breck P. Kent/Animals Animals/Earth Scenes; 157, Joyce Warren/USGS Photo Library; 159 (tl), Tui De Roy/Minden Pictures; 159 (bl), B. Murton/Southampton Oceanography Centre/Science Photo Library/Photo Researchers, Inc.; 159 (tr), Visuals Unlimited/Martin Miller; 159 (br), Buddy Mays/CORBIS; 160 (tr), Tom Bean/DRK Photo; 160 (tl), Francois Gohier/Photo Researchers, Inc.; 160, (tlc), Visuals Unlimited Inc./Glenn Oliver; 160, (tlb), E. R. Degginger/Color–Pic, Inc.; 161 (tr), Alberto Garcia/SABA/CORBIS; 161, Robert W. Madden/National Geographic Society; 162, Images & Volcans/Photo Researchers, Inc.; 163 (br), SuperStock; 163 (cr), SuperStock; 163 (tr), Roger Ressmeyer/CORBIS; 164 (tl), Yann Arthus–Bertrand/CORBIS; 165, Joseph Sohm; ChromoSohm Inc./CORBIS; 170 (bl), Robert McGimsey/USGS Alaska Volcano Observatory; 174 (tr), Alberto Garcia/SABA/CORBIS; 178 (tl), CORBIS; 178 (tr), © Bettmann/CORBIS; 178 (tc), © Sigurgeir Jonasson; Frank Lane Picture Agency/CORBIS; 179 (bl), Courtesy Christina Neal; 179 (r), Courtesy Alaska Volcano Observatory

Lab Book/Appendix "LabBook Header", "L", Corbis Images; "a", Letraset Phototone; "b", and "B", HRW; "o", and "k", images ©2006 PhotoDisc/HRW; 181 (tr), Victoria Smith/HRW, Courtesy of Science Stuff, Austin, TX; 181, (galena), Ken Lucas/Visuals Unlimited Inc.; 181 (cr), Charlie Winters/HRW; 181, 182, 183 (hematite, br), Sam Dudgeon/HRW; 184 (all), Andy Christiansen/HRW; 185, Sam Dudgeon/HRW; 186, Tom Bean; 187, 188, Sam Dudgeon/HRW; 189, Andy Christiansen/HRW; 193 (tr) Sam Dudgeon/HRW